RADIOACTIVATION
ANALYSIS

RADIOACTIVATION
ANALYSIS

BY

H. J. M. BOWEN and D. GIBBONS

WANTAGE RESEARCH LABORATORY
ATOMIC ENERGY RESEARCH ESTABLISHMENT

OXFORD
AT THE CLARENDON PRESS
1963

Oxford University Press, Amen House, London E.C.4

GLASGOW NEW YORK TORONTO MELBOURNE WELLINGTON
BOMBAY CALCUTTA MADRAS KARACHI LAHORE DACCA
CAPE TOWN SALISBURY NAIROBI IBADAN ACCRA
KUALA LUMPUR HONG KONG

PREFACE

In writing a book of this kind, it is always difficult to strike a balance between theoretical and practical aspects of the subject. We hope we have included enough information to enable the analyst to see what can be done using activation, and sufficient practical detail for him to do it.

Our colleagues have helped us in many ways, especially by reading portions of the manuscript and making suggestions for improvements. In particular, we should like to thank R. A. Allen, R. K. Barnes, G. B. Cook, G. E. Harrison, D. Mapper, C. E. Mellish, D. F. C. Morris, J. L. Putman, A. A. Smales, B. S. Smith, D. B. Smith, S. R. Stitch, and C. Whitehead for pointing out many errors, and P. A. Cawse and H. Simpson for assistance in the laboratory. Unpublished information has been supplied by a number of workers whose help is acknowledged in the text, including E. A. C. Crouch, P. H. Davenport, A. J. Fudge, H. Rauscher, A. J. Salmon, L. Salmon, I. R. Williams, E. J. Wilson, Johnson Matthey & Co. Ltd., and Thermal Syndicate Ltd. The majority of the figures are original, but we have made use of the following copyright illustrations: Fig. 3.5, K. G. Stephens and G. W. Williams, A.E.I., Aldermaston. Figs. 3.7 and 3.8, D. J. Hughes and R. B. Schwartz. Figs. 4.1 and 4.2, L. Nathans and G. D. Halpern. Fig. 4.4, N. Jarmie and J. D. Seagrave. Fig. 5.13, D. H. Peirson, by permission of Leonard Hill Ltd. Fig. 5.14, W. H. Ellett and G. L. Brownell, by permission of North Holland Publishing Co., Amsterdam. Figs. 5.16 and 5.17, J. L. Putman and W. H. Taylor, by permission of Pergamon Press. Fig. 6.2, R. A. Faires and B. H. Parks, by permission of George Newnes Ltd. Fig. 6.8, L. E. Glendenin, by permission of McGraw-Hill Ltd. Fig 10.1, E. D. Goldberg, by permission of Pergamon Press. Fig. 10.4, E. Hamilton, by permission of Meddelelser om Grønland. Fig. 11.5, C. A. Tobias.

The final responsibility for the facts and opinions expressed in this volume is our own.

H. J. M. B.

D. G.

CONTENTS

PLATES

The following figures are half-tones and appear as plates at the positions shown.

1

INTRODUCTION

MOST chemical research depends on methods of analysis, and the development of atomic science has resulted in some entirely novel methods whose full potentialities have not yet been realized. One of these methods, activation analysis, has accumulated such an extensive literature as to justify the production of the present volume (Gibbons et al., 1957 and 1960; Koch, 1960). Recent review articles (Jenkins and Smales, 1956; Loveridge and Smales, 1957; Smales and Wager, 1960; Winchester, 1960; Meinke, 1960; Leddicotte et al., 1959) and Symposia (Cook et al., 1960) make it clear that nothing short of a book of this size is sufficient to cover the whole subject. Needless to add, the rapid developments in this field will ensure incompleteness at the time of going to press, although most relevant papers prior to 1960 have been examined.

Activation differs from most other methods of chemical analysis in that it is based on the properties of nuclei and not on the behaviour of the outer electrons. This implies, firstly, that it is purely a method of elementary analysis, and can only be used indirectly, in certain special cases, to analyse for constituent molecules. Secondly, it can be used to distinguish unequivocally between different isotopes of a single element. In view of the constancy of isotopic composition of most elements, the latter characteristic is of no importance in most applications, but has its uses in geochemical problems.

The activation process involves exposure to a source of particles or photons of sufficient energy to react with the constituent nuclei. Information can sometimes be gained by studying the prompt emission during the ensuing nuclear reactions. In the majority of cases, however, it is more convenient to study the radioactive nuclides produced, since these can be detected with great sensitivity (cf. Table 2.1). Calculation of this sensitivity, together with other mathematical aspects of the activation process, as well as the laws of radioactive decay, are dealt with in Chapter 2. Although in theory activation offers an absolute method of analysis, in practice a comparative method is almost always used, whatever the activating particle may be.

There is no question that neutrons, especially thermal neutrons, have been more widely used for activation than any other type of particle. This situation has arisen from a combination of circumstances. Firstly, the absence of an energy threshold for neutron reactions means that neutrons of negligible energy can react with all nuclei. Secondly, most nuclei have a high cross-section for thermal neutrons; and thirdly, nuclear reactors, with their enormous capacity for producing neutrons, are now widely available. Although neutrons can be produced in the laboratory by nuclear reactions, and from suitable accelerating machines, as described in Chapter 3, these provide lower fluxes than those obtainable in large research reactors. With thermal neutrons, the commonest reaction occurring is the (n, γ) process, whereby each activated isotope is increased in weight by one unit. When neutrons with energies in the MeV range are employed, other reactions such as (n, p) and (n, α) processes may be important, but seldom have large cross-sections. Finally, in the case of a few of the heaviest elements, neutron bombardment may lead to fission, with the production of a spectrum of radioactive nuclides spanning half the periodic table.

Charged particles, on the other hand, have been used much less widely in analytical work. Here there is always a threshold energy which must be exceeded before activation takes place at all. There are now available exceedingly powerful sources of protons and deuterons accelerated by high-voltage machines, and the cross-sections of light elements for these particles are comparable with those for neutrons. Unfortunately these particles have very little penetrating power in solid materials, and as a consequence they raise exposed targets to high temperatures. These factors have severely limited their practical application. At energies of 1–10 MeV the predominant nuclear reactions are (p, n) or (d, n) processes, but at higher energies many other nuclear reactions occur. Among these is the process of spallation, whereby a heavy element is degraded to a series of lighter ones, which is of importance in cosmology. However, such reactions are undesirable from the point of view of activation analysis. Photon activation has also been relatively neglected. Here the threshold energies are mostly higher (6–22 MeV) and the cross-sections of most nuclides much lower, so that full exploitation of its possibilities awaits the development of more powerful photon sources. It has been used to determine deuterium and beryllium, which emit prompt neutrons when activated with photons of low energy.

Since nearly all activated nuclides emit γ-rays, it should be possible to determine the elements present in an activated sample from its γ-ray spectrum. The equipment required for this work is described in Chapter 5, and it appears that developments in this field are proceeding rapidly. The technique has been used for a great variety of qualitative and quantitative analyses, but there are several reasons why it is not universally applicable. In the first place the resolution of the method is relatively poor. Gamma spectra have broad peaks compared with those obtainable in, say, infra-red spectrometers, and have no fine structure to aid identification. As shown in Table 5.2, many nuclides may be responsible for a given peak, and so identification is not always unique. In addition, spurious peaks and undesirable background effects are caused by Compton scattering, and much effort has been devoted to eliminating this source of error. In view of these interferences, the ultimate sensitivity of gamma spectrometry is less satisfactory than that obtainable using radiochemical separation and a much simpler Geiger counter as detector. These less sophisticated detectors form the subject-matter of Chapter 6, which is largely concerned with beta counting. The preparation of samples for counting, the determination of half-life, beta energy, and self-absorption corrections are all discussed, and the advantage of the low background counts obtainable with Geiger counters is pointed out. Other types of counter, for example the proportional counter, have not been used very much for activation analysis. Autoradiography, a useful qualitative technique which has found restricted application to activated samples, is also briefly described.

Errors arising in activation analysis are different in kind from those found in classical techniques. They can come about by reason of inhomogeneities of the activating flux, by self shielding, or by interfering nuclear reactions, and so the preparation of suitable comparative standards is particularly important. On the other hand, the problem of reagent contamination, which is always present when determining trace elements by chemical methods, does not exist after activation. Since only radioactive elements are sought, it is customary to use chemical techniques which are not wholly quantitative and correct for losses as described in Chapter 8. Precipitation and solvent extraction have been very widely used, while volatilization and ion exchange are important for many radiochemical separations. Time is frequently a major limitation, since the half-life of many activated nuclides is so short. Hence attention is now focused on rapid methods of chemical separation. Neither chemical separation nor physical discrimination can give a reliable analysis if the sample is contaminated before activation.

Surface contamination can be removed after activation if the sample is a massive solid, but it is exceedingly difficult to prevent contamination of liquids. The recommendations for handling samples put forward in Chapter 9 will undoubtedly be improved as practical experience grows. However, it is clear that all samples are contaminated by handling, which should therefore be restricted to a minimum.

Practical applications of activation analysis constitute the bulk of the literature on the subject, apart from review articles. A condensed summary of these results, classified as geochemical, biological, and other applications, is set out in Chapters 10–12. It must be understood that it has not been possible to treat any detailed investigation as thoroughly as it merits, nor has it been easy to decide how much background knowledge should be inserted. In any rapidly expanding field it is difficult to pick out the part played by a single technique without either over-emphasizing or omitting all others, but it is hoped that a satisfactory compromise has been reached. Some attempt has also been made to emphasize the many gaps in our knowledge of elementary abundance which remain to be filled.

The last chapter in this book differs from all the others in its essentially practical character. Since techniques of radiochemical separation are mostly published in atomic-energy establishment reports, which have a restricted circulation, an attempt has been made to collect together techniques for all the stable elements which either have been adapted to, or appear suitable for, activation analysis. In some cases (e.g. magnesium, aluminium, lead, and the rare gases) the techniques have not been properly tested and are only inserted for completeness. In any case, it must be emphasized that the methods should always be tested prior to any particular application, partly to obtain the requisite dexterity, but mainly to ensure that no radionuclide other than that desired is coming through and interfering with the determination. Once such an interfering nuclide is identified, it is a relatively simple matter to adjust the chemical procedure to eliminate it.

2

THEORY OF ACTIVATION ANALYSIS

WHEN a material is bombarded or irradiated by the nuclear particles produced in a nuclear reactor, particle accelerator, or other suitable source, some of the atoms present in the sample will interact with the bombarding particles. These atoms may be converted into different isotopes of the same element, or isotopes of different elements, depending on the nature of the bombarding particles. In many cases, the isotopes produced are radioactive and are termed radioisotopes. If the radioactivity which is induced in one component of the material can be distinguished or separated from all other radioactivities arising at the same time, or originally present, then the amount of this induced radioactivity is a measure of the parent isotope, and therefore of the parent element, present in the original material.

Radioactive decay

Since induced radioactivity is measured in terms of the rate of decrease or decay of the radioactive atoms rather than in direct terms of the number of radioactive atoms present, it is worth while to mention briefly the laws of radioactive decay.

Radioactive decay is a purely random process and the probability of a given radioactive nucleus disintegrating is fixed and is independent of the presence or absence of other radioactive nuclei. Thus, the rate at which these radioactive nuclei disintegrate is dependent simply on the number present at any time and is expressed by the relationship

$$\frac{dN}{dt} = -\lambda N, \tag{1}$$

where N is the number of radioactive atoms at any time t,
   λ is the radioactive disintegration constant.

The constant λ is a characteristic of the radioactive nuclei under consideration.

Integration of (1) gives

$$N = N_0 e^{-\lambda t}, \tag{2}$$

where N_0 is the number of radioactive atoms present at time $t = 0$.

If the time $t_{\frac{1}{2}}$ is measured during which the number of radioactive atoms decreases to half the number originally present,

$$\tfrac{1}{2}N_0 = N_0 e^{-\lambda t_{\frac{1}{2}}}, \tag{3}$$

hence

$$\ln 2 = \lambda t_{\frac{1}{2}}, \tag{4}$$

and

$$t_{\frac{1}{2}} = \frac{0\cdot 693}{\lambda}. \tag{5}$$

Thus, $t_{\frac{1}{2}}$ is a function of λ and is therefore also a nuclear constant. It is known as the half-life and is a characteristic of the nuclei under decay. Radioactive nuclei of different atomic weights and/or different atomic numbers mostly have different half-lives (Strominger, Hollander, and Seaborg, 1958), but occasionally two half-lives may be the same or too similar for any distinction to be made. Thus manganese 56 and nickel 65 have half-lives of 2·58 hours and 2·56 hours respectively.

Production of radioisotopes

When a radioisotope is produced at a constant rate, the rate of accumulation of the isotope is given by the difference between the rate of production and the rate of decay of the isotope. Thus

$$\frac{dN}{dt} = P - \lambda N, \tag{6}$$

where P is the rate of production of radioactive nuclei. Solution of (6) gives

$$N = \frac{P}{\lambda}(1 - e^{-\lambda t}) + N_0 e^{-\lambda t}. \tag{7}$$

In most cases, N_0, the number of radioactive atoms present initially, is zero. Hence

$$N = \frac{P}{\lambda}(1 - e^{-\lambda t}), \tag{8}$$

and the rate of disintegration of these radioactive atoms at any time is given by

$$A = \lambda N = P(1 - e^{-\lambda t}). \tag{9}$$

Fig. 2.1 shows a typical growth curve in which it can be seen that the saturation activity S which occurs after an infinite irradiation time is reached within 1 per cent. after about seven half-lives.

From (9),

$$A_t = P(1 - [\tfrac{1}{2}]^{t/t_{\frac{1}{2}}}), \tag{10}$$

and when $t = t_{\frac{1}{2}}$,

$$A_{t_{\frac{1}{2}}} = P(1 - \tfrac{1}{2}) = \tfrac{1}{2}P. \tag{11}$$

Thus, unless it is absolutely essential to obtain the maximum activity possible, it is rather pointless to irradiate the material for much more than one half-life, as seven times as much irradiation will only produce twice as much activity. It is also worth noting that for irradiation times shorter than one half-life, the relationship between induced activity and irradiation time is approximately linear.

FIG. 2.1. Growth of radioactivity.

In some instances, as will be seen later, it may be more convenient to measure the radioactivity of a daughter product of the activated species, rather than measure the activated species itself. In these circumstances, the rate of production of the daughter (d) is given by the rate of decay of the parent (p):

$$P_d = \lambda_p N_p = P_p(1-e^{-\lambda_p t}). \tag{12}$$

Thus, during activation of the parent, the rate of accumulation of the daughter is given by the difference between the rate of production from the parent and the rate of decay of the daughter:

$$\frac{dN_d}{dt} = P_p(1-e^{-\lambda_p t})-\lambda_d N_d. \tag{13}$$

The solution of this equation for the boundary conditions $N_d = 0$ when $t = 0$ is

$$N_d = \frac{P_p}{\lambda_d}(1-e^{-\lambda_d t})+\frac{P_p}{\lambda_d-\lambda_p}(e^{-\lambda_d t}-e^{-\lambda_p t}), \tag{14}$$

and the daughter activity at any time during activation of the parent

$$A_d = \lambda_d N_d = P_p(1-e^{\lambda_d t})+\frac{\lambda_d P_p}{\lambda_d-\lambda_p}(e^{-\lambda_d t}-e^{-\lambda_p t}). \tag{15}$$

The two limiting conditions of equation (15) are obtained when the half-life of the daughter is much shorter than that of the parent

$$A_d = P_p(1-e^{-\lambda_p t}),\qquad(16)$$

and when the half-life of the daughter is much longer than that of the parent

$$A_d = P_p(1-e^{-\lambda_d t}).\qquad(17)$$

In equation (16) the daughter activity will reach half saturation in one parent half-life, while in equation (17) it will reach half saturation in one daughter half-life.

Activation analysis

When materials are irradiated for activation analysis the rate of production is effectively constant, regardless of the nature of the bombarding particles (subject, of course, to the flux of these particles remaining constant), since the number of inactive atoms which are activated is such a small fraction of the total present. Hence equation (9) derived above may be applied.

The rate of production

$$P = f\sigma N_i,\qquad(18)$$

where N_i is the number of inactive atoms present, f is the flux of bombarding particles (in particles/cm²/sec), and σ is the activation cross-section for the reaction (in cm²) and is a measure of the tendency of the inactive atoms to interact with the bombarding particles. Hence the rate of disintegration or activity of the radioisotopes produced is given by

$$A = f\sigma N_i(1-e^{-\lambda t}).\qquad(19)$$

Since few elements are monoisotopic, only the fraction ϕ of the inactive atoms will take part in the reaction, where ϕ is the fractional abundance of the isotope concerned. Also, the number of atoms can be obtained from the weight W of the element present, its atomic weight M, and Avogadro's number. Hence

$$A = f\sigma\,\frac{W\phi}{M}\,(1-e^{-\lambda t})\times 6\cdot02\times10^{23}.\qquad(20)$$

In general, however, the activity will not be determined until a time T after the bombardment has ended, so that the radioactive atoms produced will have decayed by a factor $e^{-\lambda T}$. Hence

$$A = f\sigma\frac{W\phi}{M}(1-e^{-\lambda t})(e^{-\lambda T})\times 6\cdot02\times10^{23}.\qquad(21)$$

If this equation is rewritten

$$W = \frac{MA}{f\sigma\phi}\frac{e^{\lambda T}}{(1-e^{-\lambda t})\times 6\cdot 02\times 10^{23}}, \tag{22}$$

then, in principle, all the factors on the right are known or can be measured. Thus, it should be possible to calculate the weight of the element present. In practice, however, σ is not known with sufficient accuracy, f cannot be determined accurately, and it is not always easy to determine the absolute disintegration rate A. Consequently, a comparison procedure is invariably used, and the amount of activity from the sample is compared with that from a standard amount of the element being determined. It is then a simple matter to calculate the weight of the element in the sample from the relationship

weight of element in sample

$$= \text{weight of element in standard} \times \frac{C_x}{C_s}, \tag{23}$$

where C_x is the observed counting rate of the sample, and C_s that of the standard, measured under comparable conditions.

Sensitivity of the method

If irradiation is carried out for a sufficient number of half-lives so that the factor $(1-e^{-\lambda t})$, known as the saturation factor, becomes effectively unity and, if the activity is determined within a small fraction of a half-life after irradiation ceases, the weight of the element in the samples is given by

$$W = \frac{MA}{f\sigma\phi\times 6\cdot 02\times 10^{23}}, \tag{24}$$

and therefore the sensitivity of the method will be greater the higher the efficiency of the detection equipment, the lower the atomic weight of the element, the greater its activation cross-section, the greater its isotopic abundance, and the greater the flux of bombarding particles.

The efficiency of detection will be dealt with more fully later; it is sufficient to point out at this stage that efficiencies of 10–40 per cent. can be achieved without much difficulty, but 100 per cent. efficiency is only possible in favourable cases and then only with special apparatus and technique. The atomic weight is, of course, fixed for any particular element, but this dependence shows that, all other things being equal, the method of activation analysis is more sensitive for the lighter elements. The activation cross-section is also fixed for any given activation process, but is really the main factor affecting the sensitivity of the method since it can vary from less than a thousandth of a barn to several thousand barns (1 barn $= 10^{-24}$ cm²) depending on the isotope and the method of activation. The isotopic abundance is also a fixed quantity, which varies widely through the periodic table, being unity for arsenic 75 and 0·0072 for uranium 235. Thus the sensitivity for monoisotopic elements is often better than for others. Multi-isotopic elements, on the other hand, offer a choice of radioactive isotopes and selection can then be made of the optimum conditions. However, if the half-lives of the several radioisotopes produced are fairly similar, difficulty may be experienced in determining these to prove the purity of the radioactivity being measured, and can lead to complicated extrapolations if the activities of samples and standards are not measured within a very short space of time. Finally, the flux of bombarding particles can only be as high as the maximum available in the irradiation equipment and can vary from about 10^4 neutrons/cm²/sec for a laboratory radium/beryllium neutron source to 10^{15} n/cm²/sec† for some atomic reactors. Cyclotrons and electrostatic generators, producing other particles, can give fluxes from 10^8 to 10^{15} particles/cm²/sec.

Thus it will be seen that, for given equipment, and a given element, the sensitivity of determination by activation analysis is fixed, since it is not practicable to determine less than a certain level of activity with a given apparatus. This activity level is usually taken as being equal to the background counting rate (i.e. the counting rate which is recorded even in the absence of a sample, due to natural activity in the material of the apparatus, to cosmic rays, and to inadequately shielded radioactive materials in the neighbourhood). If a simple Geiger–Muller counter assembly is used, and such an apparatus is in fact used more frequently than any other at present, then this lower limit is about 10 counts/min at an efficiency of about 10 per cent., corresponding to a disintegration rate of 100 disintegrations/min. If a flux of 10^{12} n/cm²/sec is assumed, corresponding to the maximum available in the Harwell reactor BEPO, then the sensitivity may be reduced to

$$\frac{M \times 100/60}{10^{12} \times \sigma_i \times 10^{-24} \times 6·02 \times 10^{23}} = \frac{M}{0·36\sigma_i}\mu\mu\text{g} \simeq \frac{3M}{\sigma_i}\mu\mu\text{g}, \qquad (25)$$

where σ_i is the activation cross-section in barns and incorporates ϕ. This then represents a handy formula for assessing the feasibility of any particular determination in the Harwell reactor and demonstrates the basically high sensitivity of the method since units of $\mu\mu$g are used. Similar expressions are readily obtained for other irradiation units and

† n = neutron(s).

measuring equipment. Jenkins and Smales (1956) have listed calculated sensitivities for the determination of most elements by neutron activation analysis, while Anders (1960 a) has listed experimentally determined neutron activation sensitivities (Table 2.1).

Other advantages

While the high sensitivity of the method of activation analysis is probably its most outstanding advantage, the fact that it is possible to eliminate errors due to contamination by impurities in reagents during processing is nearly as important. Once the sample has been removed from the irradiator, the analysis becomes one for the radioactive isotope of the element and not for the element itself. Thus it is possible to add several mg of the inactive element to act as a carrier for the trace quantity of radioactive atoms through any chemical purification stage, though care must be taken to ensure identity of chemical form. Incidentally, this introduces a further advantage in that the analysis is no longer on the micro-scale and conventional purification techniques of precipitation, etc., can be employed. Because several mg of the element are now present, the few μg of the element that are likely to arise from reagents are now negligible. Yet a further advantage arises in this carrier technique. If a known weight of carrier is added, and the weight of the final precipitate after purification is determined, it is possible to calculate the chemical yield of the process and so correct for any losses of radioactivity during this stage, since the radioactive yield will be the same as the chemical yield. Thus the purification need not be quantitative; centrifuging may be used instead of filtration without worrying about the small amount of precipitate which floats away with the supernatant solution, solutions need not be transferred quantitatively from one vessel to another, and purification procedures may be employed which, although highly specific, are not used in conventional analysis because of the low recoveries they introduce.

Finally, the remaining advantage of activation analysis is its specificity. Since the nuclear properties of a radioactive isotope, such as half-life, beta energy, and gamma energy are uniquely characteristic of that isotope, it is possible by measuring these quantities to ensure that the activity measured is appropriate to the element being determined. These factors, coupled with a specific radiochemical purification procedure where appropriate, all contribute to the high specificity of the activation method. While it is true that some radioisotopes have one nuclear property in common, it would be very strange if all were the

TABLE 2.1

Neutron activation sensitivities using a flux of 10^{12} n/cm²/sec

Element	Activated form	Half-life	Radio-chemical (a)	Gamma spectrometry (b)
Aluminium	Al 28	2·3 min	Low	3×10^9 (1·78 MeV)
Antimony	Sb 122	2·8 d	1×10^{11}	..
	Sb 122 (m)	3·5 min	..	4×10^8 (0·06 MeV)
Argon	A 41	1·8 hr	2×10^{10}	..
Arsenic	As 76	26·8 hr	2×10^{11}	1×10^7 (0·56 MeV)
Barium	Ba 139	85 min	1×10^{10}	2×10^8 (0·16 MeV)
Bismuth	Bi 210	5·0 d	2×10^8	..
Bromine	Br 80 (m)	4·6 hr	1×10^{11}	..
	Br 80	17·6 min	..	2×10^8 (0·64 MeV)
Cadmium	Cd 115	54 hr	1×10^{10}	..
	Cd 111 (m)	48·6 min	..	7×10^7 (0·24 MeV)
Caesium	Cs 134	2·3 y	2×10^{10}	..
	Cs 134 (m)	3·2 hr	..	2×10^8 (0·13 MeV)
Calcium	Ca 45	152 d	1×10^8	..
Cerium	Ce 141	32 d	1×10^{10}	..
	Ce 139 (m)	55 sec	..	1×10^7 (0·09 MeV)
Chlorine	Cl 38	37·3 min	2×10^9	7×10^7 (1·64 MeV) ⟵ se
Chromium	Cr 51	27 day	1×10^{10}*	..
	V 52	3·7 min	..	6×10^6 (1·47 MeV)
Cobalt	Co 60	5·2 y	2×10^{10}	..
	Co 60 (m)	10·5 min	..	8×10^9 (0·06 MeV)
Copper	Cu 64	12·8 hr	1×10^{11}	..
	Cu 66	5·1 min	..	3×10^8 (1·04 MeV)
Dysprosium	Dy 165	2·3 hr	1×10^{13}	..
	Dy 165 (m)	1·3 min	..	1×10^{11} (0·11 MeV)
Erbium	Er 171	7·5 hr	1×10^{11}	1×10^8 (0·11 MeV)
Europium	Eu 152 (m)	9·3 hr	1×10^{13}	2×10^7 (0·84 MeV)
Fluorine	O 19	29·4 sec	..	5×10^7 (0·19 MeV)
Gadolinium	Gd 159	18 hr	2×10^{10}	..
	Gd 161	3·6 min	..	6×10^7 (0·36 MeV)
Gallium	Ga 72	14·1 hr	1×10^{11}	2×10^8 (0·84 MeV)
Germanium	Ge 75	82 min	2×10^9	5×10^7 (0·26 MeV)
	Ge 75 (m)	48 sec	..	5×10^8 (0·13 MeV)
Gold	Au 198	2·7 d	2×10^{12}	1×10^9 (0·41 MeV)
Hafnium	Hf 181	45 d	2×10^{10}	..
	Hf 179 (m)	19 sec	..	2×10^{10} (0·22 MeV)
Helium	H 3	12·4 y†	2×10^6	..
Holmium	Ho 166	27·2 hr	2×10^{12}	5×10^8 (0·08 MeV)
Indium	In 116	54 min	1×10^{12}	7×10^{10} (1·27 MeV)
Iodine	I 128	25 min	1×10^{10}	3×10^9 (0·46 MeV)
Iridium	Ir 194	19 hr	1×10^{12}	8×10^8 (0·30 MeV)
	Ir 192 (m)	1·4 min	..	1×10^9 (0·06 MeV)
Iron	Fe 59	45 d	1×10^8	..
	Mn 56	2·6 hr	..	7×10^5 (0·85 MeV)
Krypton	Kr 85	4·4 hr	2×10^{11}	..
Lanthanum	La 140	40 hr	2×10^{11}	1×10^8 (0·50 MeV)
Lead	Pb 209	3·3 hr	2×10^6	..
Lithium	H 3	12·4 y†	2×10^{10}	..
Lutecium	Lu 177	6·8 d	2×10^{12}	2×10^8 (0·20 MeV)
	Lu 176 (m)	3·7 hr	..	2×10^9 (0·08 MeV)
Magnesium	Mg 27	9·6 min	2×10^5	5×10^7 (0·84 MeV)

TABLE 2.1 (cont.)

Element	Activated form	Half-life	Radio-chemical (a)	Gamma spectrometry (b)
Manganese	Mn 56	2·6 hr	1×10^{12}	7×10^7 (0·85 MeV)
Mercury	Hg 203	48 d	1×10^{10}	..
	Hg 199 (m)	42 min	..	9×10^6 (0·16 MeV)
Molybdenum	Mo 99	67 hr	1×10^9	..
	Mo 101	14·6 min	..	1×10^8 (0·19 MeV)
Neodymium	Nd 147	11·6 d	2×10^{10}	..
	Nd 149	2 hr	..	3×10^8 (0·11 MeV)
Nickel	Ni 65	2·6 hr	1×10^9	1×10^6 (1·12 MeV)
Niobium	Nb 94 (m)	6·6 min	2×10^2	3×10^7 (0·87 MeV)
Osmium	Os 193	31 hr	1×10^{10}	..
	Os 190 (m)	9·5 min	..	1×10^7 (0·34 MeV)
Oxygen	F 18	112 min	2×10^7	..
Palladium	Pd 109	13·4 hr	1×10^{11}	..
	Pd 109 (m)	4·8 min	..	6×10^8 (0·18 MeV)
Phosphorus	P 32	14·3 d	2×10^{10}	..
Platinum	Pt 197	18 hr	1×10^{10}	..
	Pt 199	31 min	..	9×10^7 (0·19 MeV)
Potassium	K 42	12·4 hr	1×10^{10}	2×10^6 (1·53 MeV)
Praseodymium	Pr 142	19·3 hr	2×10^{11}	6×10^6 (1·57 MeV)
Rhenium	Re 188	17 hr	1×10^{12}	..
	Re 188 (m)	18·7 min	..	4×10^9 (0·06 MeV)
Rhodium	Rh 104 (m)	4·3 min	2×10^3	1×10^{10} (0·55 MeV)
	Rh 104	44 sec	..	1×10^{11} (0·05 MeV)
Rubidium	Rb 86	19 d	2×10^{10}	..
	Rb 86 (m)	1·0 min	..	4×10^8 (0·56 MeV)
Ruthenium	Ru 105	4·5 hr	1×10^{10}	2×10^7 (0·73 MeV)
Samarium	Sm 153	46 hr	1×10^{12}	1×10^9 (0·11 MeV)
Scandium	Sc 46	85 d	2×10^{11}	..
	Sc 46 (m)	19·5 sec	..	3×10^{10} (0·14 MeV)
Selenium	Se 81 (m)	57 min	2×10^8	..
	Se 77 (m)	17·5 sec	..	2×10^9 (0·16 MeV)
Silicon	Si 31	2·6 hr	1×10^9	7×10^5 (1·26 MeV)
	Al 28	2·3 min	..	4×10^7 (1·78 MeV)
Silver	Ag 110 (m)	270 d	2×10^9	..
	Ag 110	24·2 sec	..	6×10^7 (0·66 MeV)
Sodium	Na 24	15 hr	1×10^{11}	8×10^7 (1·37 MeV)
Strontium	Sr 89	54 d	1×10^8	..
	Sr 87 (m)	2·8 hr	..	5×10^7 (0·39 MeV)
Sulphur	P 32	14·3 d§	2×10^8	..
Tantalum	Ta 182	111 d	1×10^{11}	..
	Ta 182 (m)	16·5 min	..	5×10^7 (0·17 MeV)
Tellurium	Te 127	9·3 hr	2×10^9	..
	Te 131	25 min	..	3×10^8 (0·15 MeV)
Terbium	Tb 160	73 d	2×10^{11}	1×10^7 (0·30 MeV)
Thallium	Tl 204	2·7 y	1×10^9	..
	Tl 206	4·2 min	..	3×10^7 (0·06 MeV)
Thorium	Th 233	22 min	2×10^9	2×10^9 (0·07 MeV)
	Pa 233	27·4 d	1×10^{11}	..
Thulium	Tm 170	129 d	2×10^{11}	1×10^7 (0·08 MeV)
Tin	Sn 121	27 hr	2×10^9	..
	Sn 125 (m)	9·5 min	..	1×10^8 (0·32 MeV)
Titanium	Ti 51	5·8 min	1×10^3	2×10^8 (0·32 MeV)

TABLE 2.1 (*cont.*)

Element	Activated form	Half-life	Radio-chemical (a)	Gamma spectrometry (b)	
Tungsten	W 187	24 hr	2×10^{11}	2×10^{8}	(0·07 MeV)
Uranium	U 239	23·5 min	1×10^{9}	2×10^{10}	(0·10 MeV)
	Np 239	2·3 d	1×10^{11}	..	
Vanadium	V 52	3·7 min	..	4×10^{10}	(1·47 MeV)
Xenon	Xe 133	5·3 d	2×10^{9}	..	
Ytterbium	Yb 175	4·2 d	2×10^{11}	..	
	Yb 177	1·9 hr	..	7×10^{7}	(0·13 MeV)
Yttrium	Y 90	61 hr	1×10^{11}	..	
	Y 89 (m)	16·1 sec	..	7×10^{7}	(0·91 MeV)
Zinc	Zn 69	52 min	2×10^{9}	..	
	Zn 69 (m)	13·8 hr	..	4×10^{6}	(0·44 MeV)
Zirconium	Zr 97	17 hr	1×10^{8}	4×10^{5}	(0·75 MeV)

Notes. (a) The values quoted are approximate counts per minute per g calculated for use with a Geiger counter operating at 10 per cent. efficiency for beta particles or positrons of maximum energy greater than 0·2 MeV, and at 1 per cent. efficiency for particles of lower energy (†). In some cases (*) gamma photons per minute are quoted instead. The irradiations are assumed to have been made at a thermal neutron flux of 10^{12} n/cm²/sec to saturation (with a maximum of one month) and to have been followed by a 2-hour radiochemical purification. Where fast-neutron reactions are involved (§), a flux of ∼ 10^{11} n/cm²/sec of effective energy greater than 1 MeV is assumed. For further details see Jenkins and Smales (1956).

(b) The values quoted are experimentally determined counts per minute ($\times 10^{4}$) per g for the photopeak of the energy stated on a multichannel analyser using a 7·5 × 7·5 cm sodium iodide crystal, at 28·6 per cent. of 4π, solid angle. The irradiations were made at a neutron flux of 10^{8} n/cm²/sec for 5 minutes followed by 1 minute delay before counting. The neutron energy distribution was that obtained by the moderation of 2 MeV neutrons with a 60-cm cube of paraffin wax. For further details see Anders (1960 a).

same. Thus, manganese 56 and nickel 65 which have similar half-lives and also similar beta energies (0·65, 1·04, 2·81 MeV; and 0·60, 1·01, 2·10 MeV respectively) have quite different gamma energies (0·85, 1·81, 2·12 MeV; and 0·37, 1·12, 1·49 MeV respectively) so that they are readily distinguishable. It is not always possible to measure every nuclear property of the radioisotope produced, but it is usually possible to measure sufficient of these to confirm unequivocally the identity and purity of the isotope being measured.

Disadvantages

It is only fair to list the disadvantages of activation analysis, but fortunately these are comparatively few. The main disadvantage is that a nuclear reactor is necessary for highest sensitivity. Many analyses do not require all the available sensitivity, however, and laboratory neutron sources or neutron generators have often proved adequate (De and Meinke, 1958; Meinke, 1960). A further disadvantage is that activation analysis only measures the total weight of an element and takes no account of different states of combination. Thus, no distinction could be made between, say, organically bound chlorine and ionic chlorine by this technique.

There are other disadvantages in activation analysis, concerned with some of the precautions which must be taken to avoid errors, but these will be considered in Chapter 7.

3

ACTIVATION BY NEUTRONS

NEUTRONS are produced by a variety of physical processes, many of which have been suggested as sources for activation analysis. Relatively small, portable neutron sources can be made utilizing nuclides undergoing spontaneous fission, or those which produce neutrons by nuclear reactions. These all give low fluxes, and the available flux is the biggest single factor limiting the sensitivity of neutron activation. Suitable machines can be used to accelerate charged particles which then yield secondary beams of neutrons from suitable targets. These give larger fluxes, but in practice neither of these types of source is used a great deal, especially when a nuclear reactor is available. Some of the sources yielding low fluxes will be described before the advantages and disadvantages of activation in reactors are considered.

Portable sources of neutrons

Among the many photonuclear reactions that have been investigated, the $H^2(\gamma, n) H^1$ and $Be^9(\gamma, n) Be^8$ reactions have much the lowest threshold energies, 2·2 and 1·7 MeV respectively. Hence a mixture of antimony 124 and beryllium is a commonly used neutron source, since the active nuclide emits 1·71 and 2·04 MeV γ-rays and has a half-life of 60 days. The neutrons produced are fast and have to be slowed down with graphite or paraffin wax for most analytical applications. One curie of antimony 124 sealed in a beryllium cup can yield up to 10^4 n/cm²/sec (Fig. 3.1). This is sufficient to activate a number of elements, including scandium, manganese, vanadium, cobalt, rhodium, iridium, indium, silver, and several lanthanides. Some potential applications have been described by De and Meinke (1958).

Portable neutron sources employing the (α, n) reaction give larger fluxes, but are also more expensive, than those based on photonuclear reactions. The reaction of choice is the $Be^9(\alpha, n) C^{12}$ conversion, but the source of alpha particles must be determined by cost, availability, and the need for screening off γ-rays (Hess, 1957; Shiokawa and Yagi, 1959). Polonium (Mayr, 1954), radium (Govaerts, 1955; Gueben and Govaerts, 1957; Kusaka, 1960; Meinke and Anderson, 1953; Aoki and

FIG. 3.2. Van de Graaff accelerator at Aldermaston. This can be used to accelerate beams of protons or deuterons to 6 MeV.

FIG. 3.1. Antimony 124/Beryllium neutron source (suspended from wire) and shield.

FIG. 3.3. BEPO, the Harwell reactor which burns natural uranium and uses graphite as a moderator. The maximum flux is 1.2×10^{12} neutrons/cm²/sec.

Okada, 1959), actinium (Meinke, 1958), plutonium (Stewart, 1953; Sheldon and Williams, 1954; Varres, 1960), and americium (Strain *et al.*, 1960) have all been suggested and the fluxes to which they give rise are listed in Table 5.1. Of these, polonium gives the fewest γ-rays, but it is a volatile element and hence somewhat difficult to handle. The neutrons produced are mainly fast, with energy peaks in the 3–5 MeV region. A radon-beryllium source was used for the first activation analyses ever carried out, involving two lanthanides with unusually large cross-sections, dysprosium and europium (Hevesy and Levy, 1936 and 1938).

An extremely promising source of neutrons is the nuclide californium 252, which has a half-life of 2·6 years. This undergoes spontaneous fission and a 10 mg source will provide as many as 3×10^{10} neutrons per second (Anon., 1956); these neutrons have a mean energy of 1·5 MeV. At present this isotope, which has to be made artificially, is in very short supply.

Accelerating machines

Beams of protons and deuterons from accelerating machines can also be used to produce neutrons. The most efficient conversion reactions are the $Li^7(p, n) Be^7$, $H^3(d, n) He^4$, and $Be^9(d, n) B^{10}$ reactions, but neutrons are also released during the bombardment of many light elements. These neutrons are more or less monoenergetic, depending on the incident energy, which is always in the MeV range, but this has not been utilized for activating specific nuclides. Peck and Eubank (1955) have described how the Cockcroft–Walton accelerator can be modified for producing fast neutrons at fluxes up to 2×10^{10} n/cm^2/sec. However, Shideler, Wahlgren, and Meinke (1960) describe a similar machine giving much lower fluxes which require a considerable thickness of shielding to protect the operator. Modifications to the van de Graaff accelerator (Fig. 3.2) can yield thermal neutron fluxes of $2·5 \times 10^8$ n/cm^2/sec (Burrill and Gale, 1954; Atchison and Beamer, 1956; Wagner *et al.*, 1960) and cyclotrons have also been used as neutron generators on occasion. Photon fission of uranium 235 has been used by Poole and Rae (1960) to generate 3×10^{17} neutrons per second in pulses of 0·2 microsecond duration. These neutrons have a mean energy of 0·8 MeV and are associated with a very high flux of 30 MeV photons from the linear accelerator. The photons would activate many elements more strongly than would the neutrons. Pulsed neutron sources of this or other kinds could perhaps be usefully employed in activating nuclides of very short half-life: they are fully described by Burrill and MacGregor (1960).

Reactors

None of the neutron sources mentioned above compares in intensity with the neutrons available from controlled nuclear fission in a large reactor, of which a typical example is shown in Fig. 3.3. The production of neutrons during fission of heavy nuclei, first discovered by von Halban, Joliot, and Kowarski (1939), has been widely studied in view of its technological significance. The fission of uranium 235 by thermal neutrons produces, on average, 2·47 neutrons for each atom decomposed. The corresponding figure for plutonium 239 is 2·91. By concentrating these fissionable nuclides, and controlling the neutron density by suitably placed moderators, it is possible to obtain fluxes as high as 10^{15} n/cm^2/sec. Certain low-powered research reactors can have fluxes as low as 4×10^7 n/cm^2/sec and all others have fluxes between these limits.

There are a number of technical difficulties associated with the use of reactors for activation analysis. In the first place, the neutrons in a reactor are not all 'thermal', that is, in the energy range close to 0·025 eV, but some are 'epithermal', with energies up to 1 MeV, and others have energies exceeding 1 MeV and are termed 'fast'. The ratio of fast to slow neutrons in a reactor core depends on the type of fuel, the moderator, and the geometry of the system. Fast neutrons can be converted to thermal neutrons by inserting a suitable thickness of graphite between the reactor and the sample, but this may cut down the flux several hundredfold. Fortunately the energy distribution of neutrons in most reactors, for example the Harwell reactor BEPO, is of the type shown in Fig. 3.4. Since the bulk of the neutrons are thermal, effects due to the remainder can often be neglected.

Flux variations in reactors can be considerable, as shown in Fig. 3.5. Here the thermal neutron flux is greatly depressed in the neighbourhood of the fuel elements. Fortunately these variations are known to reactor physicists, and in practice it is not difficult to find a position in BEPO, for example, where the flux varies no more than 2 per cent. over the length of a 3-inch can.

The core of a reactor also possesses a high flux of γ-rays, and occasionally (γ, n) reactions can interfere with an analysis. More often, however, they have a negligible effect or even assist in the activation of the desired nuclide.

Most reactors with a flux of 10^{13} n/cm²/sec or greater operate at a relatively high temperature. This may preclude the use of liquids, biological material, and polythene containers unless special precautions are taken. It should also be remembered that no reactor has yet been built specifically for activation analysis. Hence regions of high flux may be difficult of access (e.g. under 20 feet of water shielding) and expensive to employ.

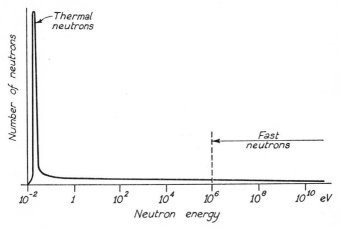

FIG. 3.4. Distribution of neutron energies in a reactor.

Since interest is shifting to nuclides of shorter half-life, the engineering problems involved in transporting activated samples from reactor cores to the laboratory in the shortest possible time have been investigated (Meinke, 1959 b). Lengths of aluminium tubing are used as guides, and small plastic containers, known as 'rabbits', are blown in or out of the reactor using compressed air. It is possible to transmit a rabbit from a reactor to the laboratory in a few seconds: Fig. 9.2 shows the type of rabbit used at Harwell.

Finally, the use of high fluxes results in shielding problems, since even canning materials of the highest purity become extremely radioactive after exposure to them. For example, after 30 minutes' exposure to a flux of 10^{14} n/cm²/sec, a gramme of aluminium would have an activity of 140 curies. Most reactor cans weigh at least 10 grammes and contain impurities which contribute substantially to the induced activity.

A recent development is the construction of relatively low-priced pulsed reactors, in which a supercritical state is maintained for an extremely short period. For example, the TRIGA reactor is capable of yielding 8×10^{15} n/cm^2/sec during a 40 millisecond pulse, and this might be used to activate short-lived nuclides. In future years it may be possible to produce neutrons by fusing light nuclei at extremely high temperatures. The reactions

$$H^2 + H^2 \to He^3 + n^1$$

and

$$H^2 + H^3 \to He^4 + n^1$$

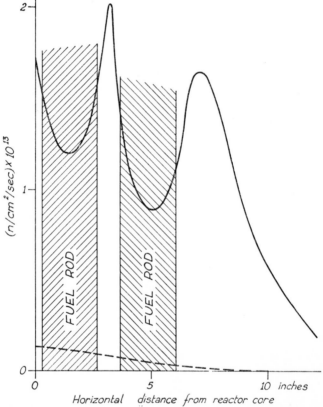

FIG. 3.5. Variation in thermal (——) and epithermal (- - - -) neutron fluxes across a reactor core, showing depressions inside the fuel rods. MERLIN enriched uranium reactor, moderated with light water and running at 1 MW. Reproduced by permission of K. G. Stephens and G. W. Williams, A.E.I., Aldermaston.

are both exothermic and should take place at a temperature of about 10^7 degrees. The technical difficulties of producing such temperatures are formidable but neutrons have in fact been produced by electrical discharges through deuterium gas. The highest neutron flux so far reported from this source is only 10^7 neutrons per discharge, but

TABLE 3.1

Thermal neutron outputs or fluxes obtainable from various sources

Source	Neutron output or flux	Other radiations	$T°$ C	$t_{\frac{1}{2}}$ or pulse	Reference
1 curie $Sb^{124}+Be^9$	$3·2\times10^6$ n/sec	γ	ambient	60 d	Atkins and Smales, 1959
1 curie $Po^{210}+Be^9$	$2·5\times10^6$ n/sec	α	,,	138 d	R.C.C. Catalogue, 1960
1 curie $Ac^{227}+Be^9$	$1·8\times10^7$ n/sec	α, γ	,,	22 yr	
1 curie $Ra^{226}+Be^9$	$1·3\times10^7$ n/sec	α, γ	,,	1600 yr	Stewart, 1953
0·9 curie (13·5 g) $Pu^{239}+Be^9$	$1·2\times10^6$ n/sec	α, γ	,,	$2·4\times10^4$ yr	Anon., 1956
24 curies (30 mg) Cf^{252}	10^{11} n/sec	α, γ	hot	2·2 yr	Poole and Rae, 1960
Linear accelerator $\gamma+U^{235}$	5×10^9 n/pulse	γ	100° C	$0·2\times10^{-6}$ sec	Peck and Eubank, 1955
Cockcroft–Walton $d+H^3$	10^{10} n/cm²/sec	α, γ	ambient	...	Taylor and Havens, 1950
Cyclotron $d+Be^9$	10^{12} n/sec	d, γ	100° C	...	Atchison and Beamer, 1956
van de Graaff $d+Be^9$	$2·5\times10^8$ n/cm²/sec	d, γ	60° C	...	
GLEEP, Harwell	$3·7\times10^{10}$ n/cm²/sec	γ	80° C	...	
BEPO, Harwell	$1·5\times10^{12}$ n/cm²/sec	γ	40° C	...	I.A.E.A., 1959
DIDO, Harwell	10^{14} n/cm²/sec	γ	100° C	...	
M.T.R., Idaho	5×10^{14} n/cm²/sec	γ	100° C	...	
TRIGA	8×10^{15} n/cm²/sec	γ	ambient	0·04 sec	Davenport, 1959
Thermonuclear reaction	10^7 n/pulse	γ	high	0·001 sec	
20 kton atomic bomb	4×10^{24} neutrons	γ	10^6 °C	10^{-6} sec	Cowan, 1960
1 Mton H-bomb	2×10^{27} ,,	γ	,,	,,	

developments in this field are likely to be rapid and may lead to even higher neutron densities than are obtainable in reactors. A neutron is produced for each 10^{-5} ergs used in the reaction, so that discharges of 100 megajoules, which would be needed to sustain the high temperatures, could give rise to about 10^{20} neutrons with energies in the MeV range. These would have to be slowed down, and might give rise to a flux of 10^{15} n/cm²/sec over a large area outside the apparatus.

Reactions of neutrons

The binding energy E of a nucleus, which is the energy required to split it into its component protons and neutrons, can be calculated from the simple formula

$$E = 931(1 \cdot 008145Z + 1 \cdot 008986N - M) \text{ MeV},$$

where Z is the number of protons, N the number of neutrons, and M the mass of the nucleus (relative to $O^{16} = 16 \cdot 000$). If the binding energy

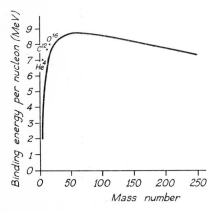

FIG. 3.6. Binding energy per nucleon as a function of mass number.

per nucleon, $E/(N+Z)$, is plotted against the mass number $(N+Z)$, the curve shown in Fig. 3.6 is obtained. Hence for all but the lightest nuclei, the binding energy per nucleon is $8 \cdot 0 \pm 0 \cdot 5$ MeV.

Because they carry no charge, neutrons can penetrate atomic nuclei without having to overcome any electrical energy barrier. A nucleus which gains a neutron increases its energy by 6–8 MeV plus any kinetic energy which the neutron may have possessed. Sometimes the resulting nucleus is stable, but if it is not, its mode of decomposition depends on the kinetic energy of the incident neutron. Thermal neutrons, which have a mean energy of $0 \cdot 025$ eV, generally give rise to (n, γ) reactions, while (n, p) and (n, α) reactions mostly take place with fast neutrons. This is because it requires less energy to expel a photon than a particle from a nucleus. Fast neutrons, with kinetic energies greater than 1 MeV, can give rise to many alternative types of nuclear reaction. Thus most $(n, 2n)$ reactions have a threshold energy of about 10 MeV, $(n, 3n)$ reactions require about 30 MeV, and so on. When 100 MeV neutrons are used spallation reactions occur, in which the target nuclei are broken down and give rise to a mixture of lighter nuclides: this type of reaction makes activation analysis unnecessarily complicated, and there are other cogent reasons for restricting activation to low-energy neutrons for analytical work. In the first place, low-energy neutrons activate chiefly by the (n, γ) process with the minimum of side reactions, and in addition the cross-sections of most elements are largest for slow neutrons. The recoil energies of nuclei undergoing (n, γ) processes only suffice to shift the atoms a few Ångströms (Novey, 1944; Yosim and Davies, 1951; Pauly, 1955) so it is unlikely that many activated atoms will be driven out of the sample into its container and vice versa. The latter possibility should be considered when thin samples undergo (n, p) and (n, α) reactions, where the recoil distances are of the order of microns (Baulch and Duncan, 1958; Süe, 1955 a; Pauly, 1955). Fast neutrons also increase the likelihood of Szilard-Chalmers reactions, which can convert some activated nuclides to chemical forms which do not readily equilibrate with added carrier in the separation process (Nilsson, 1956; Harbottle and Sutin, 1959).

A hazard may arise from radiation damage to the sample, if this evolves volatile products and builds up a high pressure inside a sealed container. Fortunately this hazard is only appreciable for irradiations in high fluxes for periods of a week or more. Under these conditions aqueous solutions may evolve an explosive mixture of hydrogen and oxygen, nitrates evolve oxygen, ammonium salts give nitrogen and hydrogen, and acetates give carbon dioxide and methane. For example, 1 g ammonium bromide yields 11 ml gas (at N.T.P.) after 150 hours at 10^{11} n/cm^2/sec in BEPO (Taylor, 1961).

Although the cross-sections for neutrons have been extensively studied for every element in the periodic table, the energy range to be covered is so wide that data are seldom complete. At low energies the neutron-capture cross-sections are often inversely proportional to the neutron velocity (Whitehouse and Putman, 1953), but at higher energies so-called resonance peaks occur, as shown in Figs. 3.7 and 3.8. The wide range of values obtained makes it necessary to employ log-log scales in these figures. The behaviour of silicon is typical of the majority of elements, while cadmium is unusual in its very high cross-section for neutrons with low energies.

The geometrical cross-sections of nuclei are of the order of 2·5 barns, which makes it a little difficult to understand how certain elements have vastly greater cross-sections for neutrons of particular energies. The element cadmium, as shown in Fig. 3.8 has a cross-section of 7000

barns at about 0·1 eV and dysprosium 164 has a cross-section as large
as $2·6 \times 10^6$ barns. The explanation of these anomalies lies in the wave-
like properties of the neutron. At thermal energies of 0·025 eV, for
example, the wavelength of a neutron is about 0·04 mm, so that it can
interact with nuclei over a correspondingly large volume.

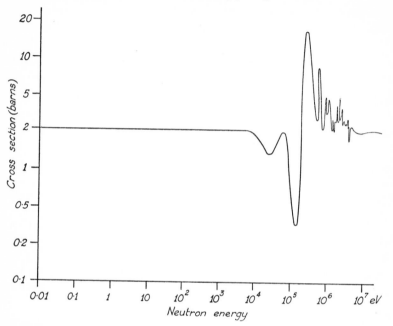

FIG. 3.7. Cross-section of silicon as a function of neutron energy: from
Hughes and Schwartz, 1958.

There are no methods known for calculating neutron activation cross-
sections from other physical constants, and the empirical values show
no obvious regularities (see Chapter 13). The values for thermal neutrons
have been plotted against half-life of the daughter nuclide by Meinke
and Anderson (1953), and a glance at their graph shows that, in general,
nuclides with odd mass numbers have larger cross-sections than those
with even mass numbers. (A notable exception is dysprosium 164,
which has the largest cross-section known.) This may be connected
with the greater stability of even nuclides and hence their relative
abundance in the universe. Several useful tabulations of neutron cross-
sections (Hughes and Schwartz, 1958) and other activation data (Rochlin,
1957; Koch, 1960) now exist.

Thermal neutrons have been extensively used for activation analysis
by (n, γ) reactions since the discovery of this reaction by Lea in 1934

and its pioneering applications by Hevesy and Levy (1936, 1938). In almost every case the γ-ray has not been measured, but the nuclide produced has been determined with or without chemical separation. Occasionally the photons have been observed by recording their tracks on a nuclear emulsion which was insensitive to neutrons (Hillert, 1951; Mayr, 1954), or counted directly (Galuzo, 1958).

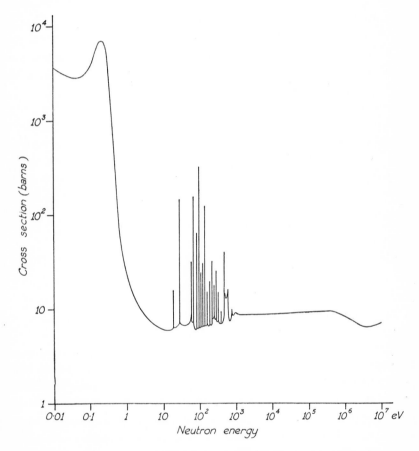

FIG. 3.8. Cross-section of cadmium as a function of neutron energy: from Hughes and Schwartz, 1958.

The occurrence of fast neutron reactions, mostly (n, p) and (n, α), in reactors has been reviewed by Mellish, Payne, and Otlet (1957), Fink (1957), and by Lbov and Naumova (1959). (n, p) reactions have not found much application in practice, though they have been used to determine the rare nuclide He^3 in natural gases (Coon, 1949) and in meteorites (Fireman and Schwarzer, 1957). Other applications include the determination of oxygen in metals (Coleman and Perkin, 1959 and 1960; Lbov and Naumova, 1959) and of aluminium in minerals (Brownell *et al.*, 1957). The relatively low cross-sections for fast neutrons render (n, p) reactions less sensitive for analytical purposes than (n, γ) reactions, as is well shown by the work of Turner (1956), who determined silicon and aluminium by activation with 14 MeV neutrons obtained by bombarding tritium targets with deuterons. This author gives data for a number of other elements, including Cl, Cr, Cu, Fe, Mg, O, P, V, and Zr, which could be determined using short irradiation times. Gibbons and Simpson (1960 *b*) have determined sulphur in the presence of phosphorus making use of the $S^{32}(n, p) P^{32}$ reaction and subtracting contributions from the $P^{31}(n, \gamma) P^{32}$ reaction.

Although the first (n, α) reactions to be discovered were those of nitrogen, oxygen, fluorine, and neon (Feather, 1932), these reactions have been used mainly for determining two light nuclides with outstandingly large cross-sections for this type of reaction, lithium 6 and boron 10. The reactions concerned are

$$\mathrm{Li^6} + n^1 \xrightarrow{\ 950\ \mathrm{barns}\ } \mathrm{H^3} + \mathrm{He^4} + 4{\cdot}5\ \mathrm{MeV},$$

$$\mathrm{B^{10}} + n^1 \xrightarrow{\ 4020\ \mathrm{barns}\ } \mathrm{Li^7} + \mathrm{He^4} + 2{\cdot}5\ \mathrm{MeV}$$

and only in the first case is one of the product nuclides unstable. In practice the nuclides have always been determined from the number of alpha-particles (or tritons) produced. In the original application to lithium 6 by Glueckauf, Kitt, and Barker (1949), the alpha-particles were counted with a scintillation counter but, apart from the work of Wänke and Morse (1955), all subsequent workers have measured particle tracks or total blackening produced in nuclear emulsions. The techniques have been made quite sensitive (10^{-11} g for $\mathrm{Li^6}$ (Picciotto and Van Styvandael, 1951); 10^{-9} g for $\mathrm{B^{10}}$ (Mayr, Bruner, and Brucer, 1953)), but are liable to interference by proton tracks produced by the $N^{14}(n, p) C^{14}$ reaction. It requires some skill to distinguish these tracks from alpha particle tracks when the photographic plate is viewed under a microscope. The bibliography can be consulted for further references on this type of activation: for lithium, see Ficq (1951 and 1954), Herr (1953), Fireman and Schwarzer (1956), Keinberger *et al.* (1957), Dent and Sheppard (1957), and Coleman (1960); for boron, see Hillert (1951), Cuer and Longchamp (1951), Faraggi, Kohn, and Doumerc (1952), Mayr (1954), and Edwards (1956). Calcium has also been measured by the (n, α) reaction (Wänke, 1958), and fluorine gives rise to 7·4-second nitrogen 16 which is detectable by its 6·4 MeV photon (Anders, 1960 b). Some workers have pointed out the possibility of second-order reactions occurring, for example $In^{116} (n, \gamma) In^{117} (n, \gamma) In^{118}$. The extent to which double neutron capture occurs is a function of the square of the flux, but does not affect analyses carried out by a comparison of sample and standard. $(n, 2n)$ reactions have been found useful in determining lead and thallium (Reed et al., 1959).

A few of the very heaviest nuclides can be determined by (n, f) reactions. Fission was first discovered by Meitner and Frisch in 1939, and has been extensively studied since that time. Certain nuclides, for example uranium 235 and plutonium 239, will undergo fission when bombarded with thermal neutrons, while others like thorium 232 and uranium 238 require bombardment with neutrons with energies in the MeV range before fission occurs. Fission of elements as light as tantalum can be accomplished when neutrons with energies of 100 MeV or more are used for bombardment. The energy released in fission of uranium 235 is about 200 MeV and most of this appears as kinetic energy of fission-product nuclides. The latter include all the elements from zinc to dysprosium in the periodic table, and the majority are both neutron-rich and radioactive. Hence there are two methods of measuring the extent of the (n, f) reaction. One involves counting the number of fission fragments produced, using either nuclear emulsions (Curie and Faraggi, 1951) or an ionization counter (Stewart and Bentley, 1954). An equally useful method is to isolate a fission product whose yield in fission is known, and hence to calculate the original content of the fissionable nuclide. It is not even necessary to know the fission yield if a uranium standard is available. This procedure has been employed by Smales (1952), Reed and Turkevich (1955), and Mackintosh and Jervis (1957) who isolated barium 140, by Fisher and Beydon (1953) who isolated tellurium 132, and by Ebert et al. (1959) who isolated xenon 133. If uranium 235 is being determined by activation in a nuclear reactor, care must be taken that fast neutron fission of uranium 238 does not produce comparable amounts of fission products to slow neutron fission of the light isotope. This interference can be avoided by using a thermal neutron column, surrounded by graphite, for activation (Seyfang and Smales, 1953) or by using very short activation times (May and Leveque, 1957). Uranium, and to a lesser extent thorium, can interfere with the determination of a large number of elements by activation because they produce so many fission products.

Fortunately uranium can be quantitatively removed from samples before activation by solvent extraction (Stewart and Bentley, 1954; Morrison and Freiser, 1957), but in practice it is preferable to correct counts for the uranium content, when this is known. Loveridge *et al.* (1960) give practical examples of this correction in the determination of strontium.

4

ACTIVATION BY PARTICLES OTHER
THAN NEUTRONS

RADIOACTIVATION can be brought about by almost any particle under suitable conditions. γ-rays, neutrons, protons, deuterons, tritons, and α-particles have all been used, but practically all the analytical work so far has been carried out using thermal neutrons. The main reasons for this fact are, as will be shown, technical rather than theoretical. If neutrons are used for activation, neutron-rich isotopes are normally produced, that is, those isotopes with a large ratio of neutrons to protons in their nuclei. However, at least 50 per cent. of the known radioisotopes are proton-rich, and must be prepared by bombardment with protons or some other particle which expels a neutron. Hence in order to appreciate the full potentialities of activation analysis, it is necessary to consider the methods which have been used to prepare proton-rich isotopes. Each of these has certain disadvantages which has limited its range of application in analysis. Some of these disadvantages are inherent and others may be overcome by future technical developments. The methods will be considered in turn, starting with activation by photons of high energy, or γ-rays.

γ-ray activation

Photon activation was first reported by Chadwick and Goldhaber (1934). A number of workers have studied the physical processes involved in activation by γ-rays, and while the activation process itself is by no means understood, the empirical observations can be summarized quite simply. The cross-section of any nuclide for γ-rays depends on their energy. There is always a threshold energy, below which no activation is observed, and a maximum energy beyond which the cross-section for the reaction studied decreases markedly. Typical plots of cross-section against photon energy are shown in Fig. 4.1.

As Odeblad (in Yoe and Koch, 1957) has pointed out, the decrease in cross-section after the maximum is reached is caused by competition from interfering nuclear reactions. In nearly every case the (γ, n)

threshold is the lowest, but at higher energies other reactions such as $(\gamma, 2n)$ and $(\gamma; p, n)$ become important at the expense of the (γ, n).

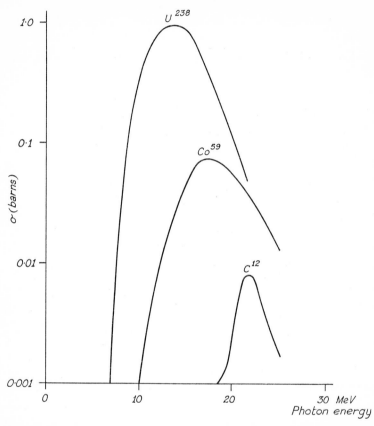

Fig. 4.1. Cross-sections of (γ, n) reactions of carbon 12, cobalt 59, and uranium 238 as a function of photon energy: from Nathans and Halpern, 1954.

Fig. 4.2 shows the threshold energy dependence on mass number, and also the energies at which the cross-sections are maximal. Apart from the nuclides deuterium and beryllium 9, which are anomalous, the threshold energies decrease fairly smoothly from about 22 MeV for helium to 6 MeV for uranium. 15–25 MeV is the most efficient range of photon energies for activation. Problems involved in producing such photons from linear accelerators are discussed by MacGregor (1957 a). The cross-sections for photons increase with atomic number from 9 millibarns for carbon 12 to nearly 1 barn for uranium 238. MacGregor (1957 b) has given a useful list of activities caused by bombarding elements with photons of 20 and 25 MeV, from which the data of Table

4.1 have been abstracted. The cross-sections for the medium-weight elements in the periodic table are therefore much smaller than the cross-sections for (n, γ) reactions. This is probably the main reason for the lack of interest in this means of activation. Large X-ray machines and linear accelerators are becoming more widely used, but they cannot always produce photons of sufficient energy for activation. Gamma

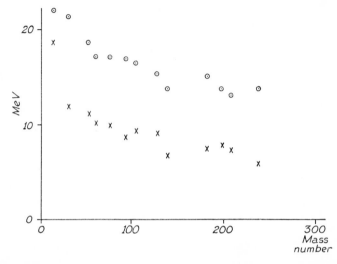

FIG. 4.2. Threshold energies (X) and energies of maximum cross-section (◯) for (γ, n) reactions as a function of mass number: from Nathans and Halpern, 1954.

radiation from nuclear reactors, fission products, cobalt 60, and other commonly used sources has a mean energy around 1 MeV, which is inadequate for activation work. Self-shielding and canning problems scarcely exist for photon activation because of the high energies involved. However, the fluxes available are not generally as large as neutron fluxes. A typical electron linear accelerator might deliver 100 rads per second, which corresponds to $1\cdot9 \times 10^{11}$ photons/cm²/sec, though the largest accelerator in the U.S.A. can yield 7×10^{14} 20 MeV photons/cm²/sec at full power. These photons are spread from the maximum energy to zero in a bremsstrahlung distribution, and only a small percentage may have sufficient energy for activation. Interfering reactions can often be prevented by keeping the energy of the photons below the threshold for the competing processes. In view of their lower threshold energy and higher cross-section it would seem logical to test photon activation of some of the heavy elements which are not strongly activated by neutrons, for example niobium and lead. So far analyses

TABLE 4.1

Activities produced by (γ, n) reactions using 10 kW linear accelerators (from MacGregor, 1957): irradiation time $\leqslant$ 1 hour

Active nuclide	$t_{\frac{1}{2}}$	mc/g produced by 20 MeV photons	mc/g produced by 25 MeV photons
C^{11}	20 m	2	80
N^{13}	10 m	9	40
O^{15}	2 m	5000	40,000
F^{18}	1·9 h	7	15
Ne^{19}	18 s	8	45
Na^{22}	2·6 y	0·002	0·004
Mg^{23}	12 s	10	58
Al^{26}	6·5 s	50	130
Si^{27}	4·9 s	15	60
P^{30}	2·6 m	60	110
S^{31}	3·2 s	18	70
A^{39}	265 y	0·0001	0·0002
Ca^{39}	1 s	9	40
Cr^{49}	42 m	3	6
Mn^{54}	310 d	0·025	0·035
Fe^{53}	8·9 m	6	16
Fe^{55}	2·9 y	0·004	0·009
Co^{58}	72 d	0·075	0·15
Ni^{57}	1·5 d	1·4	3
Cu^{62}	10 m	240	240
Cu^{64}	12·8 h	7	13
Zn^{63}	38 m	110	250
As^{74}	17 d	0·4	0·55
Br^{78}	6·4 m	120	160
Br^{80}	18 m	90	180
Br^{80m}	4·6 h	6	11
Rb^{86}	19 d	0·14	0·29
Sr^{85}	65 d	0·011	0·018
Y^{88}	2 h	7	10
Zr^{89}	3·3 d	2	4
Zr^{89m}	4·4 m	210	400
Nb^{92}	22 h	11	17
Mo^{91}	75 s	4	8
Mo^{91m}	16 m	21	40
Mo^{99}	2·9 d	0·6	0·8
Rh^{102}	210 d	0·05	0·075
Ag^{106}	24 m	200	300
Ag^{108}	2·3 m	200	300
In^{114}	1·2 m	100	140
In^{114m}	49 d	0·37	0·55
Sb^{120}	16 m	240	300
Sb^{122}	2·8 d	3	4
I^{126}	13 d	0·8	1·1
Ta^{180}	8·1 h	40	60
Au^{196}	5·6 d	2	3
Th^{231}	1·1 d	13	22
U^{237}	6·7 d	2	3

by the (γ, n) reaction have been confined to the light elements deuterium, beryllium, carbon, oxygen, and nitrogen.

Haigh (1953, 1954) has used the (γ, n) reaction to determine deuterium in water and body fluids. About a curie of sodium 24 was employed as a source of energetic γ-rays, the disadvantage of the short half-life of this isotope being compensated by its ready availability. The 2·76 MeV γ-rays resulting from the decay of sodium 24 can only activate deuterium and beryllium 9, which have unusually low threshold energies. Beryllium can be determined using γ-rays with an energy greater than 1·63 MeV, as described by Gaudin and Pannell (1951), who used a curie of antimony 124 as a γ-ray source. Both determinations were based on counting the number of neutrons emitted during the reaction, as the products are stable or of negligible half-life. Similar apparatus has been employed by Baranov et al. (1959 and 1960) for determining deuterium and by Odeblad (1956 a), but here the neutron detection was carried out by activating indium foils. Further work on beryllium has been carried out by Aidarkin et al. (1957), Mezhiborskaya (1959), Brownell (1959), Wagner et al. (1960), Milner and Edwards (1959), and Bowie et al. (1960).

The type of experimental equipment is quite different from that normally employed in activation work and is shown in cross-section in Fig. 4.3. The sample is surrounded by an annular source of γ-rays (or vice versa), which is in turn surrounded by a ring of boron-trifluoride counters, or an annular ionization chamber. Polythene and lead are used for shielding neutrons and γ-rays respectively. The polythene also acts as a moderator to thermalize the neutrons produced. If the sample contains neutron absorbers such as cadmium, boron, or lithium, or if it has an appreciable moderating action on the neutron energies, it may be necessary to correct for this by analysing a standard of similar composition. Using this type of equipment Haigh was able to determine 200 p.p.m. of deuterium oxide in water (twice the natural concentration), and Gaudin and Pannell could detect as little as 1 p.p.m. of beryllium in ores.

As early as 1949, Mayneord, Martin, and Layne bombarded the bodies of dead rats with photons of energies up to 24 MeV. By plotting decay curves immediately after activation, they were able to demonstrate at least two distinct activities, with half-lives of 2·1 minutes and 20 minutes respectively. These were shown to be caused by O^{15} and C^{11}, which are formed in rather low yield by bombarding stable oxygen and carbon at these energies. The activation process accounted for only about

0·012 per cent. of the photon absorption, which was largely due to Compton scattering and pair production. Subsequently Baldwin and Clark (1953) found O^{15}, C^{11}, and N^{13} activities in blocks of yeast irradiated with 100 MeV photons, and Basile, Hure, Leveque, and Schuhl (1954) showed that 24 MeV photons could be used to determine oxygen in pure chemicals. However, the sensitivity was poor, as 1 milligramme

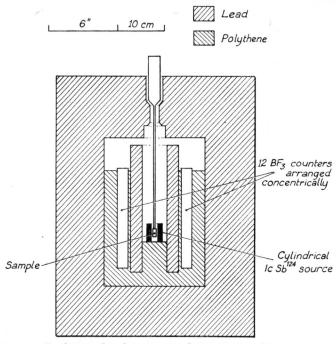

FIG. 4.3. Equipment for photoneutron determination of beryllium: from Iredale, 1960.

of oxygen in the sample gave only 20 counts per minute immediately after activation. Other workers have determined oxygen in alumina, beryllium, carbon, etc. (Asada *et al.*, 1957; Breger *et al.*, 1957; Beard *et al.*, 1959) by this technique.

Even lower sensitivities are obtained when reactions other than (γ, n) transitions are used. Harbottle (1954) studied the activation of indium by γ-rays from cobalt 60. The nuclide In^{115} is specifically activated by 1·04 MeV photons to an isomeric state with a 4·5-hour half-life, but the cross-section is only 10^{-9} barn and the activity produced is only about 1 dpm/g/kilorad/hr.† The only advantage of the method is its specificity, but in order to utilize it in analytical work it would

† dpm = disintegration(s) per minute.

be necessary to develop monochromatic photon sources delivering at least 10^9 rad/hour, which are not available today. A number of stable nuclides have radioactive isomers, including Ge, As, Se, Kr, Sr, Y, Zr, Nb, Rh, Pd, Ag, Cd, In, Sn, Te, Xe, Ba, Lu, Hf, Ta, W, Os, Pt, Au, Hg, and Pb. Cross-sections for Rh, Sr, Ag, Cd, and In have recently been reported by Ikeda, Yoshihara, and co-workers (1956, 1958, 1959), who are using these reactions as flux monitors.

Activation by positively charged particles

It has already been mentioned in Chapter 3 that the binding energy of a neutron or a proton to all except the lighter nuclei is approximately 8 MeV. Hence if a nucleus takes up a particle containing x nucleons, it will increase its energy by $8x$ MeV less the binding energy of the particle itself. There will, however, be an activation energy for the process which will depend on the number of positive charges on the nucleus.

Table 4.2 summarizes the data on these quantities for important charged particles.

TABLE 4.2

Particle	Number of nucleons	Charge	Binding energy (MeV)	Energy gain of target nucleus (MeV)
p	1	1	. .	8
d	2	1	2	14
t	3	1	8·5	15·5
He^3	3	2	8	16
α	4	2	28	4
Li^7	7	3	39	17
C^{12}	12	6	91	5
N^{14}	14	7	105	7
O^{16}	16	8	127	1

From this table we see that the most efficient charged particles for activation are deuterons and tritons, as these give the maximum gain in energy to the target nucleus with the smallest activation energy. Helium 3 nuclei give up slightly more energy but require twice as much momentum to overcome the potential barrier to entering the nucleus.

Proton activation

The simplest charged particle that can be used for activation purposes is the proton. Proton beams of moderate intensity can be produced in cyclotrons and van de Graaff machines, and are widely used for the production of isotopes. The most common nuclear reaction taking place when protons of 1–5 MeV are used for bombardment is the (p, n)

reaction. This reaction has a cross-section whose energy dependence resembles that of the (γ, n) reactions shown in Fig. 4.1. There is generally a threshold energy and an energy of maximum cross-section. The threshold energies increase, while the cross-sections decrease with increasing atomic weight. For light elements the cross-sections are between 10 and 500 millibarns (Ajzenberg and Lauritsen, 1955; Endt and Kluyver, 1954; Endt and Braams, 1957). Other reactions such as (p, α),

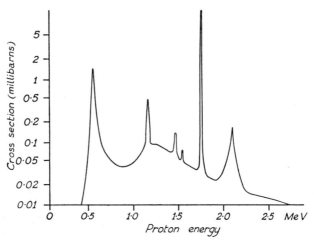

Fig. 4.4. Cross-section for the reaction $C^{13}(p, \gamma) N^{14}$ as a function of photon energy: from Jarmie and Seagrave, 1956.

(p, t), (p, pn), and $(p, 2n)$ can have cross-sections of this magnitude at equivalent energies (Jarmie and Seagrave, 1956; Martin, Livingston, Murray, and Rankin, 1955). (p, γ) reactions all seem to have very much smaller cross-sections, between 5 and 500 microbarns for light elements (Jarmie and Seagrave, 1956). (p, γ) and (p, α) reactions have maximum cross-sections at two or more peak energies. This type of behaviour is well shown in the curve for the energy dependence of the cross-section of the $C^{13}(p, \gamma) N^{14}$ reaction, which has six peaks between 0·5 and 3·1 MeV (Fig. 4.4).

Gill (1958) gives a useful table of the products of proton bombardment of light nuclides, from helium 4 to silicon 30. Table 4.3 is taken from his work and further data are tabulated by Koch (1960). Practical yields of 22 MeV proton irradiation of many other elements can be found in the compilation of Martin *et al.* (1955). At very high proton energies, spallation reactions occur which are undesirable from the point of view of activation analysis.

TABLE 4.3

Products of proton bombardment of the light elements (after Gill, 1958)

Nuclide bombarded	(p, n)	$(p, 2n)$	(p, d)	$(p, 2p)$	(p, α)	(p, t)	(p, γ)	(p, He^3)
Li^6							54-d Be^7	
Li^7	54-d Be^7			0.8-s He^6				
Be^9		0.8-s B^8		0.8-s Li^8		54-d Be^7		
B^{10}	19-s C^{10}				54-d Be^7	0.8-s B^8	20-m C^{11}	
B^{11}	20-m C^{11}	19-s C^{10}		2×10^6-y Be^{10}				
C^{12}	0.01-s N^{12}		20-m C^{11}			19-s C^{10}	10-m N^{13}	
C^{13}	10-m N^{13}	0.1-s N^{12}		0.02-s B^{12}		20-m C^{11}		
N^{14}	1.2-m O^{14}		10-m N^{13}		20-m C^{11}	0.01-s N^{12}	2-m O^{15}	
N^{15}	2-m O^{15}	1.2-m O^{14}		5000-y C^{14}		10-m N^{13}		
O^{16}			2-m O^{15}		10-m N^{13}	1.2-m O^{14}	1.1-m F^{17}	
O^{17}	1.1-m F^{17}			7.4-s N^{16}		2.1-m O^{15}	1.9-h F^{18}	
O^{18}	1.9-h F^{18}	1.1-m F^{17}		4.1-s N^{17}				7.4-s N^{16}
F^{19}	18-s Ne^{19}		1.9-h F^{18}			1.1-m F^{17}		
Ne^{20}	0.4-s Na^{20}		18-s Ne^{19}		1.1-m F^{17}		23-s Na^{21}	1.9-h F^{18}
Ne^{21}	23-s Na^{21}	0.4-s Na^{20}		11-s F^{20}	1.9-h F^{18}	18-s Ne^{19}	2.6-y Na^{22}	
Ne^{22}	2.6-y Na^{22}	23-s Na^{21}						11-s F^{20}
Na^{23}	12-s Mg^{23}		2.6-y Na^{22}			23-s Na^{21}		
Mg^{24}	2.1-s Al^{24}		12-s Mg^{23}		23-s Na^{21}		8-s Al^{25}	2.6-y Na^{22}
Mg^{25}	8-s Al^{25}	2.1-s Al^{24}		15-h Na^{24}	2.6-y Na^{22}	12-s Mg^{23}	7-s Al^{26}	
Mg^{26}	7-s Al^{26}	8-s Al^{25}		1-m Na^{25}				15-h Na^{24}
Al^{27}	4-s Si^{27}		7-s Al^{26}			8-s Al^{25}		
Si^{28}			4-s Si^{27}		8-s Al^{25}		4-s P^{29}	7-s Al^{26}
Si^{29}	4-s P^{29}			2.3-m Al^{28}	7-s Al^{26}	4-s Si^{27}	2.6-m P^{30}	
Si^{30}	2.6-m P^{30}	4-s P^{29}		7-m Al^{29}				2.3-m Al^{28}

There are a number of technical snags in the application of proton beams in analytical work. A small cyclotron with a beam current of 1–2 microamps is shown in Fig. 4.5. For all charged particle beams the number of particles per second is equal to 6×10^{12} times the beam current in microamps. In the larger cyclotrons, such as that described by Martin *et al.* (1955), with a beam current of up to a milliamp, the beam intensity may approach 6×10^{15} protons/second. This compares favourably with the largest available neutron fluxes, but gives rise to intense heating of the target because of the low penetration of protons. The large cyclotron mentioned above has a maximum operating voltage of 22 MeV, which for a 1-milliamp beam current means that any target must dissipate 22 kilowatts of energy. This can be accomplished by forced water cooling, but as Reid (1947) remarks, even where targets have a high boiling-point and good thermal conductivity, there are frequent losses of active material by evaporation. Even more important is the low penetrating power of protons compared with neutrons or γ-rays (Odeblad, 1956 *a*). This is illustrated by the graph in Fig. 4.6. Even with the most powerful cyclotrons, samples are restricted to a thickness of 0·5 mm or less, and the canning of such material in thin aluminium or tantalum decreases the sample thickness still further. From this it should be obvious that standards for proton activation should differ as little as possible in chemical nature from samples being analysed. In view of the instability of beams of charged particles, standards should be activated at the same time as the samples, preferably on a rotating disk in the beam (Odeblad, 1956 *b*). A stationary target holder designed by Gill (1958) is illustrated in Fig. 4.7.

Proton activation has only been used for analysis by a few workers. As little as 3×10^{-9} g of boron in silicon is detectable by the $B^{11}(p, n) C^{11}$ reaction (Gill, 1958); in this work the sample was etched after activation to avoid contamination. Point (1958) used 0·6 MeV protons to determine carbon in steel by the $C^{12}(p, \gamma) N^{13}$ reaction. The low-energy protons only penetrated 0·003 mm into the steel. Although the cross-section for the reaction is low ($< 0·0001$ barn), the (p, γ) cross-sections for other elements like boron and silicon are even lower, and Point found that he could determine 20 p.p.m. of carbon without chemical separation and without interference from other activated species. In earlier work Von Ardenne and Bernhard (1944) could not detect less than 400 p.p.m. of carbon in steel by this method.

Rubin, Passell, and Bailey (1957) used 2 MeV protons to activate fluorine in various glasses. The γ-rays from the reaction $F^{19}(p; \alpha, \gamma) O^{16}$

Fig. 4.5. General view of frequency modulated cyclotron at Harwell, used for accelerating beams of protons to 20 MeV for activation analysis.

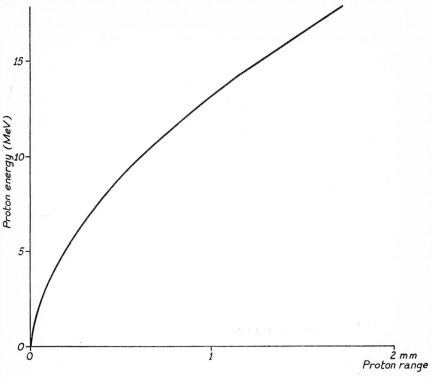

FIG. 4.6. Range of protons in aluminium as a function of proton energy:
from Gill, 1958.

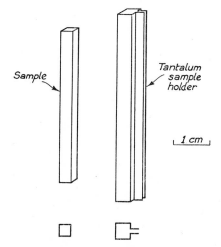

Fig. 4.7. Size of target and its holder for proton activation in the Harwell
cyclotron: from Gill, 1958.

have unusually high energies of 6–7 MeV, and were readily detected by a suitably biased scintillation counter. These authors consider that 1 p.p.m. of fluorine could be detected by this method, though their counting geometry set a practical limit of 1000 p.p.m.

An ingenious method for determining oxygen 18 has been described by Fogelstrom-Fineman, Holm-Hansen, Tolbert, and Calvin (1957). When O^{18}-labelled water was used to grow the alga *Chlorella*, it was metabolized and many products of photosynthesis were labelled with the heavy isotope. The products were separated by chromatography and the amounts of oxygen 18 in them estimated by activation with 4·5 MeV protons, which gave rise to 1·8 hour fluorine 18 by a (p, n) reaction. Since filter paper contains 50 per cent. oxygen, corresponding to 10 μg O^{18} per cm^2, and the method can detect 0·1 μg of O^{18}, the chromatograms were transferred to metal foils for activation. Aluminium was found to be too impure for this purpose, but pure tantalum was suitable. The amount of fluorine 18 produced was estimated by gamma spectroscopy. Other reactions which might be used by analysts are $Be^9 (p, t) Be^7$, $Al^{27} (p, 3pn) Na^{24}$, and $Si^{30} (p, n) P^{30}$ (Gill, 1958). Dick (1960) has used activation with 7 MeV protons to determine copper and nickel in an ore, using the reactions $Ni^{62} (p, n) Cu^{62}$ and $Cu^{63} (p, n) Zn^{63}$. The prompt neutrons emitted by the $Li^7 (p, n) Be^7$ reaction cannot be used to detect the small amounts of lithium present in most rocks (Sippel and Glover, 1960).

Deuteron activation

The main reactions used for activation are (d, n), (d, p), and (d, α). The first two occur at energies of 1–2 MeV, but the third, and other reactions like (d, t) and $(d; p, \alpha)$ have a threshold energy exceeding 5 MeV.

Although yields generally increase with increasing deuteron energy, the occurrence of side reactions may complicate the situation for subsequent analytical work. Cross-sections are energy dependent, and are in the range 0·1–1 barns for light elements but fall to 0·001 barns for cadmium in the middle of the periodic table (Jarmie and Seagrave, 1956; Anders and Gardner, 1957).

The remarks made concerning protons with regard to their production, flux density, and low penetration, apply equally to deuterons, which have been more widely used than protons for activation analysis, though their use has been restricted to the lighter elements. Since the (d, p) reaction gives an identical product to the commonly used (n, γ) reaction it has not found important applications.

The (d, n) reaction has been used to determine carbon in metals by a number of workers. Von Ardenne and Bernhard first described the technique in 1944. The product, nitrogen 13, has a 10-minute half-life, and these authors found they could determine 500 p.p.m. of carbon in steel using 0·8 MeV deuterons. The nuclide copper 62, arising from a (d, n) reaction on nickel, was thought to be the main interference. Later work by Riezler (1949) showed that deuterons with energies above 4 MeV gave rise to large quantities of cobalt 55 by the $Fe^{54}(d, n)$ reaction. Nevertheless Curie (1952, 1953) used 6·7 MeV deuterons to activate carbon in steels and determined the nitrogen 13 produced by an autoradiographic method. Albert, Chaudron, and Süe (1953) also used deuterons of this energy, but separated the activated nitrogen 13 by a rapid Kjeldahl distillation, and in this way were able to detect as little as 0·25 μg of carbon in the original metal. Carbon has also been determined in organic compounds, sealed in silica microtubes, by Süe (1953), but both silicon and oxygen give rise to interfering activities. The estimation of boron, nitrogen, and oxygen in pure chemicals by (d, n) activation has been described by Süe (1953, 1955 b, 1956). The detection limits are 0·5 μg, 1 μg, and 0·01 μg respectively, showing that the methods are promising and might repay further study.

An ingenious method for the analysis of surfaces has been put forward by Rubin, Passell, and Bailey (1957). These workers bombarded steel with deuterons of energy less than 2 MeV and measured the scattered protons from (d, p) reactions with a scintillation counter. In this way they were able to calculate the amounts of carbon, nitrogen, and oxygen in the surface. Also mentioned in the same paper is the determination of sodium in glass by the $Na^{23}(d, p)Na^{24}$ reaction, which had previously been described by Laing, Jones, Emhiser, Fitzgerald, and Bachman (1951) for refractory materials, and by Riezler (1949) for aluminium. Other elements such as silicon (Riezler, 1949; Süe, 1953), phosphorus (Odeblad and Tobias, 1954; Odeblad, 1956 b; Odeblad et al., 1958), and potassium (Süe, 1955 b) have been detected or determined by (d, p) reactions. Sippel and Glover (1960) recommend the technique for aluminium, magnesium, phosphorus, and sodium in rocks. Odeblad emphasizes the extreme sensitivity of the method for thin sections of biological tissue, where, for example, 10^{-12} g of phosphorus can be detected after activation.

The (d, α) reaction has been used by Süe (1956) and Süe and Albert (1956) to determine sulphur in amounts down to 1 μg. The activation product, phosphorus 30, has a half-life of only 2·5 minutes, which makes chemical separation difficult. The competing reaction $S^{33}(d, n)\,Cl^{34}$ gives less than 1 per cent. interference under suitable conditions. The determination of calcium by the $Ca^{36}(d, \alpha)\,K^{38}$ reaction was very insensitive. However, magnesium in steel has been determined by the $Mg^{24}(d, \alpha)\,Na^{22}$ reaction (Hoste, 1960). Some (d, α) cross-sections are tabulated by Hall and Meinke (1959).

Triton activation

There are no readily available sources of tritons, and the cross-sections of triton-induced reactions have scarcely been investigated (Kundu and Pool, 1948). However, Osmond and Smales (1954) showed that oxygen content could be determined by triton activation, though the sensitivity was no better than that obtainable by more conventional methods. Oxygen was determined in beryllium metal by mixing the powdered metal with excess lithium fluoride and bombarding with neutrons. Two reactions took place: $Li^6(n, \alpha)\,H^3$ and $O^{16}(H^3, n)\,F^{18}$. The fluorine 18 was then determined by chemical separation and counting. One major factor limiting sensitivity was the oxygen content of the lithium fluoride used, which gave rise to a high blank. Similar results have been reported by Bate and Leddicotte (1958), Lbov and Naumova (1959), and Born and Riehl (1960).

Alpha particle activation

Artificial radioactivity was first discovered by the $Al^{27}(\alpha, n)\,P^{30}$ reaction (Joliot and Curie, 1934). Activation by alpha particles has been very little used for analysis, probably because of the limited fluxes available. (α, n) and (α, p) reactions have cross-sections of the order of 0·1 barns, and (α, γ) reactions have very much smaller cross-sections. The graphs of energy against cross-section for these reactions generally show peaks at a number of energy levels.

The technique of alpha activation has been thoroughly described by Odeblad (1954, 1956 b). Polonium 210, with a half-life of 140 days, is the best portable α-source, since the only other radiation emitted by this isotope is a weak γ-ray, and a suitable source holder is shown in Fig. 4.8. The amounts that have been used, about 1 curie, give rise to fluxes of about 10^{12} alpha particles/cm²/sec at 0·5 mm from the source. The radiation has little penetrating power, but the low flux means that there are no problems due to heating of the target and there is none of the instability often found in beams of particles from large machines.

Beryllium, which is not activated by neutrons, can be determined by activation with alpha particles. The $Be^9(\alpha, n)\,C^{12}$ reaction gives rise

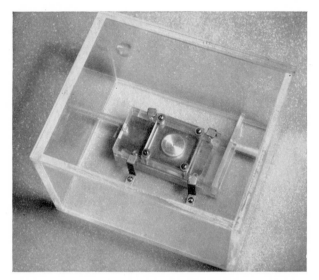

FIG. 4.8. Holder for Polonium 210 α-source in gas-tight Perspex box.

to 4·4 MeV γ-rays which can easily be counted on a gamma spectrometer, but the lowest recorded sensitivity is 5 μg (Odeblad and Nati, 1955; Gold, 1957; Cantwell et al., 1958; Plaksin et al., 1960). Dick (1960) used 15 MeV alpha particles from a cyclotron to induce the $Be^9(\alpha, 2n)C^{11}$ reaction. In most other applications described in the literature, the lowest recorded sensitivity was 100 μg or greater, e.g. boron by the $B^{10}(\alpha, n)N^{13}$ reaction (Sippel and Glover, 1960); copper by the $Cu^{63}(\alpha, n)Ga^{66}$ reaction (King and Henderson, 1939); aluminium by the $Al^{27}(\alpha, n)P^{30}$ reaction (Odeblad and Odeblad, 1956); sodium by the $Na^{23}(\alpha, n)Al^{26}$ reaction (Odeblad, 1954). This could be improved by using larger sources of alpha radiation, and Odeblad claims a sensitivity of 10^{-12} g for iron using the $Fe^{56}(\alpha; p, n)Co^{58}$ reaction.

Other particles

Current developments in nuclear physics are so rapid that beams of particles heavier than those so far used may soon be readily available. Activation by bombardment with beams of carbon and oxygen nuclei, for example, has already been achieved, but has not yet found application in analysis. Improvements in the fluxes of proton and deuteron beams will improve the sensitivity, and greater knowledge of cross-sections for reactions of the heavier elements should lead to more applications of the methods described in this chapter.

5

GAMMA SCINTILLATION SPECTROMETRY

GAMMA scintillation spectrometers have several uses in activation analysis. Firstly, they are of value in methods involving a full radiochemical purification, as a means of testing the success or otherwise of the separation procedure. Secondly, under suitable conditions, they may be used as qualitative tools to determine the nature of the trace impurities which may be present in the sample. Thirdly, they may be used as quantitative tools to measure the γ-rays emitted by the desired trace element in the presence of radiations from other impurities or from the matrix itself. It is thus possible for the radiochemical purification step to be considerably simplified or even eliminated completely.

With this technique it is possible, using suitable electronic equipment, to obtain the counting rate for γ-rays of a selected energy in the presence of radiation of different energy or type. This is the nuclear radiation analogue of light spectrometry; the energy of the γ-ray characterizes the radioisotope and its associated counting rate is a measure of the amount of the isotope present in the sample.

Interaction of gamma radiation with matter

In order to appreciate the application and problems of the technique of gamma spectrometry it is necessary to consider the various ways in which gamma radiation can interact with matter—interactions which are characterized by the fact that each gamma photon is removed individually from the incident beam in a single event. In the energy range from a few eV to about 5 MeV there are three basic processes by which gamma photons may interact with matter and be removed from the incident beam. There are other forms of interaction (Cook and Duncan, 1952) but these are negligible in scintillation spectrometry.

1. *The photoelectric effect*—in which a photon gives all its energy to a bound electron which uses part of the energy to overcome its binding to the nucleus and absorbs the rest as kinetic energy. Photoelectrons may be ejected from any of the orbital energy levels, but a free electron cannot become a photoelectron since a third body (a nucleus) must be present to conserve momentum. Theoretical analyses of this effect

have been made (Siegbahn, 1955 a) and it has been shown that the probability of photoelectric absorption increases rapidly with the binding energy of the electron, so that at gamma energies greater than the binding energies of the K and L shells, absorption due to outer shells is negligible. The probability of the photoelectric effect occurring is approximately proportional to the fourth power of the atomic number of the absorbing material, and inversely proportional to the third power of the energy of the gamma radiation (Goodman, 1947). Thus, it occurs most noticeably with the heavy elements and with low-energy gamma radiation (below about 0·5 MeV).

A subsidiary effect due to the photoelectric process is the production of secondary X-radiation. After the photoelectron has been ejected from an inner orbit, it is replaced by an electron from an outer orbit, and as this latter electron moves from one energy level to the other it emits its excess energy as the characteristic X-radiation of the element. This X-radiation can then interact with the absorbing material in the same way as gamma radiation but, as it has a very low energy, it is absorbed readily.

2. *The Compton effect*—in which the gamma photon is deflected by the orbital electrons. Provided the gamma energy is appreciably greater than the electron binding energy, the gamma photon is deflected as though the electron were free and at rest and an elastic collision had taken place. The scattered photon has, of course, less energy than the incident gamma radiation and it can be shown (Siegbahn, 1955 b) that it has energy

$$h\nu' = \frac{h\nu}{1+(h\nu/mc^2)(1-\cos\theta)},$$

where

$h\nu$ is the original energy of the photon,

$h\nu'$ is the energy of the scattered photon,

θ is the scattering angle,

m is the rest mass of the electron,

c is the velocity of light.

Thus the energy of the scattered photon varies with the angle of scatter, which will itself vary from event to event. In the same way, the energies of the scattered electrons cover a continuous range up to a maximum of

$$E_e = \frac{E}{1+mc^2/2E},$$

where E is the energy of the incident gamma photon.

This represents the maximum energy which can be transferred to an electron by the Compton process and corresponds to a scatter angle of 180°.

The probability of the Compton effect occurring is proportional to the atomic number of the absorbing material, and is inversely proportional to the energy of the gamma radiation. The Compton effect is much less important than the photoelectric effect below 0·5 MeV but predominates above 1·0 MeV.

3. *Pair production*—in which the gamma photon interacts with the Coulomb field surrounding a nucleus or an electron, and disappears with the creation of an electron-positron pair with kinetic energy equal to the energy of the incident gamma photon less the mass equivalent of the two new particles ($2mc^2 = 1·02$ MeV). Thus, this effect can occur only with gamma radiation of energy greater than 1·02 MeV, but thereafter the effect increases steadily with energy. When the positron slows down it annihilates with any convenient electron and produces two 0·51 MeV γ-rays which may then themselves undergo photoelectric or Compton interaction. The probability of pair production is proportional to the square of the atomic number and so this effect is also important in heavy elements.

Phosphors

In the above interactions secondary electrons are produced with all, or part, of the original gamma energy. If the interactions occur in a phosphor, the subsequent de-excitation and recombination of these electrons converts their energy into light pulses or scintillations, the brightness of which is proportional to the total energy absorbed. The most important scintillation process is that due to the photoelectric effect, since this produces light pulses of constant intensity (apart from a statistical spread). The Compton effect, however, produces a continuous distribution of pulses owing to the different angles through which the original γ-rays are scattered, and pair production can result in up to three extra photopeaks: the original γ-ray less 0·51 MeV (if one annihilation γ-ray escapes from the phosphor), the original γ-ray less 1·02 MeV (if both annihilation γ-rays escape), and a peak at 0·51 MeV due to annihilation radiation from the material surrounding the phosphor being detected.

These various effects may be illustrated by reference to the hypothetical gamma spectrum of Fig. 5.1 where photoelectric peaks, pair production peaks, and back-scatter peaks are all present. It will be seen that the individual peaks have a spread of energy which, incidentally, approximates to a Gaussian distribution (Connally and Leboeuf, 1953). This spread is due to the statistical nature of the photomultiplication process, non-uniformity of the photocathode, and imperfections in the crystal. The sharpness of the peak is a measure

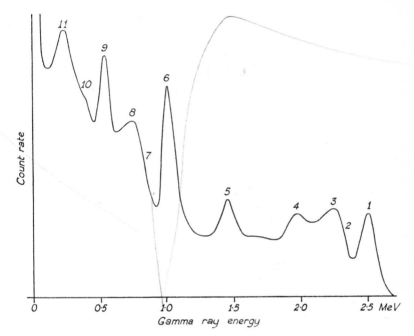

FIG. 5.1. Hypothetical gamma spectrum.

Key. 1. High-energy photopeak at 2·50 MeV. 2. Compton edge of (1) at 2·37 MeV. 3. Compton peak of (1). 4. Pair production with one photon lost at 2·50−0·51 = 1·99 MeV. 5. Pair production with both photons lost at 2·50−1·02 = 1·48 MeV. 6. Low-energy photopeak at 1·00 MeV. 7. Compton edge of (6) at 0·80 MeV. 8. Compton peak of (6). 9. 0·51 MeV peak of annihilation radiation. 10. Compton edge of (9). 11. Backscatter peak from surroundings.

of the resolution of the apparatus and is expressed as $100d/V$ per cent. (Fig. 5.2 A) where d is the peak width at half height, and V is the peak position in the same units as d. The resolution is usually 8–10 per cent. for a good $2·5 \times 3·5$-cm sodium iodide crystal, and can never be less than 6·6 per cent. (Morton, 1949). It is sometimes more convenient to express the resolution as shown in Fig. 5.2 B in terms of the peak to valley ratio h/r of cobalt 60, a measurement which requires no knowledge of the peak position. Ratios of between 2·5 and 3·0 are quite common.

The phosphor must be selected with these facts in mind, together with the aim of obtaining as bright a scintillation as possible for a given gamma energy. The phosphor should therefore have a high atomic number in order to favour the photoelectric effect. Crystals of sodium iodide are generally used as these have a fairly high effective atomic number, they can be obtained reasonably transparent to the light they emit, and they have a favourable scintillation brightness for a given gamma energy.

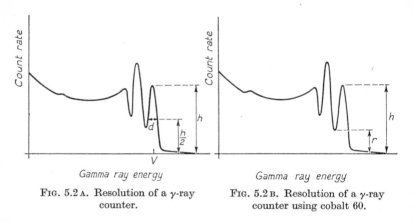

FIG. 5.2 A. Resolution of a γ-ray counter.

FIG. 5.2 B. Resolution of a γ-ray counter using cobalt 60.

It should be remembered that, because of the finite resolving time of the apparatus, a sequence of events, such as two successive Compton scatterings followed by a photoelectric event together with photo-electric absorption of the residual X-ray, will be observed as one single scintillation, indistinguishable from that produced by total photo-electric absorption. Consequently, the crystal chosen should be as large as possible to allow such multiple processes to occur and to reduce the chance of any of the secondary radiation escaping from the crystal without being detected. A larger crystal, however, has a higher cosmic background and also a poorer resolution since it is likely to have more lattice imperfections. A $2 \cdot 5 \times 3 \cdot 5$-cm crystal is a useful compromise for most purposes, although some workers prefer a $7 \cdot 5 \times 7 \cdot 5$-cm crystal, especially when low-activity samples are involved. Fig. 5.3 compares the sensitivities and resolving powers of two such crystals for the twin photopeaks of cobalt 60.

Auxiliary equipment

The light pulse or scintillation produced in the phosphor is very weak and must be converted into a voltage pulse by a multistage photo-multiplier and then further amplified by a linear amplifier to a pulse several volts in magnitude before it can be recorded. It is usual to feed the output from the photomultiplier to the amplifier via a cathode follower unit which matches the impedances of the two stages, and also enables the amplifier and subsequent electronic equipment to be operated some distance away from the detector assembly if necessary.

Some information can be obtained with regard to the pulse height or energy distribution by feeding the output of the amplifier into a

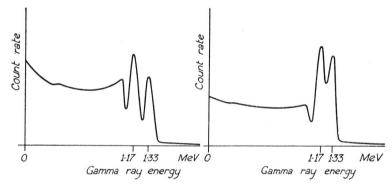

FIG. 5.3 A. Cobalt 60 gamma spectrum from a 2·5 × 3·5-cm sodium iodide crystal.

FIG. 5.3 B. Cobalt 60 gamma spectrum from a 7·5 × 7·5-cm sodium iodide crystal.

standard scaler via a simple discriminator—a device which only allows pulses of voltage greater than the set discriminator voltage to be passed to the scaler. The count rate is then determined in the normal way, and is redetermined as the discriminator voltage is increased, so reducing the number of pulses detected by the scaler. If the count rate is plotted against the discriminator voltage in half-volt steps, a trace similar to Fig. 5.4 is obtained for a simple γ-ray emitter. Such a trace is not very useful at first sight but, if it is now redrawn so that the difference between successive readings is plotted against discriminator voltage, the differential spectrum of Fig. 5.5 is obtained.

Such a differential spectrum can be obtained more easily by means of a single channel pulse height analyser or kicksorter. This device passes only those pulses whose heights lie between two fairly close limits as set by the controls of the instrument. It does in fact consist of two discriminators, and is arranged so that pulses which are less than the first discriminator setting are rejected in the normal way, and pulses which are greater than the second discriminator setting are also rejected. Only those pulses whose heights lie between the two discriminator settings are detected. This acceptance band is referred to as the counting channel and the difference between the upper and lower limits is

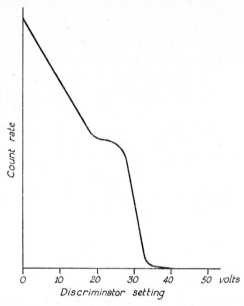

FIG. 5.4. Pulse height distribution curve for caesium 137.

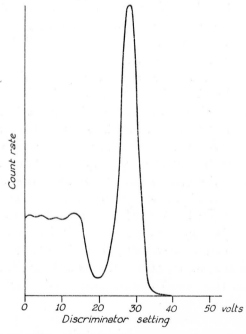

FIG. 5.5. Differential pulse height spectrum for caesium 137.

FIG. 5.6. Automatic multi-channel recorder for gamma spectroscopy.

the channel width δV. If the channel is moved along the voltage (or energy) scale to position V, the count rate in the channel will vary and will in fact show the proportion of pulses with heights between the two new limits $(V; V+\delta V)$. In this way, a picture of the pulse height distribution is obtained as before.

The channel position can usually be varied stepwise manually, or continuously and automatically. In the former case, the count rates are measured on a scaler and individually plotted against voltage or energy. In the latter case, the count rate is measured continuously on a ratemeter, the output of which is fed to a recorder. The chart drive of the recorder is geared to a potentiometer which in turn alters the channel position in the pulse-height analyser.

The multipeak analyser

This is a form of multiple-channel analyser in which there are several independent channels, usually about five. Although the channels are adjustable, the spectrum is not scanned as in the single channel analyser, but the different channels are set to positions corresponding to the peaks expected and the counts in each channel are recorded. It is, of course, necessary to allow for the contribution of the Compton continuum of the higher energy peaks to the counts in the lower channels. This system has no advantages in qualitative analysis, where a complete scan is usually required, and its advantages in quantitative analysis are rather dubious because of the contribution of the Compton continuum of the higher energy peaks to the counts in the lower channels. As will be seen later, it is this factor which is one of the most serious drawbacks in gamma spectrometry.

Multichannel analysers

These differ from multipeak analysers in that the channels are all adjacent, covering a continuous energy range, and can be moved as a block to any part of the spectrum. They usually contain anything from 20 to 400 channels or more, but 100 or 256 channel analysers are probably most popular. The count rates in the individual channels may be recorded, simultaneously by separate scalers and registers, or displayed as counts registered in binary or decimal form on a cathode-ray tube (Fig. 5.6). More ambitious apparatus stores the information and then prints this out on paper tape while a second spectrum is being recorded, and can even be made to plot the spectrum automatically.

The main advantage of the multichannel analyser over the single-channel analyser is the rate at which information can be obtained, this being proportional to the number of channels. This is very important when low activities or isotopes of short half-life are involved.

Compton elimination

In order to determine the radioactivity associated with a particular γ-ray energy, it is necessary to measure the number of counts in the

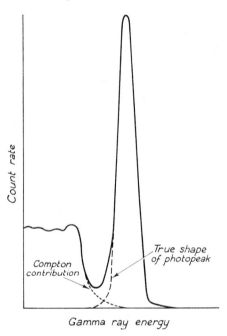

FIG. 5.7. Distortion of photopeak by Compton scattering.

photopeak. Under ideal conditions this can be done in three ways: by measuring the height of the photopeak, by measuring the number of counts in the channel corresponding to the centre of the photopeak, or by measuring the area under the photopeak. The reproducibility of such measurements is about 10 per cent., 5 per cent., and 2 per cent. respectively, but varies slightly from one type of equipment to another.

Because of the statistical spread of the trace, there is an unavoidable error in all these measurements, due to the foot of the Compton edge running into the beginning of the photopeak, resulting in the photopeak being unsymmetrical, as shown in Fig. 5.7. This error is quite low in pure one-component systems and will be similar for both sample and standard, but if the radioactivity is so pure it is easier to determine it by simple counting. In multicomponent systems the position is further complicated since, if a low-energy γ-ray has to be measured in the presence of a high-energy one, the former may coincide with the Compton continuum of the latter as in Fig. 5.8. Under these conditions, simple measurement of total peak height or counts in the channel is not adequate and it is preferable to measure the peak area, but only that part of the peak area which is due to the low-energy γ-ray.

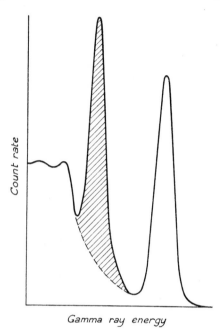

FIG. 5.8. Distortion of photopeak by high-energy γ-ray.

Various techniques are used to obtain this value. The simplest is to draw a straight or estimated curved line across the bottom of the peak as shown in Fig. 5.8. Such a method is only approximate, however, and a more accurate method is to obtain a pure sample of the high-energy component, record its spectrum and, after normalizing the trace, subtract the second trace from the first to leave the spectrum of the low-energy component only. Since the result is now the difference between two statistically varying quantities, the accuracy is less than for a one-component system. Also, the error is cumulative and in multicomponent systems can become excessive.

It is not always convenient, however, to obtain a pure radioisotope at a moment's notice. Instead, it is possible to make use of previously determined gamma spectra. Several excellent compilations of gamma spectra are now available (Salmon, 1959; Heath, 1957) and, provided these have been determined with the same size and type of crystal, they may be normalized and used in the peak stripping technique (Heath, 1957; Heath and Schroeder, 1957), involving simple graphical subtraction.

Another method intended to eliminate the effects of Compton continua, caused by the peak being measured and, more particularly, by

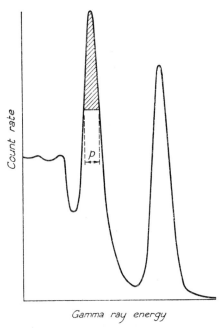

Fig. 5.9. Measurement of photopeak by integration of area above point of set width p.

higher energy peaks, is due to McIsaac (1956). This method depends on determining graphically the point at which the peak has a set width and then integrating the peak area above this point with a planimeter (Fig. 5.9). The characteristic width p is chosen to be well above the Compton continuum for the worst peak to be measured, and it can be shown that the ratios of such areas are in the same ratios as the true activities, despite the varying Compton contributions. The application of this technique is, however, limited to regions where the Compton continuum is reasonably flat, and recalibration is necessary if the resolution of the apparatus should change.

This technique has also been applied to multichannel analysers in a way which obviates the necessity for plotting the spectrum graphically before estimating peak areas (Covell, 1959). Use is made of the digital nature of the information presented on these instruments. The channel which gives the highest count rate in the peak is determined and termed C_0, and n, channels are counted off on either side of C_0 such that C_n and C_{-n} contain counts about half-way between that in C_0 and those in the channels at the minima at either side of the peak (Fig. 5.10).

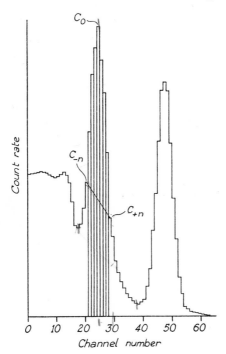

FIG. 5.10. Measurement of a photopeak on a multichannel analyser.

The area above the line C_{-n}—C_{+n} may then be expressed (in channels × counts, which is a form of area) by the formula

$$\text{area} = \sum_{m=-n}^{+n} A_m - (n+\tfrac{1}{2})(A_{-n}+A_{+n}),$$

where A_m is the number of counts in the mth channel.

This technique is very rapid and eliminates the errors which must arise in transposing from counts to a graph and back to counts again, but it can only be used on instruments which have a sufficiently narrow channel width for a reasonable number of channels to occur in the peak being measured.

The effect of Compton continua from higher energy radiation, on the photopeak being measured, is illustrated in Fig. 5.11. The caesium

137 activities, measured by peak height, by peak area, and by Covell's method, in the presence of increasing amounts of cobalt 60 activity are plotted against the amount of cobalt 60. The difference between the methods is apparent from the way the observed activities deviate from the theoretical activities, and it can be seen that Covell's method is superior to the other two.

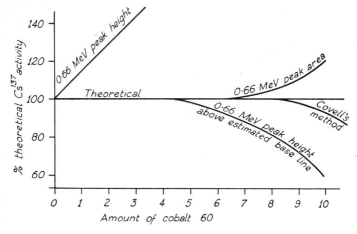

Fig. 5.11. Measurement of 1 mμc caesium 137 in presence of cobalt 60.

Compton subtraction can also be done electronically (Peirson, 1955, 1956) using a technique which not only subtracts the Compton continuum due to high energy peaks, but also subtracts that due to the photopeak being observed, thus leaving a pure photopeak, the area or height of which is easily measured (Fig. 5.12). Use is made of the fact that anthracene produces little or no photoelectric effect with γ-rays and is essentially a Compton absorber.

The apparatus consists of a two-crystal spectrometer in which the γ-ray source is exposed simultaneously to sodium iodide and anthracene scintillation detectors (Fig. 5.13). The Compton continua from the two crystals are equalized for count rate (by adjusting the position of the source between the two crystals) and for energy calibration (by adjusting the high-voltage supplies to the two photomultipliers). The count rate calibration can be made at any one energy and holds good over the range for which pulse amplitude is proportional to energy in both counters. Thus, for ease of adjustment, it is preferable to equalize the two traces using a monoenergetic γ-ray source of high purity, and then run the unknown sample under identical conditions. The energy calibration will hold good over a range of higher energies. At lower energies, the proportion of scattered radiation which is absorbed by a subsequent event (giving a pulse indistinguishable from a single photoelectric pulse) increases more rapidly for sodium iodide than for

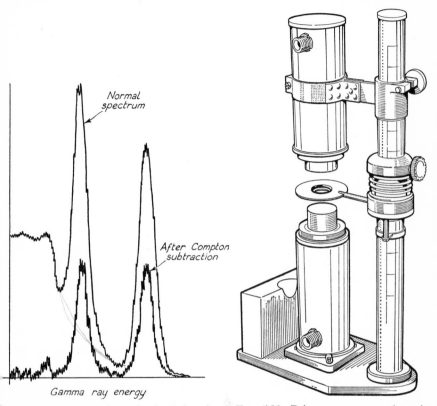

FIG. 5.12. Compton subtraction by Peirson's method.

FIG. 5.13. Peirson gamma spectrometer with sample holder between the anthracene and sodium iodide crystals. After Peirson, 1955.

anthracene, resulting in a certain amount of mis-matching. However, at low energies, the Compton effect is much reduced, so it is still possible to balance the two Compton continua to within 5 per cent. of the photoelectric peak height.

Duplication of amplifiers, pulse height analysers, and ratemeters is avoided (to reduce the effects of electronic drift) by using a synchronous electronic switch. This switch connects each photomultiplier in turn for 0·5-second periods to the amplifier and, at the same time, rearranges the circuitry of the ratemeter so that sodium iodide pulses increase the ratemeter reading and anthracene pulses reduce it. Thus, for equal count rates in the two crystals, the net effect, and the ratemeter output, is zero.

Peirson and Iredale (1957) have further modified the apparatus to include (1) a lead shield fitted to the anthracene crystal to reduce the number of quanta scattered back into the sodium iodide crystal, (2) a thermostatically controlled enclosure for the two crystals to eliminate the mis-match which occurs, if the ambient temperature varies by more than 5° C, owing to the different pulse height/temperature characteristics of the two crystals, (3) an energy-dependent channel width in the pulse-height analyser. Instead of maintaining a constant-width channel while the pulse height is scanned, a device is used giving a channel width proportional to pulse height, so compensating for the greater efficiency of the crystals for low-energy γ-rays and ensuring that no peak is distorted by being scanned with too large a channel width.

This subtraction technique is very valuable in eliminating or considerably reducing the Compton continuum and facilitating the observation of a low-energy peak in the presence of one or more of higher energy. It is therefore of considerable use in qualitative analysis. In quantitative analysis, however, there are disadvantages. Firstly, since the sodium iodide crystal is connected to the apparatus for only half the time, the effective count rate (and therefore the sensitivity of detection) is reduced by a factor of two. Secondly, when a low-energy peak is being measured in the presence of the Compton continuum due to a high-energy γ-ray, the final ratemeter output is the small difference between two large quantities and is therefore less accurately recorded. Higher accuracy can be obtained by using longer sweep times and integration times in the ratemeter, but only when the life of the radioactivity is long enough to permit this. Finally, the human error is still present, since the matching of the two traces must be done visually. Nevertheless, the technique is often of value in obviating a tedious radiochemical separation.

Albert (1953) described a method of reducing Compton continua on a purely electronic basis. The normal sodium iodide crystal and radioactive sample are completely surrounded by a cluster of sodium iodide crystals coupled to several photomultipliers. The combined pulses from the outer photomultipliers are fed into an anticoincidence unit together with the pulses from the central detector. If a Compton event occurs in the central crystal and the scattered γ-ray escapes, there is a good chance that it will be detected in the outer crystal assembly. The anticoincidence unit allows pulses to pass from the central detector only if they are *not* accompanied by a simultaneous pulse in the surrounding system. In this way, photoelectric or total absorption pulses are registered, but Compton pulses (accompanied by an event in the outer detector) are not.

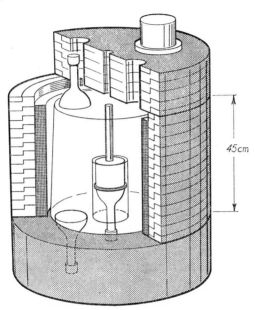

FIG. 5.14. Anticoincidence gamma spectrometer: the 12·5 × 14-cm sodium iodide crystal is surrounded by a 45 × 45-cm plastic scintillator wired in anticoincidence, inside a mercury-lined lead castle. After Ellett and Brownell, 1960.

The difficulty here is, of course, in obtaining sufficient phosphor to surround the central detector completely. Other workers (Bell, 1954) have used a tank full of a liquid scintillator for the same purpose, as it is obtainable more readily, while Ellett and Brownell (1960) have used a large plastic scintillator in the same way (Fig. 5.14).

Although this technique eliminates the human error in matching, it introduces further problems of its own. The principal one is due to the large outer assembly showing a high natural background, resulting in a high random coincidence rate. In other words, there is an appreciable chance that a background event in the outer crystal will occur at the same time as a photoelectric or total absorption event in the centre crystal; consequently the latter will not be recorded even though it is not a Compton event, and so the effective count rate and sensitivity of the apparatus are reduced.

Another form of Compton elimination, which is less satisfactory but none the less important, operates by coincidence rather than by anti-coincidence and is known as a Compton pair spectrometer (Hofstadter and McIntyre, 1950). In this instrument the energy absorbed by those Compton encounters which scatter the incident rays through a defined

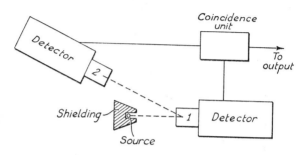

FIG. 5.15. Compton pair spectrometer.

angle is measured. The apparatus consists of two sodium iodide crystals and associated photomultipliers (Fig. 5.15). The sample is placed close to crystal (1), but is screened from crystal (2) by a lead shield which is designed to allow γ-rays scattered back from crystal (1) to reach crystal (2) while screening direct radiation from the sample. The two photomultiplier outputs are fed into a coincidence unit which allows pulses to pass from detector (1) only when a pulse occurs simultaneously in detector (2). Thus, pulses due to the photoelectric effect or total absorption in crystal (1) will not be counted as they will not give rise to an event in crystal (2). On the other hand, those Compton events which give rise to scattered gamma rays which are deflected at the correct angle to be detected in crystal (2) will be registered. If these pulses are analysed, they will form a low-energy peak related to the original gamma energy and the relative position of the two crystals by the standard Compton relationship.

This method is relatively insensitive, since only those Compton events which result in the correct angular scatter are registered, and the angular acceptance of crystal (2) must be kept small to limit the energy spread and give a narrow energy peak in the final output. Consequently, an appreciable amount of radioactivity is necessary for the equipment to function adequately and, unfortunately, in activation analysis the amount of activity available is generally small.

It has already been stated that the main purpose in eliminating the Compton effect is to prevent the Compton continuum of a high-energy γ-ray obscuring the photopeak of a low-energy ray. Putman and Taylor (1957) developed, for this purpose, a modification of the Peirson apparatus which was much easier to set up. The apparatus was in fact very similar to that of Peirson except that both crystals were of sodium iodide and were completely screened from each other. The sample

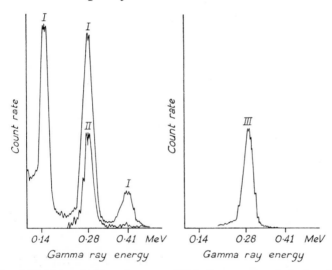

Fig. 5.16. Determination of mercury 203 in the presence of selenium 75.

I. Mercury 203 photopeak swamped by selenium 75 activity.
II. Mercury 203 photopeak after subtraction of selenium 75 activity.
III. Mercury 203 photopeak from equal amount of pure mercury.

containing the unknown activity, together with a higher energy component, was examined on one crystal, and a comparable amount of a pure sample of the higher energy component was exposed to the second crystal. The position and height of the high energy peaks were then matched as with the Peirson apparatus, but the matching was easier as it was done on the photopeaks, which had a more definite shape than the Compton edge, and the responses of the two crystals were much more similar.

The two outputs were subtracted electronically as before, all pulses from the higher energy component being subtracted from the output of the first crystal, leaving only those due to the low-energy γ-ray. This is the electronic version of the graphical method mentioned earlier and suffers from the same errors, but is less tedious. Putman and Taylor demonstrated the value of their technique by determining mercury 203 in the presence of selenium 75. This was a severe test, for not only was the Compton continuum of the 0·405 MeV selenium 75 γ-ray present, but also a 0·27 MeV selenium 75 γ-ray which was almost indistinguishable from the 0·28 MeV mercury 203 γ-ray. However, after subtraction, the mercury 203 activity was determined to within 7 per cent. of its true value (Fig. 5.16).

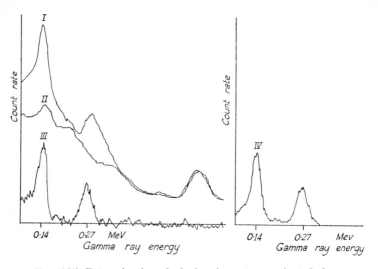

Fig. 5.17. Determination of selenium in neutron-activated glass.
    I. Gamma spectrum of glass containing added selenium.
   II. Gamma spectrum of glass containing no added selenium.
  III. Curve I–curve II.
  IV. Gamma spectrum of selenium standard.

Putman and Taylor (1958) also applied this technique to the special case of the determination of a trace impurity present in a matrix which could be obtained in an identical state but without the trace impurity. Putman and Taylor analysed glass to which had been added a trace of selenium as a decolourizer. After irradiation the two glass samples (with and without selenium) were counted on the two crystals, and the high-energy responses were matched. After subtraction the selenium activity alone remained, and the selenium content of the glass was found by comparing this activity with a selenium standard which had been irradiated at the same time (Fig. 5.17).

Applications of γ-ray spectrometry

(a) *Qualitative.* The use of the γ-ray spectrometer as a qualitative tool in activation analysis is limited to the identification of possible trace impurities prior to a quantitative analysis, and to the confirmation of the purity of a separated species after a radiochemical purification step. Such applications hinge on the ability of the spectrometer to determine γ-ray energies.

After determining the gamma spectrum of the sample, the apparatus is calibrated with γ-ray emitters of known energy (Table 5.1) (Marion,

TABLE 5.1
Gamma-ray calibration standards (Marion, 1960)

Radioisotope	Gamma energy (MeV)	Half-life (days)
Americium 241	0·060	177,000
Cobalt 57	0·122	268
Cerium 141	0·146	32·5
Indium 114m	0·190	50·0
Mercury 203	0·279	46·9
Chromium 51	0·321	27·8
Gold 198	0·412	2·70
Beryllium 7	0·478	53·4
Caesium 137	0·662	10,200
Iodine 131	0·724	8·07
	0·638	
	0·364	
	0·284	
	0·080	
Manganese 54	0·835	314
Zinc 65	1·114	244
	0·511	
Scandium 46	1·118	83·9
	0·892	
Sodium 22	1·274	942
	0·511	
Cobalt 60	1·333	1920
	1·173	
Yttrium 88	1·841	105
	0·900	
Antimony 124	2·088	60·6
	1·692	
Thorium 228	2·614	697

1960). At least two such standards should be used, one above and one below the unknown energy, and preferably three standards should be used so that the linearity of the energy scale can be checked at the same time. The instrument should preferably be calibrated for each measurement to avoid errors due to electronic drift, which can cause apparent peak shifts of about 10 per cent. or more in a matter of a few hours unless the equipment is very stable.

In multichannel analysers the channel with the highest activity in a peak may be taken as the centre of the peak for energy measurement purposes. With sweep analysers, however, this is not necessarily the case unless the ratemeter is operated on the same count-rate range and time constant setting for both sample and reference standards. Because of the nature of the ratemeter circuitry, the output to the recorder lags behind the input to the ratemeter and the amount of lag depends on the settings of the ratemeter controls. Obrink and Ulfendahl (1959) devised a reversible scanning instrument to overcome this error. The procedure was simply to scan the spectrum from low energy to high, then put the machine into reverse and scan from high energy to low. On the first run the recorded peak is at too high an energy, and at too low an energy on the second. The average of the two peak positions then gives the true γ-ray energy.

Having determined the γ-ray energy, reference may be made to a classification of radioisotopes by γ-ray energy (Table 5.2); if necessary, a pure sample of the supposed isotope may be analysed for comparison purposes. If several radioisotopes have the same γ-ray energy as the unknown, the half-life of the γ-ray activity must be determined, by following the decay of the photopeak, in order to resolve the situation.

(b) *Quantitative.* The quantitative application of γ-ray spectrometry hinges on the measurement of the heights or areas of photopeaks. This procedure has been discussed thoroughly above. The specific applications of the technique to the determination of trace impurities are far too numerous to be described. A few procedures will be discussed to illustrate the applicability of the method.

A wide range of impurities in drinking water have been determined by γ-ray spectrometry coupled with very simple chemical separations (Blanchard, Leddicotte, and Moeller, 1959). These included As, Br, Cl, I, Cu, Mn, Na, Rb, Sr, and Zn. It was claimed that the limit of detection with this technique was considerably less than with conventional analytical methods, and that elements previously undetected in drinking water could be detected and determined quantitatively.

In a paper describing a method for the determination of gold in biological materials, Gibbons (1958) described a full radiochemical procedure capable of giving a precision of 2 per cent., and also a rapid method using γ-ray spectrometry giving a precision of 5–10 per cent. The latter method used a simple chemical precipitation step to separate the gold activity from the sodium activity which formed over 99 per cent. of the activity of the sample in most cases, and the spectrometer could then determine the gold activity in the presence of other minor activities which might have been present. This rapid method was four times quicker than the full radiochemical method.

TABLE 5.2

Radioisotopes produced by (n, γ) reactions classified by γ-energy
(Salmon, 1959; Mateosian and McKeown, 1960)

γ-Energy (MeV)	Nuclide	Half-life	Associated energies
0·041	Nb⁹⁴ᵐ	6·6 min	
0·042	Os¹⁹¹	15 days	0·129
0·068	Ta¹⁸²	111 days	1·20, 1·12, 0·23, 0·150, 0·100
0·069	Sm¹⁵³	47 hours	0·103
0·070	Pt¹⁹⁹	29 min	0·71, 0·54, 0·48, 0·32, 0·197
0·072	Os¹⁹¹ᵐ	14 hours	
0·073	Os¹⁹³	31 hours	0·56, 0·46, 0·37, 0·32, 0·28, 0·25, 0·139
0·074	U²³⁹	23·5 min	
0·077	Pt¹⁹⁷	18 hours	
0·080	Ho¹⁶⁶	27·3 hours	1·53, 1·36
0·080	Ce¹⁴⁴	285 days	0·134
0·084	Tm¹⁷⁰	127 days	
0·087	Tb¹⁶⁰	73·5 days	1·27, 1·18, 0·96, 0·89, 0·41, 0·29, 0·20
0·087	Pd¹⁰⁹	13·6 hours	
0·088	Te¹²³ᵐ	104 days	0·159
0·089	Lu¹⁷⁶ᵐ	3·7 hours	
0·091	Nd¹⁴⁷	11·6 days	0·52
0·094	Dy¹⁶⁵	140 min	0·36, 0·27
0·100	Se⁸¹ᵐ	56·5 min	
0·100	Nd¹⁴⁹	2·0 hours	0·65, 0·54, 0·44, 0·21
0·100	Ta¹⁸²	111 days	1·20, 1·12, 0·23, 0·150, 0·068
0·103	Sm¹⁵³	47 hours	0·069
0·105	Sm¹⁵⁵	23·5 min	
0·106	Te¹²⁹ᵐ	33 days	
0·110	Te¹²⁵ᵐ	58 days	
0·110	Yb¹⁶⁹	33 days	
0·110	Pm¹⁵¹	27·5 hours	0·21
0·111	Er¹⁷¹	7·5 hours	0·31, 0·29
0·113	Lu¹⁷⁷	7·0 days	0·21
0·114	Yb¹⁷⁵	4·2 days	0·40, 0·28
0·115	Gd¹⁵⁹	18·0 hours	0·36, 0·170
0·117	Nd¹⁵¹	15 min	0·42
0·120	Ba¹³¹	13 days	0·62, 0·49, 0·24, 0·21
0·120	Eu¹⁵²	13 years	0·34
0·122	Eu¹⁵²	9·2 hours	0·97, 0·85, 0·34
0·122	Eu¹⁵⁴	16 years	0·24
0·128	Cs¹³⁴ᵐ	3·1 hours	
0·129	Os¹⁹¹	15 days	0·042
0·130	Ru¹⁰⁵	4·5 hours	0·73
0·132	Hf¹⁸¹	46 days	0·48
0·133	Hg¹⁹⁷ᵐ	23 hours	0·164
0·134	Ce¹⁴⁴	285 days	0·080
0·134	W¹⁸⁷	23·9 hours	0·68, 0·48
0·137	Re¹⁸⁶	3·70 days	
0·139	Os¹⁹³	31 hours	0·56, 0·46, 0·37, 0·32, 0·28, 0·25, 0·073
0·140	Tc⁹⁹ᵐ	6·04 hours	
0·140	Se⁷⁵	127 days	0·27
0·145	Te¹³¹	24·8 min	0·59, 0·45
0·145	Ce¹⁴¹	33 days	
0·147	Yb¹⁷⁷	1·8 hours	1·23, 1·08

F

TABLE 5.2 (contd.)

γ-Energy (MeV)	Nuclide	Half-life	Associated energies
0·150	Ta^{182}	111 days	1·20, 1·12, 0·23, 0·100, 0·068
0·150	Cd^{111m}	48·6 min	0·25
0·152	Sr^{85m}	70 min	0·23
0·154	Ta^{182m}	16·5 min	0·180
0·155	Re^{188}	16·7 hours	1·13, 0·93, 0·83, 0·63, 0·48
0·159	Te^{123m}	104 days	0·088
0·159	Au^{199}	3·15 days	0·21
0·160	Sn^{117m}	14 days	
0·162	Ba^{140}	12·8 days	0·30
0·163	Ba^{139}	85 min	
0·164	Hg^{197m}	23 hours	0·133
0·170	Gd^{159}	18·0 hours	0·36, 0·115
0·180	Mo^{99}	67 hours	0·78, 0·74, 0·36
0·180	Ta^{182m}	16·5 min	0·154
0·190	In^{114m}	49 days	0·72, 0·55
0·197	Pt^{199}	29 min	0·71, 0·54, 0·48, 0·32, 0·070
0·20	Tb^{160}	73·5 days	1·27, 1·18, 0·96, 0·89, 0·41, 0·29, 0·087
0·21	Ge^{77}	12 hours	1·09, 0·79, 0·71, 0·62, 0·54, 0·41, 0·36, 0·26, 0·21
0·21	Ba^{131}	13 days	0·62, 0·49, 0·24, 0·120
0·21	Nd^{149}	2·0 hours	0·65, 0·54, 0·44, 0·100
0·21	Pm^{151}	27·5 hours	0·110
0·21	Lu^{177}	7·0 days	0·113
0·21	Hf^{180m}	5·5 hours	0·44, 0·33
0·21	Au^{199}	3·15 days	0·159
0·21	Np^{239}	2·33 days	0·28
0·22	Ru^{97}	2·44 days	
0·23	Sr^{85m}	70 min	0·152
0·23	Ta^{182}	111 days	1·20, 1·12, 0·150, 0·100, 0·068
0·24	Ba^{131}	13 days	0·62, 0·49, 0·21, 0·120
0·24	Eu^{154}	16 years	0·122
0·25	Os^{193}	31 hours	0·56, 0·46, 0·37, 0·32, 0·28, 0·139, 0·073
0·25	Cd^{111m}	48·6 min	0·150
0·26	Ge^{77}	12 hours	1·09, 0·79, 0·71, 0·62, 0·54, 0·41, 0·36, 0·21
0·27	Se^{75}	127 days	0·140
0·27	Dy^{165}	140 min	0·36, 0·094
0·28	Pm^{149}	54 hours	
0·28	I^{131}	8·14 days	0·36
0·28	Np^{239}	2·33 days	0·21
0·28	Ce^{143}	33 hours	
0·28	Os^{193}	31 hours	0·56, 0·46, 0·37, 0·32, 0·25, 0·139, 0·073
0·28	Yb^{175}	4·2 days	0·40, 0·114
0·29	Tb^{160}	73·5 days	1·27, 1·18, 0·96, 0·89, 0·41, 0·20, 0·087
0·29	Er^{171}	7·5 hours	0·31, 0·111
0·30	Tc^{101}	14·0 min	
0·30	Ba^{140}	12·8 days	0·162
0·31	Er^{171}	7·5 hours	0·29, 0·111
0·31	Ir^{192}	74 days	0·60, 0·47
0·31	Pa^{233}	27·4 days	
0·32	Ti^{51}	5·8 min	
0·32	Cr^{51}	27·8 days	
0·32	Rh^{105}	36·5 hours	

TABLE 5.2 (contd.)

γ-Energy (MeV)	Nuclide	Half-life	Associated energies
0·32	Os^{193}	31 hours	0·56, 0·46, 0·37, 0·28, 0·25, 0·139, 0·073
0·32	Ir^{194}	19 hours	
0·32	Pt^{199}	29 min	0·71, 0·54, 0·48, 0·197, 0·070
0·33	La^{140}	40·0 hours	2·50, 1·60, 0·81, 0·49
0·33	Hf^{180m}	5·5 hours	0·44, 0·21
0·34	Eu^{152}	9·2 hours	0·97, 0·85, 0·122
0·34	Eu^{152}	13 years	0·122
0·36	Ge^{77}	12 hours	1·09, 0·79, 0·71, 0·62, 0·54, 0·41, 0·26, 0·21
0·36	Mo^{99}	67 hours	0·78, 0·74, 0·180
0·36	I^{131}	8·14 days	0·28
0·36	Gd^{159}	18·0 hours	0·170, 0·115
0·36	Dy^{165}	140 min	0·27, 0·094
0·37	Ni^{65}	2·56 hours	1·49, 1·12
0·37	Os^{193}	31 hours	0·56, 0·46, 0·32, 0·28, 0·25, 0·139, 0·073
0·39	Sr^{87}	2·8 hours	
0·39	Sn^{113}	112 days	
0·40	Yb^{175}	4·2 days	0·28, 0·114
0·41	In^{116m}	54·3 min	2·09, 1·49, 1·27, 1·09
0·41	Tb^{160}	73·5 days	1·27, 1·18, 0·96, 0·89, 0·29, 0·20, 0·087
0·41	Au^{198}	2·7 days	
0·41	Ge^{77}	12 hours	1·09, 0·79, 0·71, 0·62, 0·54, 0·36, 0·26, 0·21
0·42	Nd^{151}	15 min	0·117
0·44	Zn^{69m}	13·8 hours	
0·44	Nd^{149}	2·0 hours	0·65, 0·54, 0·21, 0·100
0·44	Hf^{180m}	5·5 hours	0·33, 0·21
0·45	Ag^{110}	270 days	1·52, 1·39, 0·88, 0·68
0·45	I^{128}	25 min	
0·45	Te^{131}	24·8 min	0·59, 0·145
0·46	Os^{193}	31 hours	0·56, 0·37, 0·32, 0·28, 0·25, 0·139, 0·073
0·47	Ir^{192}	74 days	0·60, 0·31
0·48	Hf^{181}	46 days	0·132
0·48	W^{187}	23·9 hours	0·68, 0·134
0·48	Re^{188}	16·7 hours	1·13, 0·93, 0·83, 0·63, 0·155
0·48	Pt^{199}	29 min	0·71, 0·54, 0·32, 0·197, 0·070
0·49	Ba^{131}	13 days	0·62, 0·24, 0·21, 0·120
0·49	La^{140}	40·0 hours	2·50, 1·60, 0·81, 0·33
0·50	Ru^{103}	39·8 hours	
0·51	Cu^{64}	12·8 hours	
0·51	Zn^{65}	250 days	1·12
0·51	Sr^{85}	65 days	
0·51	Ru^{106}	1·0 year	0·62
0·51	Nd^{147}	11·6 days	0·091
0·54	Pt^{199}	29 min	0·71, 0·48, 0·32, 0·197, 0·070
0·54	Te^{129}	72 min	
0·54	Ge^{77}	12 hours	1·09, 0·79, 0·71, 0·62, 0·41, 0·36, 0·26, 0·21
0·54	Nd^{149}	2·0 hours	0·65, 0·44, 0·21, 0·100
0·55	As^{76}	26·8 hours	1·20, 0·64
0·55	Br^{82}	36·0 hours	1·30, 1·03, 0·77
0·55	In^{114m}	49 days	0·72, 0·190
0·56	Os^{193}	31 hours	0·46, 0·37, 0·32, 0·28, 0·25, 0·139, 0·073

TABLE 5.2 (contd.)

γ-Energy (MeV)	Nuclide	Half-life	Associated energies
0·57	Sb[122]	2·8 days	0·68
0·59	Te[131]	24·8 min	0·45, 0·145
0·60	Cs[134]	2·3 years	0·79
0·60	Ir[192]	74 days	0·47, 0·31
0·61	Sb[124]	60 days	2·10, 1·69
0·62	Ru[106]	1·0 years	0·51
0·62	Ge[77]	12 hours	1·09, 0·79, 0·71, 0·54, 0·41, 0·36, 0·26, 0·21
0·62	Br[80]	18 min	
0·62	Ba[131]	13 days	0·49, 0·24, 0·21, 0·120
0·63	Ga[72]	14·3 hours	2·50, 2·20, 0·83
0·63	Re[188]	16·7 hours	1·13, 0·93, 0·83, 0·48, 0·155
0·64	As[76]	26·8 hours	1·20, 0·55
0·65	Nd[149]	2·0 hours	0·54, 0·44, 0·21, 0·100
0·66	Cs[137]	30 years	
0·67	Nb[97]	74 min	
0·68	Ag[110]	270 days	1·52, 1·39, 0·88, 0·45
0·68	Sb[122]	2·8 days	0·57
0·68	W[187]	23·9 hours	0·48, 0·134
0·69	Pr[144]	17·0 min	2·19, 1·50
0·71	Ge[77]	12·0 hours	1·09, 0·79, 0·62, 0·54, 0·41, 0·36, 0·26, 0·21
0·71	Pt[199]	29 min	0·54, 0·48, 0·32, 0·197, 0·070
0·72	In[114m]	49 days	0·55, 0·190
0·73	Ru[105]	4·5 hours	0·130
0·74	Mo[99]	67 hours	0·78, 0·36, 0·180
0·75	Zr[95]	65 days	
0·75	Zr[97]	17·0 hours	
0·77	Br[82]	36·0 hours	1·30, 1·03, 0·55
0·77	Nb[95]	35 days	
0·78	Mo[99]	67 hours	0·74, 0·36, 0·180
0·79	Cs[134]	2·3 years	0·60
0·79	Ge[77]	12·0 hours	1·09, 0·71, 0·62, 0·54, 0·41, 0·36, 0·26, 0·21
0·80	Po[210]	138·4 days	
0·81	La[140]	40·0 hours	2·50, 1·60, 0·49, 0·33
0·82	Mn[56]	2·58 hours	2·06, 1·77
0·83	Ga[72]	14·3 hours	2·50, 2·20, 0·63
0·83	Re[188]	16·7 hours	1·13, 0·93, 0·63, 0·48, 0·155
0·84	Mg[27]	9·45 min	1·02
0·85	Eu[152]	9·2 hours	0·97, 0·34, 0·122
0·88	Ag[110]	270 days	1·52, 1·39, 0·68, 0·45
0·89	Sc[46]	85 days	1·12
0·89	Tb[160]	73·5 days	1·27, 1·18, 0·96, 0·41, 0·29, 0·20, 0·087
0·90	Rb[88]	17·8 min	1·86
0·93	Re[188]	16·7 hours	1·13, 0·83, 0·63, 0·48, 0·155
0·96	Tb[160]	73·5 days	1·27, 1·18, 0·89, 0·41, 0·29, 0·20, 0·087
0·97	Eu[152]	9·2 hours	0·85, 0·34, 0·122
1·02	Mg[27]	9·45 min	0·85
1·03	Br[82]	36·0 hours	1·30, 0·77, 0·55
1·04	Cu[66]	5·1 min	
1·08	Rb[86]	19·5 days	
1·08	Yb[177]	1·8 hours	1·23, 0·147

$$\text{T\scriptsize ABLE } 5.2 \; (contd.)$$

γ-Energy (MeV)	Nuclide	Half-life	Associated energies
1·09	Ge^{77}	12·0 hours	0·79, 0·71, 0·62, 0·54, 0·41, 0·36, 0·26, 0·21
1·09	In^{116m}	54·3 min	2·09, 1·49, 1·27, 0·41
1·10	Fe^{59}	45 days	1·28
1·12	Sc^{46}	85 days	0·89
1·12	Ni^{65}	2·56 hours	1·49, 0·37
1·12	Zn^{65}	250 days	0·51
1·12	Ta^{182}	111 days	1·20, 0·23, 0·150, 0·100, 0·068
1·13	Re^{188}	16·7 hours	0·93, 0·83, 0·63, 0·48, 0·155
1·17	Co^{60}	5·27 years	1·33
1·18	Tb^{160}	73·5 days	1·27, 0·96, 0·89, 0·41, 0·29, 0·20, 0·087
1·20	As^{76}	26·8 hours	0·64, 0·55
1·20	Ta^{182}	111 days	1·12, 0·23, 0·150, 0·100, 0·068
1·23	Yb^{177}	1·8 hours	1·08, 0·147
1·26	Si^{31}	2·62 hours	
1·27	In^{116m}	54·3 min	2·09, 1·09, 0·41
1·27	Tb^{160}	73·5 days	1·18, 0·96, 0·89, 0·41, 0·29, 0·20, 0·087
1·28	Fe^{59}	45 days	1·10
1·30	Br^{82}	36·0 hours	1·03, 0·77, 0·55
1·33	Co^{60m}	10·1 min	
1·33	Co^{60}	5·27 years	1·17
1·36	Ho^{166}	27·3 hours	1·53, 0·080
1·37	Na^{24}	14·9 hours	2·75
1·39	Ag^{110}	270 days	1·52, 0·88, 0·68, 0·45
1·49	In^{116m}	54·3 min	2·09, 1·27, 1·09, 0·41
1·49	Ni^{65}	2·56 hours	1·12, 0·37
1·50	Pr^{144}	17·0 min	2·19, 0·69
1·52	Ag^{110}	270 days	1·39, 0·88, 0·68, 0·45
1·53	K^{42}	12·5 hours	
1·53	Ho^{166}	27·3 hours	1·36, 0·080
1·57	Pr^{142}	19·2 hours	2·10
1·60	Cl^{38}	37·3 min	2·15
1·60	La^{140}	40·0 hours	2·50, 0·81, 0·49, 0·33
1·69	Sb^{124}	60 days	2·10, 0·61
1·77	Mn^{56}	2·58 hours	2·06, 0·82
1·86	Rb^{88}	17·8 min	0·90
2·06	Mn^{56}	2·58 hours	1·77, 0·82
2·09	In^{116m}	54·3 min	1·49, 1·27, 1·09, 0·41
2·10	Pr^{142}	19·2 hours	1·57
2·15	Cl^{38}	37·3 min	1·60
2·19	Pr^{144}	17·0 min	1·50, 0·69
2·20	Ga^{72}	14·3 hours	2·50, 0·83, 0·63
2·50	Ga^{72}	14·3 hours	2·20, 0·83, 0·63
2·50	La^{140}	40·0 hours	1·60, 0·81, 0·49, 0·33
2·75	Na^{24}	14·9 hours	1·37
3·10	Ca^{49}	8·5 min	4·05
4·05	Ca^{49}	8·5 min	3·10

N.B. Some of the low-energy γ-rays are not actually emitted, as they are fully converted internally. Many of the energies are the subjects of disagreement between different workers.

Westermark and Fineman (1959) described a rapid method for the analysis of cobalt in reactor grade steel by determination of 10·5-minute cobalt 60m. A fast chemical procedure was used to separate the cobalt from the steel, and this separation also rendered self-absorption of the soft gamma radiation negligible. This chemical separation was necessary because of interference by manganese 56 activity, but if the Mn/Co ratio in the steel was less than 10/1, it was possible to determine the cobalt activity directly on the steel sample, thus making the method non-destructive.

Another non-destructive method for cobalt in steel is due to Salmon (1957 b). This is an interesting technique in that it depends on the determination of cobalt 60 which has γ-rays of almost the same energy as iron 59. Nevertheless, it is possible to differentiate between the two activities by making use of the fact that the two cobalt γ-rays are emitted almost simultaneously, i.e. in coincidence, whereas the two iron γ-rays are emitted independently. Two spectrometers are used; one is permanently 'focused' on the lower energy peak at about 1·2 MeV and the other is swept through the spectrum in the normal way. The outputs from the two pulse height analysers are fed into a coincidence unit which ensures that, in the sweep spectrometer, only those pulses which are in coincidence with the low-energy pulses detected by the fixed spectrometer are recorded. In this way the spectrum of the high-energy cobalt 60 γ-ray is recorded alone, and can be determined in the presence of more than twenty-five times as much iron 59 activity (equivalent to about 100 p.p.m. of cobalt in steel).

Other non-destructive methods of analysis include the determination of a whole range of trace impurities in transistor-grade silicon (Morrison and Cosgrove, 1955), the detection and determination of copper, manganese, and sodium in aluminium (Iredale, 1957; Peirson and Iredale, 1958), and also copper and manganese in biological materials (Fineman, Ljungren, Erwall, and Westermark, 1957).

Advantages and disadvantages

Activation analysis using the γ-ray spectrometer offers most of the advantages of the radiochemical method with regard to specificity, avoidance of contamination, and high sensitivity, although the sensitivity is generally somewhat less favourable than with the radiochemical method. Its further advantages are that it is more rapid, giving a considerable saving in man-hours and enabling radioisotopes with shorter half-lives to be considered; it often enables a radiochemical separation to be simplified or even eliminated which is particularly advantageous when the separation is tedious or difficult; it is often non-destructive; and finally, several impurities can easily be determined on the one sample.

The technique is not without its disadvantages, however. The less favourable sensitivity has already been mentioned, and precision is also less than with the radiochemical method. The instrument is an expensive piece of equipment compared with the simple Geiger counter assembly.

Finally, it must be said that neither the radiochemical method nor the spectrometric method is generally superior to the other. The various aspects of each analytical problem must be considered and one method or the other, or a combination of the two, used as the situation demands.

Future developments

It would seem (Kuykendall *et al.*, 1960) that developments in this technique will lead to fully automated activation analyses, using computers to examine and measure the photopeaks in a γ-ray spectrum and to identify the radioisotopes responsible and calculate the amounts present.

6

THE DETERMINATION OF RADIOACTIVITY

Preparation of samples for counting

THE first essential in any method of radioactivity determination is that the sample and standard should be suitably prepared before the determination is made.

Thus metal specimens should have their surfaces cleaned with a suitable etching fluid, appropriate to the metal, to remove any surface contamination which may have arisen before or during irradiation, as by contact with the canning material. If this etch is made under the correct conditions, it can be assumed that the loss in weight of the metal sample will be negligible. For maximum accuracy the sample may be reweighed after the analysis is complete, when its radioactivity is low enough for it to be handled more easily. In a similar way, possible surface contamination can be removed from other solid samples such as some biological specimens, plastics, glass, etc., by using an appropriate solvent, by paring the surface with a knife, or by using a suitable abrasive.

Liquids and powders cannot be treated in this way and it is necessary to ensure that the irradiation container is scrupulously clean so that no contamination can occur. The sample should, however, be transferred from the irradiation container to a suitable inactive container (for gamma counting) or to a standard counting tray or liquid counter (for beta counting) so that any radioactivity induced in the original container is eliminated.

Ideally the sample and standard should have the same shape and size and have comparable activities. If the analysis is to be non-destructive there is not much that can be done with the sample, although the standard can often be chosen to match it. For low-energy gamma counting and, more particularly, for beta counting of solid samples, sample size and shape can be very important. The sample should be as thin as is convenient and the counter should be equally sensitive to all parts of it. For many beta counters a thin disk is best. For powders, such conditions are easily met by spreading the sample in an even layer on the bottom of an aluminium tray, of which several styles are avail-

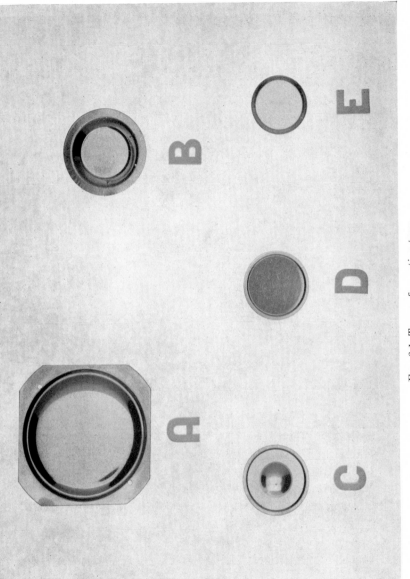

FIG. 6.1. Types of counting tray.

A. 5 cm. diameter, suitable for weak beta-emitters. C. 2·5 cm. diameter with central depression.
B. 3 cm. diameter, 3 mm. deep, suitable for most radionuclides. D. 2·5 cm. diameter, 1 mm. deep, suitable for mounting filter-papers.
E. 2 cm. diameter, 1 mm. deep, without lip.

able (Fig. 6.1). Whole solid specimens must, however, be preshaped and this can be done more conveniently before irradiation or even when the sample is taken. In circumstances where no adjustment can be made, it is essential that the standard be as similar as possible to the sample, and an allowance must be made for any dissimilarity when assessing the accuracy of the final result. The conditions for comparing sources of γ-rays of energy greater than about 0·2 MeV are less stringent.

Liquid samples represent a special case and are conveniently measured by a standard liquid counter for beta activities of energy > 0.5 MeV. The sample should be diluted with a miscible solvent to fill the active volume of the counter. Low-energy beta activities can be measured on liquid samples with an end-window counter or with a 2π or 4π counter, but the risk of contamination of the counter by the sample is then fairly high. Gamma activities are best determined in a standard or well-type scintillation counter.

The same criteria apply to the determination of the radioactivity of the reference standard, but there is usually more scope for fulfilling the necessary conditions. As has already been said, the ideal is for the sample and standard to be of similar size, shape, and density, which is readily achieved if they are of similar material. With the more convenient solution standards, described in Chapter 7, these conditions cannot be realized exactly, except for liquid samples. For comparison with other samples, a solution standard may be precipitated and transferred to a counting tray, transferred to a thin-walled polyethylene container of similar shape to the sample and diluted suitably, dispersed through an absorbent medium of similar size, shape, and density to the sample, or evaporated to dryness on a counting tray if the solute is non-volatile. If the conditions of the sample and standard cannot be matched sufficiently well, the error may be reduced, in some instances of gamma counting, by placing the counter at a distance sufficient for the centres of gravity of the two specimens to be regarded as being at the same distance away. Well-type scintillation counters and 4π beta counters also eliminate geometrical variations, as all radiations escaping from the standards and samples are within the detector, but there is then less scope for adjusting the counting rate to suit the recording equipment.

When the sample and standard are purified radiochemically, the measurement of the radioactivity can be made under more precisely controlled conditions. If the activity is left in solution, it can be determined by any convenient beta or gamma liquid counter, and the chemical yield for the purification process can be measured subsequently on this solution, or another aliquot, by any analytical technique such as colorimetry or gravimetry. For most analyses, and certainly for routine work, it is advantageous to precipitate the activity from solution in a suitable gravimetric form and then to make measurements of both radioactivity and chemical yield on the one precipitate.

There are two convenient ways in which a precipitate can be mounted for radioactivity measurements. The simplest is to slurry the precipitate

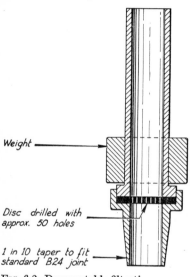

Weight

Disc drilled with approx. 50 holes

1 in 10 taper to fit standard B24 joint

FIG. 6.2. Demountable filtration apparatus: after Faires and Parks, 1960.

with a convenient liquid on to a weighed aluminium counting tray and dry the slurry to constant weight under a heat-lamp or in an analytical oven at a controlled temperature or, in some instances, in a vacuum desiccator. The form of precipitate and the slurrying fluid must be chosen by experiment to give a slurry which dries down to a smooth adherent deposit without cracking or flaking. Water, ethanol, acetone, and ether have all been used for slurrying; the more volatile solvents are to be preferred, where possible, as the drying time can then be quite short. The best type of counting tray to use is probably type B (Fig. 6.1) as this is

deep enough to hold a reasonable volume of slurry during drying. The film of dried precipitate will usually extend part or all the way up the walls of the tray, but this can be controlled by adjusting the volume of the slurry and only introduces errors when precise geometry is essential.

An alternative method, which gives very precise geometry, is specially recommended for use with low-energy beta activities. A demountable filtration apparatus in glass or Perspex, such as that described by Faires and Parks (1960) (Fig. 6.2), is used and the precipitate collected on a disk of filter paper as a well-defined circular mat. The precipitate and paper may be dried and weighed as before, using a piece of brass tubing as a paper-weight to hold the filter paper flat during drying. After weighing, the paper and precipitate may be slid onto a counting tray (type D, Fig. 6.1) and fixed down with a very small quantity of dilute cellulose acetate adhesive. This process suffers from the disadvantage that the demountable filtration apparatus must be cleaned and decontaminated after each filtration—a tedious process if a large number of samples have to be filtered. Also, the weight of the filter paper after filtration, washing and drying cannot be predicted accurately, although it should be similar to that of another disk of filter paper which has been through the same process. Errors of up to 5 per cent. can occur, however, but the use of millipore filters (Jervis, 1957) can minimize these errors.

Types of detectors

Before discussing the different ways in which ionizing radiation can be detected it is worth while recalling briefly the fundamental properties of the radiations which are likely to be encountered in activation analysis.

1. β-particles are fast electrons with energies ranging from 0 to over 3 MeV. They produce direct ionization but, having track lengths varying from a few centimetres to a few metres according to energy, they produce a low intensity of ionization compared with that of α-particles. Positrons are positive electrons with similar properties to β-particles except that when at rest they readily combine with free electrons and are annihilated to give two 0·51 MeV γ-rays.

2. γ-rays and X-rays have similar properties to each other, being forms of electromagnetic radiation, differing only in their mode of production and the energy range in which they occur. They cause ionization via secondary electrons and are very penetrating, producing only a very low ionization density.

The detectors used for measuring these radiations may be divided into three main categories which cover most types of equipment likely to be encountered, gas-filled detectors, scintillation counters, and photographic emulsions.

Gas-filled detectors

Here we shall consider the ionization chamber proper, and also the proportional counter and Geiger counter in their various forms. All three types of chamber have the same basic design; they consist of two electrodes placed in a gas to form a capacitor, which is then charged to a fixed voltage. Radiation causes ionization of this gas and allows a current to flow between the two electrodes. Once the ions in the gas have been attracted to the electrodes, the current ceases until a further ionizing event occurs. If the number of ion pairs collected is plotted against the applied voltage, a curve is obtained which has the same basic shape for any type of chamber. It can be divided into five regions (Fig. 6.3):

A, the ion chamber region; B, the proportional counter region; C, the limited proportionality region; D, the Geiger counter region; E, the continuous discharge region.

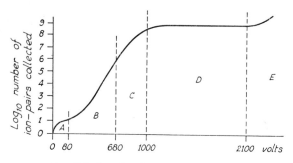

FIG. 6.3. Ion chamber operating regions.

Detectors operated in region A are called ionization chambers. Although this type of chamber is normally associated with the measurement of comparatively high activities, when the rate of collection of ion pairs is so high that in effect a steady current is obtained, it can be operated as a counting ion chamber in which an output pulse is obtained for each particle entering the sensitive volume of the counter. However, the size of the output pulses is exceptionally small and it is necessary to use a high-gain amplifier to amplify these sufficiently to operate an electronic scaler.

If the applied voltage is increased to take the counter into the proportional region B, the ions produced by the primary ionizing event are accelerated by the increased field sufficiently (i.e. to a kinetic energy greater than the ionization potential of the gas) to cause further ionization of the gas. This secondary ionization is cumulative, and results in an avalanche of ionizing collisions, with the result that the current flowing, and therefore the size of the output pulse, is much larger. This process is termed gas amplification and can give amplification factors of more than a million. The size of the amplified pulse is still proportional to the number of ion pairs produced by the primary ionizing event—hence the name proportional counter. If the output pulse is fed to electronic equipment capable of discriminating against pulses of less than a certain size, it is possible to differentiate between particles of different energies, as these will produce output pulses of different sizes proportional to the original energies.

If the applied voltage is increased still further the gas amplification increases until space charges produced in the counter begin to limit the internal fields, so that proportionality is no longer maintained (region C) though the pulse size still depends on the energy of the ionizing particle. Eventually, pulses are produced of a constant size, independent of the number of ion pairs in the primary event. The

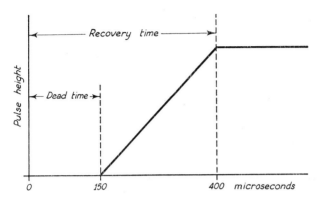

FIG. 6.4. Recovery time and dead time of a Geiger counter.

counter is then operating in the Geiger region D. Proportional counters have a faster response than counting ion chambers and give a larger output which is, however, still so low that considerable amplification is necessary before they will operate an electronic scaler. When the chamber is operated in the Geiger region D, the output pulse is constant and independent of the size of the initial ionizing event, and is of sufficient amplitude to operate an electronic scaler with little or no amplification.

In the proportional counter, since the electrons produced in the avalanche are rapidly collected by the electrodes and the space charges are small, the counter is at once ready to detect another ionizing event. In the Geiger counter the number of ions involved is much greater and the slowly moving positive ions limit the internal fields. A second avalanche cannot occur until the positive ions have moved far enough away from the positive electrode for the electron accelerating field to be re-established. The counter is therefore said to be dead for this period, which may be about 100–150 microseconds. After this dead time, the counter will not produce pulses of full amplitude until the positive ions have been completely removed. The total recovery time (Fig. 6.4) may be of the order of 300–400 microseconds and depends on the applied potential. It is therefore usual to impose an external constant paralysis time, greater than the recovery time, by electronic means.

Under these conditions, the observed counting rate C_0 is related to the true counting rate C by the relationship

$$C = \frac{C_0}{1 - C_0 T},$$

where T is the artificially imposed paralysis time in the same time units as C. C_0 may therefore be corrected for the lost counts which could have been recorded during the time the counter was paralysed.

In principle, any ionization detector can be used as either an ion chamber, a proportional counter, or a Geiger counter but, in practice, the physical design and gas filling are chosen to give optimum operating conditions in one region only.

Of the various types of gas-filled detectors, only the proportional and Geiger counters are used extensively in activation analysis and both these may take the form of end-window counters or of demountable counters of the 2π or 4π types giving correspondingly greater counting efficiencies. In principle, there is little to choose between the two, except that the Geiger counter needs less in the way of associated electronic equipment and, because of its constant pulse height output, the associated high-voltage supply does not need to be so well regulated. This counter should therefore be more reliable, but the proportional counter can count a wider range of activities and does not have the high dead-time of the Geiger counter which can necessitate large corrections being made to the observed count rate. In practice, however, it is now generally accepted that the proportional counter itself is more stable than the Geiger counter and the variation of its efficiency, outside normal statistical variation, over a period of time can, with suitable design, be reduced to less than one-quarter of that of a Geiger counter. Further discussion of the topics mentioned in this section can be found in the monograph by Wilkinson (1950).

Scintillation counters

The principles of the scintillation method for the determination of gamma radiation have been outlined in Chapter 5. In the direct scintillation method, the output from photomultiplier and amplifier is fed into a simple discriminating electronic scaler instead of into a pulse height analyser. In this way all pulses of energy greater than the setting of the discriminator are detected. The discriminator can therefore be set to eliminate electronic noise pulses or low-energy pulses due to other radioactivity.

Beta activity can be determined with similar apparatus provided that the sodium iodide crystal is replaced by one of anthracene or a suitable plastic phosphor covered with thin aluminium foil to make the system light-tight. These phosphors have a much lower density than sodium iodide and so do not back-scatter such a high proportion of the incident beta radiation, but they still have a high efficiency for the transformation of the beta particles into light quanta. Because beta particles have a much shorter range than γ-rays, the phosphors used for beta counting may be much smaller in size and still give a high conversion factor. Thus, plastic phosphors only 3 mm thick will give satisfactory results with the normal range of beta particle energies (cf. 2·5 cm thick sodium iodide crystal for γ-ray measurements).

Although no activation analysis methods using liquid scintillation counting appear to have been published, this technique is one of the most rapidly developing methods for the determination of radioactivity. It is mainly used for the determination of low-energy beta emitters such as carbon 14 or hydrogen 3, but there is no reason why it should not be used for higher-energy radiation. Liquid scintillation counting offers the advantages of virtually 4π geometry and the elimination of self-absorption and scattering losses, since the sample is dissolved directly in the scintillator. Guinn and Wagner (1957) have discussed the procedures, operational problems, and sources of error in the technique and have described suitable apparatus and liquid scintillators.

The scintillation method in general has the advantage that high counting rates can be accepted, since dead time corrections are negligible, as with the proportional counter, except at very high counting rates. It has the further advantage that both beta and gamma radiation can be measured with comparable efficiencies, simply by changing the phosphor. Its disadvantage, however, is that the background for beta counting is slightly higher than for a Geiger counter with comparable shielding. The background for gamma counting is even higher.

Counting errors

Errors in the determination of the amount of induced radioactivity are of two main types, one depending on the statistical nature of the radioactive decay process and one on the nature of the radioactive sample.

The measurement of random processes such as radioactive disintegrations is subject to fluctuation about a mean value. Even if all other counting errors, which are described later in this section, are excluded, the counting rate from a given long-lived sample will vary from measurement to measurement. On this basis, it is not possible to define a true counting rate, but only a mean counting rate about which the observed counting rate will vary according to a Poisson distribution (Yule and Kendall, 1947). The greater the number of disintegrations observed in any one measurement, the closer will that measurement approach the mean counting rate.

The effect of statistical errors on the measurement of radioactivity has often been described (e.g. Barnes, 1960), and it is not proposed to discuss the matter too deeply here. It is only necessary to point out that, for a Poisson distribution, the so-called standard deviation σ is given by

$$\sigma = \sqrt{N},$$

where N is the number of events recorded in a given observation.

Statistical theory shows that there is

(1) a 50 per cent. chance that a given result will differ from the average by less than 0·674 standard deviations,

(2) a 68 per cent. chance that a given result will differ from the average by less than one standard deviation,

(3) a 96 per cent. chance that a given result will differ from the average by less than two standard deviations.

Thus, if 10,000 counts are recorded in any one counting period, the probable variation (50 per cent. above, 50 per cent. below) from the mean count is 0·67 per cent. and there is a 96 per cent. chance that the actual variation will be less than 2 per cent. It will be seen, therefore, that it should generally be possible to reduce statistical errors to negligible proportions.

When very low counting rates have to be measured, an inconveniently long counting time is necessary to avoid statistical errors. The counter background may vary with time, so that if the sample is counted for an exceptionally long time it will be impossible to say what the background is during that time. The background counting rate may also vary between the measurement of the sample and the reference standard, whether the counting periods are long or short. For maximum accuracy it is preferable to determine the background before and after any other measurement, and take the mean of the two determinations as the true background in each case. Under less rigorous conditions, and when the background is known to be reasonably constant, it is usually sufficient to measure it at the beginning and end of each set of observations.

This background is also subject to statistical fluctuations which contribute to the variation of total counts when measuring a sample. Thus an additional fluctuation is introduced into the corrected counting rate for the sample. For the difference between a sample plus background count (A) and a background count alone (B),

$$\sigma(A-B) = \sqrt{(\sigma_A^2 + \sigma_B^2)}.$$

Thus, in measuring a counting rate which is only equal to the background (the minimum counting rate that it is worth while attempting to determine), the standard deviation for the derived activity due to the sample alone can be shown to be much higher than that due to the sample plus background. For a typical end-window Geiger counter, the background is about 10 counts per minute so, in a period of ten minutes, about 100 counts will be registered with a standard error of 10 representing 10 per cent. of the count. For a sample counting rate equal to the background, the total count registered in the same period will be 200 with a standard error of 14·14 representing 7·07 per cent. of the count. Now the activity due to the sample is the difference between the two readings (100 counts), but the standard error is

$$\sqrt{\{(10)^2 + (14\cdot14)^2\}},$$

or 17·3 per cent. of the sample activity.

The practical sensitivity of a counting technique, on which the sensitivity of activation analysis depends, is often set at the level of the background of the instrument. For example, a Geiger counter with a background of 10 counts/minute should not be used for the determination of < 10 counts/minute above this background. This implies that the minimum detectable disintegration rate is given by B/E, where B is the background and E the counting efficiency. More rigorous reasoning shows that a better measure of the ultimate sensitivity is given by E^2/B, which is known as the figure of merit (Loevinger and Bermann, 1951). This is because a low counting rate of 10 counts/minute above background will take longer to evaluate to a given statistical accuracy than a counting rate of 500 counts/minute above a background of 1,000, although this is only half the background. Figures of merit for different types of counters are given by Salmon (1959).

Self-absorption and other errors

The main type of error due to the nature of the radioactive material is that of self-absorption in the sample being counted. In simple terms this means that all the radiations produced in the sample do not manage to escape from it. The proportion which are lost in this way is dependent on the energy of the radiation and on sample thickness. Although this error manifests itself mainly when counting beta particles, it can also arise in gamma counting, particularly when low-energy γ-rays are involved.

The self-absorption of beta particles is represented by the equation

$$\frac{C_d}{C_0} = \frac{1 - e^{-\mu d}}{\mu d} \quad \text{(Glendenin and Solomon, 1950),}$$

where C_d is the observed counting rate for a sample of thickness d, C_0 is the counting rate which would have been observed in the absence of self-absorption, d is the thickness of the sample in mg/cm^2, and μ is the absorption coefficient in cm^2/mg. It can be shown that C_d becomes approximately constant when d exceeds the value $7/\mu$: this value of d is known as 'infinite thickness'.

If the samples are prepared with thickness greater than $7/\mu$, the ratio of the observed count rates will be equal to the ratio of specific activities provided both samples are of the same material and have the same area. Where precipitates are being counted, the thickness of the samples may be increased simply by using larger amounts of inactive carrier. However, since any self-absorption reduces the counting rate, the sensitivity using thick samples is less good than that obtained using thin ones.

If all samples are processed in the same way (and standards can be treated similarly) the weights of the final precipitates will be comparable so that self-absorption errors will also be comparable and may often be neglected. When low-energy beta particles are being counted (where even a slight difference in sample thickness can be important) it is necessary to determine self-absorption curves for the particular sample and apply the appropriate correction to the observed counting rates as shown in Figs. 6.5 and 6.6.

The associated counting errors of back-scattering and self-scattering are also relatively easily eliminated; the former by counting all samples on trays of uniform thickness and material; the latter by controlling sample size or by using self-absorption curves which will also include this effect.

Variations in geometrical efficiency and errors due to scattering by air and shielding materials are normally eliminated by counting all samples at a fixed distance from the counter. If the activities of the samples vary considerably, such a technique may result in the recording of a count rate which is outside the optimum range of the recording equipment. Under these circumstances it is preferable to use only a

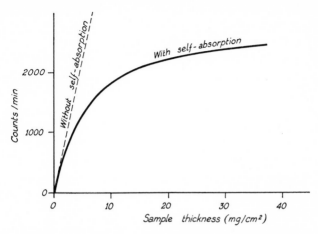

FIG. 6.5. Self-absorption of beta radiation from sulphur 35.

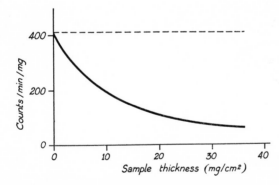

FIG. 6.6. Self-absorption of beta radiation from sulphur 35: specific activity plotted against thickness.

portion of the high-activity sample, rather than attempt to inter-calibrate the different positions of the counting assembly. Such a calibration would vary with the energy of the radiation being detected.

Further counting errors arise since it is obviously impossible to count all samples on the same counter at the same time. Thus, the first sample measured will have decayed to a certain extent by the time the second sample is measured. A correction may be applied for this decay, either mathematically using the published half-life for the particular radioisotope, or graphically using the experimental decay curve, which is usually plotted as a means of checking the radiochemical purity of the radioactivity being counted. An alternative technique has been suggested by Kemp and Smales (1960 c) for the determination of 3·8-minute vanadium 52. Two scalers and matched counters were operated from a single timing unit so that the sample and standard could be counted together. In this way the necessity to correct for decay was eliminated, assuming that the inter-calibration of the two assemblies did not vary.

It is impossible to measure the counting rate at an instant in time, but only over a period of time, i.e. that period during which measurement is made and a certain number of counts are recorded. Cook and Duncan (1952) have shown that, by plotting the activity against the mid-time of the counting period these errors can be minimized to 2 per cent. for a counting period, equal to the half-life, and only 0·6 per cent. for half a half-life. They also give a table of correction factors for activities determined over periods ranging from one-tenth of a half-life to ten half-lives (Table 6.1).

TABLE 6.1

Correction factors for counting time in decay measurements

Counting period (in half-lives)	Correction factor	Counting period (in half-lives)	Correction factor
0·0	1·000	0·9	0·984
0·2	0·999	1·0	0·980
0·3	0·998	1·5	0·955
0·4	0·997	2·0	0·925
0·5	0·994	3·0	0·841
0·6	0·993	4·0	0·738
0·7	0·990	5·0	0·635
0·8	0·987	10·0	0·218

Notes. Multiply the observed activity in the counting period by the corresponding correction factor and plot the corrected activity as if measured at the mid-time of the counting period.

Finally, when all the above counting errors have been eliminated or allowed for, it should be remembered that the electronic equipment used for radioactivity measurements is not absolutely stable and the apparent efficiency of detection may vary from time to time. Such an effect can, of course, be checked by the use of a long-lived reference sample such as uranium (in equilibrium with its decay products) for beta counting or caesium 137 for gamma counting.

Low-background counting

It is exceedingly difficult to achieve exceptionally low backgrounds with sodium iodide scintillation counters, although some improvement can be made by using a pulse height analyser as described earlier. The background activity is due to cosmic rays, to potassium 40 in the crystal, and to natural radioactivity in the glass of the photomultiplier. The background due to γ-rays can be eliminated almost entirely by shielding with 10 cm of lead with about 1 cm of mercury inside it. An anticoincidence shield may also be used. This shield consists of a guard ring of Geiger type cosmic ray counters or scintillation counters, which are all connected together, and their outputs, together with the amplified output from the photomultiplier, are fed into an anticoincidence unit where only those pulses originating in the crystal, *without* an accompanying pulse in the anticoincidence counters, are passed on. The background activity due to potassium 40 can only be reduced by using very pure sodium iodide. In the same way, the activity due to the photomultiplier can be considerably reduced by using a tube constructed of pure quartz. Such equipment is not yet available commercially.

In the case of gas-filled detectors, the background may be subdivided into that due to cosmic rays and external radiation, to electronic and electrical causes, and to radioactive contamination of materials. The background activity due to cosmic rays and other external radiation can again be reduced considerably by the use of lead/mercury shielding and an anticoincidence ring. The inner surface of the counter should preferably be plated with gold or nickel to cover up any α-ray contamination from the counter materials, and the window should be of metallized plastic film rather than mica. Electrical and electronic interference can also be eliminated by suitable apparatus and careful design. Thus, electromagnetic radiation from commutator brushes, etc., can be screened by erecting a properly earthed Faraday cage around the counter, and mains-borne interference can be suppressed by the use of adequate mains filters in all electronic units. Geiger counters are not very susceptible to internally generated electronic backgrounds owing to the large output pulses which they give, but with proportional counters it is essential to use specially smoothed high-voltage units and noise-free amplifiers.

If all these precautions are taken, then with counters of suitable design it is possible to reduce the background to about 1 count/minute for both Geiger and proportional counters. A further slight improvement can be obtained by the use of specially designed counters. In the screen wall counter due to Libby and Lee (1939), modifications are introduced to eliminate the background of electrons (formed by pair production, Compton and photoelectric effects), due to γ-rays, which have penetrated both the shielding and the outer coincidence shield, interacting with the walls of the cathode. In this counter, the outer wall of the counter is no longer the cathode; the cathode is a fine wire screen in between the central anode wire and the counter wall. The counter wall is maintained at about 100 volts positive with respect to the cathode, so that if any electrons are produced in the counter wall or between it and the cathode they are attracted back to the wall and prevented from reaching the sensitive volume of the counter between the anode and the cathode.

Another counter, due to Crouch (1959), is an internal proportional counter with a built-in anticoincidence shield. This is made by taking a screen wall counter, in which the cathode is a ring of straight wires parallel to the anode wire, and placing a second ring of wires between the cathode and the counter wall. These new wires form the anodes of an anticoincidence ring. With this type of counter backgrounds less than 0·2 counts/minute have been obtained but, unfortunately, as soon as a sample is introduced the background rises owing to interactions of γ-rays with the mass of the sample. A similar design of counter, described by Fowler (1954), has been constructed in end-window form to give a compact, anticoincidence counter with a background less than 1 count/minute.

Energy determinations

The measurement of the energies of the radiations emitted by the radioactive sample is a necessary part of activation analysis as discussed in Chapter 2. The determination of gamma energy is described in detail in Chapter 5. The determination of beta energy is a much less precise measurement due partly to the nature of the beta spectra, which are continuous and not divisible into discrete peaks as in gamma spectrometry, and partly to the method of measurement. Because beta spectra are continuous, as shown in Fig. 6.7, with an energy distribution up to a maximum level which is characteristic of the radioactive species, it is customary to measure this maximum energy rather than the shape of the energy distribution, which can be affected by the conditions of measurement.

Maximum beta energies can be determined by magnetic beta spectrometers, or by proportional counters or beta scintillation counters coupled to pulse height analysers. The former technique requires comparatively large quantities of radioactivity of the order of 10 μc (Williams, I. L., 1959) which is more than 100 times the average quantity encountered in activation analysis. While the latter techniques require smaller amounts of activity, they have not come into general use for this type of measurement. The simplest and most common method of beta energy determination is by means of an aluminium absorption curve, in which the amount of radiation able to penetrate sheets of aluminium of increasing thickness is determined and plotted against thickness of the aluminium

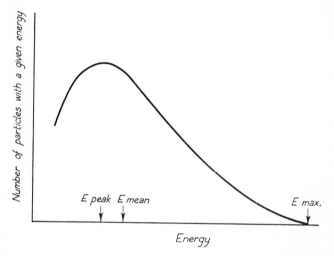

FIG. 6.7. Beta particle energy spectrum from a typical radionuclide.

in mg/cm² (Fig. 6.8). This may be done manually by placing the aluminium absorbers in between the sample and an end-window counter. More conveniently, an automatic filter changer is sometimes used in which the sample is measured for a predetermined time with each of a series of absorbers interposed in turn between it and the counter. After each measurement the time, identity of absorber, counting period, and number of counts are printed on paper tape. Some equipments are also fitted with a turntable to take several samples in turn (e.g. Fig. 6.9).

In order to determine the maximum range, an absorption curve is required in which the beta particle counting rate is reduced by a factor of at least 100, for extrapolation to a factor of about 10,000. When the counting rate is low, or when γ-rays contribute more than about 5 per cent. of the counting rate, this is impracticable. Simple identification can sometimes be achieved by direct comparison with the absorption curve of the standard, but in general the beta particle energy must be determined from the first part of the absorption curve.

Several methods for doing this have been described (Feather, 1938; Glendenin, 1948; Cook and Duncan, 1952). In principle they all depend on matching the absorption curve with that of a known nuclide such as bismuth 210, by proportionally adjusting the scale on which the absorber thickness is plotted. The maximum range can then be found,

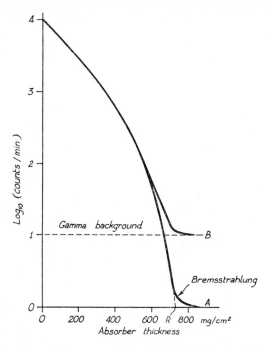

FIG. 6.8. Absorption curve for beta particles of range R in aluminium.

and the beta energy is determined graphically from this as shown in Fig. 6.10.

Determination of half-lives

The half-life of a radioactive sample is usually determined graphically by plotting the counting rate C against time. C is proportional to the radioactivity of the sample and hence to the number N of radioactive atoms present. Thus

$$\frac{C_t}{C_0} = \frac{N_t}{N_0} = e^{-0.693t/t_{\frac{1}{2}}}.$$

If $\log_{10} C_t$ is plotted against t, a straight line is obtained for a single radioactive species, from which the half-life can be found as the time taken for the activity to fall from any value to half that value (Fig. 6.11). The measurement of half-lives in this way is straightforward if

FIG. 6.9. Apparatus for the automatic determination of beta absorption curves from up to six samples.

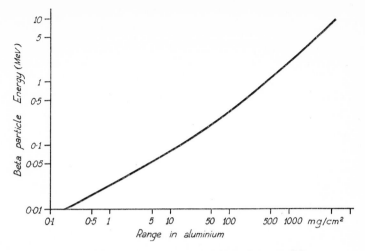

FIG. 6.10. Range-energy relationship for beta particles.

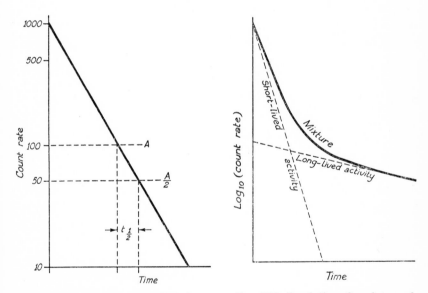

FIG. 6.11. Determination of half-life from
decay measurements.

FIG. 6.12. Resolution of a mixture of
two beta activities.

the radioactivity concerned is mono-isotopic and radiochemically pure.
If, however, a second radioactivity is present, the decay curve obtained
may be similar to Fig. 6.12. The half-life of the longer-lived component
is readily found from the tail end of the curve, when all the short-lived
activities have decayed away. The half-life of the shorter lived component may be estimated by subtracting the extrapolated contribution

of the longer-lived activity as shown. This subtraction may be repeated for multicomponent systems, but satisfactory results are only obtained when the various half-lives differ by a factor of two or more.

The situation is more complex when the different activities are not independent, but are all part of the same decay chain. If the activities are in equilibrium, then for a two-component system, the half-life

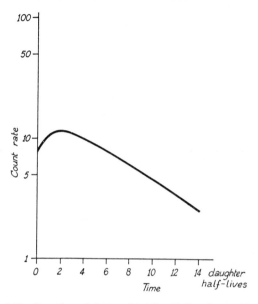

FIG. 6.13. Growth and decay of total activity of parent with a short-lived daughter.

obtained would be that of the parent if the half-life of the daughter were less. This is because the daughter cannot decay any faster than it is produced from the parent. On the other hand, if a radiochemical separation has been used which differentiates between the two components then, at the beginning of the activity measurements, little or no daughter activity will be present. Under these circumstances, a shorter-lived daughter activity will give rise to a growth curve (Fig. 6.13) from which the half-life of the daughter can be deduced. If, however, the half-life of the daughter were longer than that of the parent, then a composite decay curve would be obtained similar to Fig. 6.12.

Autoradiography

Photographic emulsions react to nuclear radiations in the same way that they react to light. Hence they can be used to give a permanent record of the radioactivity in an activated specimen, and have the advantage that the spatial distribution of induced activity can be found in a single experiment. The technique is known as autoradiography, and will only be briefly discussed here, since it has been made the subject of a monograph by Boyd (1955).

At present the technique is largely empirical. Exposure times cannot readily be calculated, and must be determined by trial and error in each application. The resolving power is limited by the size of the silver grains in the emulsion, but a resolution of 250 lines per mm can be obtained under favourable conditions: in such cases the sensitivity of the technique would be comparable with that obtainable with a low-background Geiger counter. Errors have been fully discussed by Boyd (1955). Cutting or polishing the section used for autoradiography can lead to contamination by abrasives and smearing of any fluids present in the sample: hence biological material must be frozen before it is cut. Chemical effects of certain samples, for example terpene peroxides from pine wood and sulphydryl compounds from meat, can be avoided by inserting a very thin plastic film between the sample and the emulsion. Finally there are a number of film blemishes which can be caused by faulty handling before and during development.

Two approaches have been used in connexion with activation analysis. Emulsions are sometimes employed to record prompt particles emitted during activation, but more often they are used to record secondary particles emitted during the decay of activated nuclides. An example of the first approach is the work of Herr (1953) on the determination of lithium 6 by the (n, α) reaction. Here the alpha particle tracks were readily distinguished from tracks caused by lighter particles in the nuclear emulsion. Boron 10 has been determined by a similar reaction (e.g. Mayr, 1954) as have uranium and thorium by autoradiography of the fission process (Curie and Faraggi, 1951).

The second approach is often less specific because most activated samples contain a number of nuclides emitting β- and γ-rays. The γ-rays have much less effect on emulsions than have beta particles, but the energies of the latter cannot be readily distinguished from a photographic record. However, autoradiograms of polished minerals (Goodman and Thompson, 1943), biological sections (Odeblad and Tobias, 1954), and metal surfaces (Makin, 1960) have proved useful. Specificity is greatly improved by chemical separation before or after activation, and autoradiograms of activated chromatograms are becoming more widely used (Benson et al., 1959).

7

ERRORS IN ACTIVATION ANALYSIS

JUST as the technique of activation analysis has its own special advantages, so it has its own particular set of errors. Fortunately, these errors are comparatively few and can, in general, be minimized if not eliminated. These errors may be divided into three main categories, according to whether they originate in flux variations, interfering nuclear transmutations, or processing errors.

Although activation analyses using bombarding particles other than neutrons have been described, most published work refers to the use of neutrons, and especially to slow neutrons, for activation purposes. Consequently, the following discussion applies in the main to the use of reactor neutrons; variations of these errors due to different irradiating particles will be mentioned where appropriate. In addition, the graphite-moderated natural uranium reactor will be taken as a typical source of neutrons.

Flux inhomogeneities

The normal or unperturbed flux in a reactor is not uniform throughout the reactor but decreases from the centre, the rate of decrease increasing with increasing distance from the centre (Fig. 7.1). Thus, although the flux gradient is quite low in the core of the reactor, it can be quite high near the reflector. When a sample and standard are irradiated together in an irradiation can in the core of the reactor, the low flux gradient ensures that the flux reaching the sample and standard is the same. Near the reflector, however, the flux may vary by as much as 5 per cent. across a 2·5 cm can and it is then necessary to make sure that the sample and standard are as close together as possible.

This flux gradient effect is therefore minimized by irradiations in the core of the reactor where the effect can be reduced to less than 2 per cent. However, when irradiations are made in an endless belt of graphite cups (Fig. 7.2), as is frequently the case for irradiations in the Harwell reactor BEPO, certain of the belts do not remain stationary for the whole of the irradiation period, but are wound in and out of the reactor as other samples are added or removed. Under these circumstances, it is possible for the sample to spend a significant proportion of the irradiation time in a region of high flux gradient, and due allowance should be made for this effect. It is, of course, possible to irradiate in fixed positions for irradiation times of multiples of a week (the normal period between reactor shut-downs), or in an irradiation hole for shorter periods. When, as will be discussed later, it is necessary to irradiate

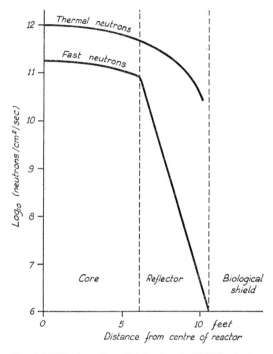

FIG. 7.1. Neutron flux distribution in BEPO reactor.

the sample away from the core of the reactor so that the maximum ratio of slow to fast neutrons can be obtained, due allowance must again be made for the increased flux gradient.

Plumb and Lewis (1955) claimed that the neutron flux distribution of the graphite reactor ORNL was sufficiently stable from week to week for the flux variation within an irradiation can to be determined by the use of monitors and corrections to be applied to subsequent irradiations. They irradiated a can containing only a thin liner of a high purity tinfoil. After irradiation the foil was cut up and the activity determined at various positions. In this way it was shown that, for a sample irradiated near the reflector of the reactor, the bulk of the neutrons came from one side of the can and from slightly above it.

A further effect must be borne in mind, however, even under conditions of apparent low flux gradient. If an irradiation can containing a material of high neutron cross-section is irradiated near to the can containing the sample under examination, it is possible for the local flux depression, caused by the high rate of absorption of neutrons in this material, to affect the flux gradient across the sample can. This situation is not likely to arise very frequently as reactor operators do not like to irradiate large quantities of materials of high neutron absorption cross-section which use up the 'spare' neutrons. When an analysis of the highest accuracy is required it is worth while inquiring as to the nature of the materials in the cans adjacent to the one containing the sample.

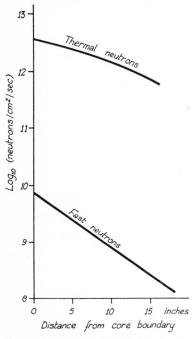

FIG. 7.3. Neutron flux distribution in DIDO reactor.

It should also be mentioned that the flux distribution shown for BEPO (Fig. 7.1) will be similar to that for other large graphite-moderated reactors but, in the more compact, enriched fuel, heavy-water moderated reactors, the flux distribution is of course quite different (Figs. 7.3 and 3.5). Much higher flux gradients are encountered especially where the core is not accessible. Consequently, the advantage of the higher flux usually associated with such reactors must be balanced against the disadvantage of this higher flux gradient. Other neutron sources such as the van de Graaff generator (Burrill and Gale, 1957) and the laboratory neutron source (Meinke and Anderson, 1953) have not only a high flux gradient but also a much lower flux than the graphite-moderated reactor.

Activation by particles other than slow or thermal neutrons also gives rise to errors due to flux variation. The flux gradient for fast neutrons in BEPO (Fig. 7.1) can be seen to increase, even more markedly than for thermal neutrons, with increasing distance from the centre of the reactor. Similarly, machines which produce beams of particles such as protons or deuterons also give rise to high flux gradients, mainly

FIG. 7.2. Graphite 'belt-stringer' used for loading samples into BEPO reactor.

due to the narrowness of the beam. Under these conditions sample size is usually limited and it is often impossible to irradiate both sample and standard in a constant flux at the same time. It is preferable to irradiate sample and standard on a rotating disk in the beam (Odeblad, 1956 b), but this is not always possible.

Even when a sample is irradiated in a uniform flux, the flux reaching the sample and standard may be quite different owing to the different inner containers used. While no attenuation of neutrons is observed for aluminium up to 2 cm thick, 1 mm of quartz reduces the flux to 95 per cent. (Plumb and Lewis, 1955). Since standards are often irradiated in solution in silica ampoules, and samples in containers of aluminium or polythene (which also gives low attenuation), this variation is worth noting. A correction can, of course, be made, since the containers are usually of reproducible thickness, but for maximum accuracy it is preferable to irradiate both samples and standards in containers of the same material and of the same shape and size.

Self-shielding

The main cause of flux variation is, however, self-shielding which results in flux depression within the sample itself. This effect applies to activation with any type of particle and depends simply on the *absorption* cross-section for that particle. (This cross-section may be quite different from the *activation* cross-section.) As succeeding layers of the sample absorb particles, the residual flux becomes less and this results in the inside of the sample becoming less active than the outside. This effect is readily demonstrated by irradiating samples of the same material but of varying size and then, after determining the activity of each, plotting a graph of specific activity against sample weight (Fig. 7.4). The deviation from the straight line which would be obtained if there were no self-shielding is readily seen.

If the self-shielding does not occur, or occurs to a lesser extent, in the standard as compared to the sample, then different specific activities will result in the two materials, and the error in the analysis will be dependent on the difference in the two self-shielding effects.

Various formulae have been put forward for calculating the effects of self-shielding. Keyes (1950) has given a simplification of the treatment of Marshak (1947) and obtained for a sphere the formula

$$f = \tfrac{3}{4}N\sigma a,$$

where f is the fractional decrease in the average neutron flux on the sample, N is the number of atoms per unit volume in the sample, σ is the neutron absorption cross-section, and a is the radius of the sample in cm. Jenkins and Smales (1956) recommend the formula

$$f_x = f_0 e^{-N\sigma x},$$

where f_0 is the flux at the surface of the sample, f_x is the flux at depth x inside the sample, and N and σ are as above. However, in neither

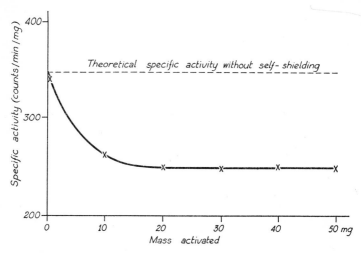

FIG. 7.4. Variation of induced specific activity with weight of sample.

of these formulae can the *thermal* neutron *activation* cross-section as given in various charts (Meinke and Maddock, 1957; General Electric Co., 1956) be used. Since the neutron energy spectrum in most nuclear reactors covers a wide energy range above the thermal energy region, and since many neutron reactions have much higher cross-sections for reactions with these epithermal neutrons, the effective cross-section for the assessment of self-shielding can be quite high. Tables of the variation of neutron absorption cross-section with neutron energy are now available (Hughes and Schwartz, 1958) but the values given are difficult to apply in practice as the neutron energy spectrum is not known accurately for all irradiation positions. The best use to be made of these various self-shielding formulae is to assess the significance of these effects, bearing in mind the value of any resonance cross-section. If self-shielding is likely to be serious, steps should be taken to eliminate or minimize it rather than attempts made to calculate and correct for the effect.

One method of eliminating self-shielding has already been mentioned, namely the irradiation of samples of varying size. From the graph of specific activity against sample weight it is possible to determine the maximum weight which will give, say, 1 per cent. self-shielding and then to limit all future irradiations to samples of that weight. If this results in inadequate sensitivity it will be necessary to tolerate higher degrees of self-shielding. Alternatively, it is possible to extrapolate

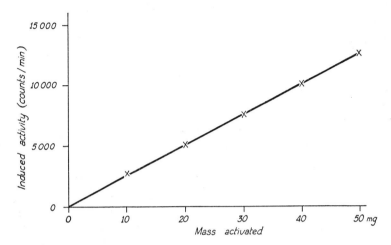

FIG. 7.5. Variation of induced activity with weight of sample.

the experimental curve and so obtain the specific activity at zero weight (i.e. the specific activity with no self-shielding) and then use this value in the calculation of the result of the analysis.

Such methods are, however, unreliable as can be seen from Fig. 7.4. Here if sample weights greater than about 20 mg had been used, a constant specific activity would have resulted, and it would have been assumed that there was no self-shielding. This effect arose because the bottoms of the irradiation containers used were not flat, and although the specific activity decreased as the containers were filled up, it reached a constant value when the addition of more solid merely increased the height of the solid in the container without affecting the average diameter of the solid presented to the flux of neutrons (Cabell and Smales, 1957). It is therefore essential to irradiate one sample of extremely small weight in order to approximate to the 'zero weight' conditions.

It is important that the results of such investigations be plotted as in Fig. 7.4 in terms of specific activity, and not in terms of induced activity as in Fig. 7.5 where the effect of self-shielding is lost. Both Figs. 7.4 and 7.5 were obtained from the same set of results.

Some authors (e.g. Long, 1951) recommend that when self-shielding is significant the material should be diluted by admixture with alumina or graphite, but it is then necessary to ensure that a completely homogeneous mix is obtained and the technique can, of course, only be applied to materials of small particle size.

As a last resort, the sample can be dissolved and diluted with water (Gibbons and Simpson, 1960 a) which then makes certain that a homogeneous mixture is obtained. All these dilution techniques, however, vitiate one of the main advantages of activation analysis, namely the elimination of reagent blanks. Since contamination after irradiation is only of minor importance, the less treatment the sample receives before irradiation the better.

A technique which has been suggested to solve this problem (Leliaert, Hoste, and Eeckhaut, 1958 a) involves the use of an internal standard. Instead of irradiating a known amount of the element as reference standard, two quantities a and b of the sample are irradiated, an amount c of the element X to be determined being 'homogeneously' mixed with b. The material of the sample should also contain an element Y with suitable nuclear characteristics to facilitate its determination. The ratio of the specific activities induced in element Y enables the ratio of the effective fluxes for samples a and b to be determined and, in fact, the two samples need not be irradiated in the same can or even at the same time. The second sample containing the known amount of added impurity acts as the reference standard and the result is calculated from the formula

$$\% X = \frac{100 c X_a Y_b}{a X_b Y_a - b X_a Y_b},$$

where

X_a is the activity due to element X in sample a,

X_b is the activity due to element X in sample b,

Y_a is the activity due to element Y in sample a,

Y_b is the activity due to element Y in sample b.

The method has the advantage that sample and standard have similar compositions, an ideal situation, but it suffers from the same disadvantage as the dilution technique in that a truly homogeneous mixture must be obtained for the method to be valid. A further difficulty is involved in the measurement of the amount of impurity added, which must of necessity be quite small and preferably comparable to the amount already present. Also, there is a possibility that some of the additive may be absorbed on the walls of the container and therefore not subject to the macro-components of the sample to the same extent as the trace impurity. Finally, element Y will only act as a true flux monitor if it absorbs neutrons in the same energy range as element X.

Preparation of standards

Since the technique of activation analysis is mainly applied to the determination of trace quantities, the element being determined is usually present in a low enough concentration for self-shielding effects to be negligible, even if the element has quite a high absorption cross-section. Self-shielding in the sample is therefore only likely when strongly absorbing elements occur in the matrix. Self-shielding in the standard is, however, directly dependent on the element being determined, and becomes important when the standard contains elements of cross-section greater than a few hundred millibarns. These are the elements which, of course, give the greatest sensitivity of analysis, and are therefore the ones which have to be determined most frequently. Consequently, the element must usually be irradiated in some diluted form.

As has already been mentioned, the ideal standard is a material closely similar, both chemically and physically, to the unknown but containing a known amount of the element to be determined. However, as one of the main reasons for using activation analysis is that the concentration of the impurity is so small that it cannot be measured accurately by other methods, such standards are not likely to be available readily. Synthetic materials can be used, but it is difficult to prepare these to contain such small quantities of impurity in accurately known amounts. The easiest way to prepare a standard which approximates to the composition of the sample is by adding a known amount of impurity to a second portion of the sample as already mentioned in the technique of Leliaert, Hoste, and Eeckhaut (1958 a). A similar procedure, but excluding the use of an internal standard for self-shielding monitoring, was used by Reed, Kigoshi, and Turkevich (1959). The trace element, in an amount more than 100 times that already present, was added in solution to a finely powdered specimen of exactly the same material as the sample, which was thoroughly mixed and dried before irradiation. Reed (1959) claimed that it was possible to prepare a uniform mixture in this way and that, although the amount of trace element was much larger than the amount in the sample, it was still sufficiently low to be regarded as a trace quantity and was affected by the macro-components in the same way as the trace impurity in the sample.

Bowen (1959 c) has used a variation of this technique when determining trace impurities in biological material. Seeds, which had been grown and collected under controlled conditions, were used as a carrier medium for the solution of the trace impurity. It was shown that the seeds would absorb comparatively large amounts of liquid and, although the general composition of the standard was not exactly the same as that of the sample it was sufficiently close to be comparable.

Gibbons and Hewlett (unpublished) used a synthetic standard when determining the strontium content of saturated brine. Safety considerations, owing to the possibility of radiolytic decomposition, necessitated the solution being evaporated to dryness prior to irradiation. In these circumstances it was a fairly simple matter to prepare a synthetic standard, of uniform composition, by adding a measured trace quantity of strontium to a pure sample of saturated brine. When the solutions were evaporated, in the actual irradiation containers, the rates of crystallization were similar and it was expected that the strontium would distribute itself, between the sodium chloride crystals and the walls of the containers, in the same way in each case. The strontium content of the sodium chloride used in preparing the pure brine solution was found by adding increasing quantities of strontium and plotting the induced strontium activity against weight of strontium added; the strontium content was then calculated by extrapolation (Fig. 7.6).

There are occasions when, although the trace element content is not unusually low, activation analysis is still applied because it is quicker, more precise, or will work with smaller samples than conventional methods for a particular determination. Under these conditions, e.g. for the determination of uranium in rocks and minerals, Smales (1952) recommends that the standard should be a mineral, similar in type to that under examination, but in plentiful supply so that good determinations can be made by classical methods. In the same way, Salmon (1957 b) used a British Standard Steel as reference when determining the cobalt content of steel by a gamma-gamma coincidence method, and Spencer, Mitchell, and King (1958) used commercially available dried human serum, of known composition, when determining macro-components of tissue, blood, saliva, urine, and faeces.

When suitable reference materials cannot be obtained or prepared, it is necessary to irradiate a pure compound of the element being determined, diluted in some suitable way. Smales and Pate (1952 a) used an arsenic standard prepared by solid dilution of arsenious oxide with aluminium oxide. The alumina was tested for arsenic content and was then mixed intimately with a weighed portion of arsenious oxide. An aliquot of this mixture was then mixed intimately with a further quantity of alumina and the process repeated until the desired dilution

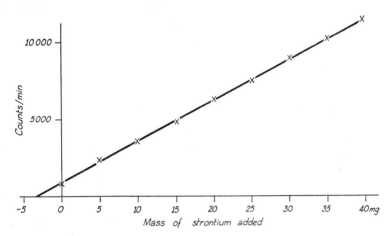

FIG. 7.6. Determination of added strontium in saturated brine.

was obtained. Portions of the final mix were tested for homogeneity and it was claimed that a satisfactory standard could be prepared in this way. The method is obviously tedious, however, and the accuracy with which the concentration of the final mixture is known must be doubtful. It is perhaps significant that Smales and his co-workers gradually turned to the use of dilute solutions as standards (e.g. Smales, Mapper *et al.*, 1959). This type of standard (i.e. a dilute solution) is now used by more than 75 per cent. of activation analysts, judging from published papers and from discussion at the Vienna Symposium (1960).

The standard solution may be irradiated in polythene tubing as this is fairly readily cleaned (Bowen, 1956 b), but it is probably worth while to standardize on silica ampoules as these are necessary anyway if long irradiation times (> 3 days) are to be used. Although some workers have used silica needles containing only a few microlitres of solution (Mackintosh and Jervis, 1957), ampoules of the type shown in Fig. 7.7 are more convenient as they are easier to fill and empty and the contents can be weighed more accurately, although the solution must be correspondingly more dilute. These ampoules are easily made from

4-mm I.D. silica tubing which can be worked with a normal oxygen-coal gas flame. They should be cleaned with hot redistilled nitric acid and with silica-distilled water, and dried in a dust-free atmosphere before use. They may be filled by means of the usual transfer pipette, which must be cleaned in the same way, and after weighing they are easily sealed at the outer constriction.

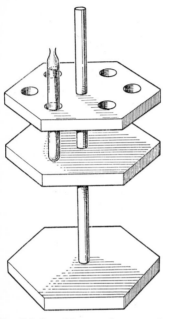

FIG. 7.8. Stand for warming ampoules with carrier after activation.

After irradiation the ampoules are centrifuged to drive all the liquid into the body of the ampoule, which can then be opened at the remaining constriction. Both the ampoules and tip are then filled with part of the carrier solution to be used in the radiochemical purification, and heated in a stand (Fig. 7.8) in a hot-water bath for a few minutes for the carrier to exchange with any of the trace element adsorbed on the walls of the ampoule. The ampoule and tip are then washed out with the remainder of the carrier solution and finally with water. Of course, if no radiochemical purification is to be done, it may not be necessary to open and empty the ampoule unless the impurity to be determined has a short-lived activity which could be masked by the 2·62-hour activity of silicon 31.

From the safety aspect, it can be stated that ampoules prepared as above have invariably passed the requirement of the Isotope Division (1957) at Harwell that sealed containers should be capable of withstanding 100° C for 24 hours. As far as radiolytic decomposition is concerned (Allen, Davis *et al.*, 1949) no serious pressure has built up in any of several hundred standards used during six years of the operation of an activation analysis service at Harwell.

The standard solution can, in general, be prepared from the normal A.R. grade of reagent, particularly when radiochemical purifications are to be used, as induced activity due to impurities in these reagents will usually be much less than that due to the element concerned. When significant amounts of high neutron-absorbing impurities are present, or where radiochemical purifications are not used, it is often

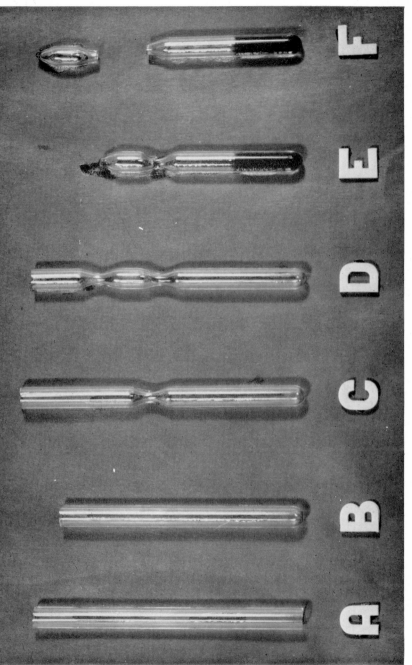

Fig. 7.7. Stages in the construction of a silica ampoule for activation: *A–D*; manufacture. *E*; filled and sealed. *F*; broken open after activation.

worth while using spectrographically standardized materials for the preparation of standards. It should be noted, however, that these materials are not always purer than A.R. materials, but the impurity content is more accurately known.

Ideally, the concentration of the standard solution should be adjusted so that the standard contains the same weight of element as that expected in the sample, dispersed over a similar volume. For routine analysis, using ampoules of the type containing 0·20–0·25 ml of solution, it is worth while standardizing on a concentration of 100 μg element/ml unless this would involve more than 100 times the weight of element expected in the sample. Differences up to this level can be balanced, in general, by dilution of the standard after irradiation without the introduction of a significant error. The concentration suggested is convenient in that it is high enough for the solution to be washed out of the ampoule easily without serious adsorption losses and yet low enough, for the majority of elements, for no self-shielding errors to be introduced. Also, although the activation technique is capable of sub-micro analysis, it is surprising how many samples analysed have impurity contents in the 10–20 p.p.m. range.

Finally, some workers, instead of sealing the solution in a silica ampoule, evaporate a few micro-litres of a stronger solution on a filter paper under an infra-red lamp (e.g. Westermark and Fineman, 1959). Such a procedure is only advisable if the trace element is non-volatile. The filter-paper disk may be sealed between two disks of polythene for protection (Mackintosh and Jervis, 1958) to give a standard which is of convenient size and shape for γ-ray spectrometry.

Interfering nuclear reactions

In addition to the activation reaction which occurs with the element being determined, the matrix material and the other impurities present are also irradiated and it is possible for the same radioelement to be produced from these materials. Thus, in reactor irradiations interference may occur due to reactions with slow neutrons, with γ-rays and, in particular, with fast neutrons. Taking the determination of arsenic as an example, radioarsenic is normally produced by the slow neutron reaction

$$_{33}\text{As}^{75} + _{0}n^{1} \longrightarrow _{33}\text{As}^{76} + \gamma,$$

but it is also possible for the same radioisotope to be produced directly from selenium,

$$_{34}\text{Se}^{76} + _{0}n^{1} \longrightarrow _{33}\text{As}^{76} + _{1}p^{1},$$

$$_{34}\text{Se}^{77} + \gamma \longrightarrow _{33}\text{As}^{76} + _{1}p^{1};$$

from bromine, $_{35}Br^{79}+_0n^1 \longrightarrow {}_{33}As^{76}+_2He^4$;

and indirectly from germanium and selenium,

$$_{32}Ge^{74}+_0n^1 \longrightarrow {}_{32}Ge^{75} \longrightarrow {}_{33}As^{75}+_{-1}e^0,$$

$$_{34}Se^{76}+\gamma \longrightarrow {}_{33}As^{75}+_1p^1.$$

In the last two reactions As^{75} is initially formed but, since this is the starting material for the original arsenic activation reaction, the amount formed will add to the amount of impurity originally present and so constitute a real interference.

A further interference arises due to the formation of radioisotopes other than the one being used for the determination. Significant amounts of As^{77} are not likely to be formed by neutron bombardment of arsenic during a normal irradiation period since a double neutron reaction is involved,

$$_{33}As^{75}+_0n^1 \longrightarrow {}_{33}As^{76}+_0n^1 \longrightarrow {}_{33}As^{77},$$

but it can be made by the reactions

$$_{32}Ge^{76}+_0n^1 \longrightarrow {}_{33}As^{77}+_{-1}e^0,$$

$$_{34}Se^{77}+_0n^1 \longrightarrow {}_{33}As^{77}+_1p^1,$$

$$_{92}U+_0n^1 \longrightarrow \text{fission products including } {}_{33}As^{77},$$

$$_{90}Th+_0n^1 \longrightarrow \text{fission products including } {}_{33}As^{77}.$$

In this instance it is comparatively easy to distinguish between the As^{76} and As^{77} activities. The maximum beta energy of As^{76} is 2·97 MeV, whereas that of As^{77} is 0·70 MeV, so that by use of a suitable filter ($\sim$ 300 mg/cm^2 of aluminium) the beta particles from As^{77} may be screened from the counter without seriously affecting those from As^{76}. The count-rate due to As^{76} will be slightly reduced, however, so that the presence of As^{77} does represent an interference by affecting the ultimate sensitivity adversely.

Fortunately the cross-sections for these (n,p), (n,α), and (γ,p) reactions are generally quite low compared to the (n,γ) activation cross-section, so that these reactions normally cause serious interference only in the presence of macro-quantities of the interfering elements which, it should be noted, are all (apart from uranium and thorium which are special cases in that they undergo fission reactions) adjacent, in the periodic table, to the element being determined. Thus, these types of interference constitute a serious limitation in the determination of arsenic in germanium, an analysis which has been discussed in some detail by Smales and Pate (1952 a).

Another example of the interference of an (n, p) reaction is in the determination of copper in zinc. It has been shown that, in the centre of BEPO, the amount of copper 64 activity produced by the reaction

$$_{30}Zn^{64} + {}_0n^1 \longrightarrow {}_{29}Cu^{64} + {}_1p^1$$

is equivalent to 708 p.p.m. of natural copper (Mellish, Payne, and Otlet, 1958) and, although this error may be reduced to ~ 1 p.p.m. by irradiating the sample at the edge of the reactor, where the flux of fast neutrons is greatly reduced, the method can only be used to determine a similar quantity of true natural copper in zinc, even though the basic sensitivity of the method is still 0·001 p.p.m. in the lower thermal flux at the edge of the reactor.

In a similar way, the (n, α) reaction results in the introduction of a spurious sodium activity equivalent to 81 p.p.m. in the determination of sodium in aluminium (Salmon, 1954). Once again, if the sample is irradiated in a part of the reactor where the fast neutron flux is sufficiently low, the slow neutron flux is also reduced and the sensitivity of the method is affected adversely.

It should be realized that it is not only major components of a sample which give rise to interfering radioactivities. Some minor constituents can also cause trouble, particularly when the trace element is present at very low levels, and has a long half-life so that long irradiation times are necessary. Thus, in the determination of cobalt via cobalt 60, any nickel present in the sample will give rise to cobalt 58 by (n, p) activation and the two cobalt activities will not be separated by a radiochemical purification. For equal weights of nickel and cobalt the error is about 0·1 per cent. As both isotopes are relatively long-lived, decay measurements would not reveal the contamination, and although, in principle, γ-ray spectrometry could identify and separate the two activities, it is quite possible that the amount of activity would be insufficient for the purpose.

In activations with fast neutrons, or with other particles, side reactions are much more important as the cross-sections for all these reactions are comparable, with the result that other trace impurities can cause tremendous interference if they are capable of being converted into the same radioisotope as that produced from the element being determined. Thus, for example, in the determination of boron by the (p, n) reaction

$$_5B^{11} + {}_1p^1 \longrightarrow {}_6C^{11} + {}_0n^1,$$

comparable amounts of radiocarbon can be formed from nitrogen by the (p, α) reaction

$$_7N^{14} + {}_1p^1 \longrightarrow {}_6C^{11} + {}_2He^4,$$

and from carbon by the $(p; p, n)$ reaction

$$_6C^{12} + {}_1p^1 \longrightarrow {}_6C^{11} + {}_1p^1 + {}_0n^1.$$

Other, more complicated reactions can also occur and the degree of complexity increases with the energy of the proton beam. If the proton energy could be kept below 5 MeV the simple reactions would predominate, but such a limitation is difficult to realize with the majority of cyclotrons.

On the credit side, it should be mentioned that these interfering reactions can occasionally be used to advantage, particularly in reactor activations. For example, by using the fast neutron reaction

$$_{16}S^{32} + {}_0n^1 \longrightarrow {}_{15}P^{32} + {}_1p^1,$$

the sensitivity for the determination of sulphur can be improved by a factor of 10 compared with the slow neutron reaction

$$_{16}S^{34} + {}_0n^1 \longrightarrow {}_{16}S^{35} + \gamma,$$

because of the increased isotopic abundance of sulphur 32 compared with that of sulphur 34 and the greater ease of detection of phosphorus 32 compared with that of sulphur 35. Under these conditions it is the slow neutron reaction

$$_{15}P^{31} + {}_0n^1 \longrightarrow {}_{15}P^{32} + \gamma$$

which represents an interference and, because the cross-section for this reaction is so high, a phosphorus content of only 1/2000 of the sulphur content will cause a 1 per cent. interference. Furthermore, such a small amount of phosphorus can usually be determined only by activation analysis; but irradiation in the core of the reactor, to determine the phosphorus content, results in interference from the sulphur present, and irradiation in the thermal column does not give sufficient sensitivity.

A useful technique (Gibbons and Simpson, 1960b), which resolves this dilemma, involves the irradiation of a sample together with phosphorus and sulphur standards in the core of the reactor, and also a second sample and a similar set of standards in another part of the reactor where the ratio of fast to slow neutrons is different, but the slow-neutron flux is still adequate for the production of detectable quantities of phosphorus 32 by the (n, γ) reaction on phosphorus 31. The phosphorus 32 content of all six specimens is then measured and the sulphur content of the sample can be calculated as follows:

Let Cu_c, Cs_c, and Cp_c be the counts from the unknown, the sulphur standard and the phosphorus standard from the centre of the reactor, and Cu_e, Cs_e, and Cp_e be the counts from the unknown, the sulphur standard and the phosphorus standard from near the edge of the reactor.

Then
$$Cs_c = K_c F_c Ws_c, \qquad Cs_e = K_e F_e Ws_e,$$
$$Cp_c = k_c f_c Wp_c, \qquad Cp_e = k_e f_e Wp_e,$$

where

F_c is the fast neutron flux at the centre,

F_e is the fast neutron flux near the edge,

f_c is the slow neutron flux at the centre,

f_e is the slow neutron flux near the edge,

Ws_c, Ws_e, Wp_c, and Wp_e are the weights of the four standards,

and K_c, K_e, k_c, and k_e are constants.

If x be the proportion of sulphur in the sample,

   y be the proportion of phosphorus in the sample,

then
$$Cu_c = K_c F_c x Wu_c + k_c f_c y Wu_c S$$
$$= \frac{Cs_c}{Ws_c} x Wu_c + \frac{Cp_c}{Wp_c} y Wu_c S.$$

Similarly
$$Cu_e = \frac{Cs_e}{Ws_e} x Wu_e + \frac{Cp_e}{Wp_e} y Wu_e S,$$

where S is the fractional reduction in the slow neutron flux due to self-shielding by the matrix.

Solving these two simultaneous equations, we find

$$x = \frac{\dfrac{Cu_c}{Wu_c} - \left(\dfrac{Cp_c}{Wp_c}\dfrac{Wp_e}{Cp_e}\right)\dfrac{Cu_e}{Wu_e}}{\dfrac{Cs_e}{Ws_e} - \left(\dfrac{Cp_c}{Wp_c}\dfrac{Wp_e}{Cp_e}\right)\dfrac{Cs_e}{Ws_e}}.$$

Hence the sulphur content may be calculated.

Other errors

Apart from statistical variations and other errors, associated with the methods of determination of the induced radioactivity, which are considered in the appropriate sections, there are other errors worthy of brief mention although these are not really characteristic of activation analysis. These are mainly associated with the treatment of the sample both before and after irradiation, and may therefore be termed loosely as processing errors.

For example, the sample may pick up contamination from the irradiation container, even though this be cleaned scrupulously, particularly when liquid samples are irradiated. Bowen (1956 b) found that polythene containers retained 3×10^{-10} grammes of manganese even after thorough cleaning.

An important contamination effect can also occur during radiochemical separations. This may manifest itself in two ways. Firstly, trace impurities other than the one being determined may be present at almost carrier-free concentrations with the result that their behaviour becomes somewhat unpredictable. Consequently, they may be absorbed on the precipitate of the desired element (e.g. phosphorus 32 on manganese dioxide), or may even coprecipitate if the chemical properties are sufficiently close. It is therefore necessary to add carriers for such trace impurities to ensure that they are not carrier-free, adding further quantities after each precipitation of the desired element to give adequate hold-back of the undesired impurity. In some instances, a better separation can be achieved by adding carriers for the unwanted impurities and then precipitating them by selective reactions to leave the desired element in solution.

Secondly, macro-quantities of other components may also contaminate the final precipitate of the trace impurity and, while this may not be apparent as erroneous activity, the amount involved may be sufficient to give a false chemical yield. This effect can occur in the determination of strontium in calcium-rich samples. Here, it is necessary to ensure that the radiochemical separation is adequately selective. The selectivity of these separations can, of course, be checked prior to an actual analysis by the use of radioactive tracers.

The chemical yield is also susceptible to the normal hazards of any analytical procedure in that physical contamination may occur due to inadequately cleaned apparatus or to ingress of dirt and rust by fallout from overhead pipes, etc. Here, of course, normal analytical precautions coupled with clean and tidy working will eliminate the errors.

Where radiochemical separations with carriers are involved, it is necessary to ensure that the carrier element and the trace element are in the same chemical form so that they behave identically in the ensuing purification; this being particularly true for the trace element being determined. When a nucleus reacts with an activating nuclear particle, the new nucleus and the residual particle may recoil with sufficient energy to overcome chemical binding forces. This is the Szilard–

Chalmers effect (Szilard and Chalmers, 1934). For example, in thermal neutron activation, the recoil energy E_r of the nucleus is given by

$$E_r = \frac{536E_\gamma^2}{M} \text{ electron volts,}$$

where E_γ is the energy of the prompt γ-ray of the (n, γ) process, and M is the atomic weight of the product nucleus. The recoiling atom travels for a short distance before it gives up all its excess energy, and may undergo various chemical reactions in the process. The activated element may be found, therefore, in a variety of chemical states, and the radiochemical purification should include as its first step an oxidation/reduction cycle if the element has more than one oxidation state.

In the analysis of biological materials, the oxidative conditions normally used for dissolving and destroying the organic material can usually be made part of this cycle. Special steps may be necessary, in, for example, the determination of organic halides where the halogen may be released in a sufficiently energetic form to escape the sample matrix and be absorbed on the walls of the container. It is then necessary to wash the container with hot, acidified carrier to ensure that the absorbed trace element exchanges with the carrier.

A further error may arise due to the sample and standard having different isotopic ratios. This is particularly true for those elements which are the end products of radioactive decay chains, e.g. Ca, A, Sr, Sn, Ba, Ce, Nd, Yb, Hf, Os, Tl, Pb, and the heavier elements (see Duckworth, 1958).

For example, Herr, Hoffmeister *et al.* (1960), using mass spectrometry, have found that the ratio of osmium 187 to osmium 186 in osmium/iridium ores and in iron meteorites varies between 0·88 and 1·41. This variation is attributed to the production of radiogenic osmium by the decay of rhenium 187. Similarly, elements present in minerals containing significant amounts of uranium may have unusual isotopic ratios, due to activation by the various uranium radiations which would affect different isotopes to different extents, or dilution by stable fission products.

The determination of uranium itself is also liable to errors of this type. Thus, natural uranium contains 99·3 per cent. of uranium 238 and 0·7 per cent. of uranium 235 of which the uranium 238 is not fissionable by slow neutrons. The uranium may be determined by activation analysis by two main methods, the first involving activation of uranium 238 to uranium 239 or neptunium 239, and the second fission of uranium 235 and determination of some convenient fission product such as barium 140. Thus, so long as the uranium standard has the same isotopic composition as the uranium in the sample, either method will give the correct result. If, however, the sample is enriched with respect to uranium 235, the fission method will give a high result and the activation method a low one. By using both methods at the same time, it is possible to determine both the uranium content and its isotopic ratio.

Finally, it may be pointed out that all measurements of weight and volume are subject to the normal analytical errors. It is preferable to keep measurements by volume to the minimum, and the preparation of reference standard solutions and the taking of aliquots should all be made by weight. The weight of the final precipitate obtained after a radiochemical purification is dependent on the variability of its composition and, in fact, the precipitate may not be a suitable weighing form for the element. Its suitability may, however, be checked by thermogravimetry (Duval, 1953). Although it is possible to obtain most elements in a weighable form by means of 'classical' precipitation steps, such a precipitate may not in fact be suitable for radioactivity measurements as it may not form a smooth adherent layer on the counting tray, or it may be too thick for the efficient counting of low-energy beta particles.

8

METHODS OF SEPARATION OF RADIONUCLIDES

ONE factor which limits quantitative analysis is the selectivity of the separation scheme or the final method of detection. This is particularly important when the element to be determined is present in trace amounts compared with other constituents, and highly selective reagents have been discovered for a number of elements (Feigl, 1958). Secondly, in the interests of accuracy it is necessary to use methods of separation, for example precipitations, which are highly efficient, and to take extensive precautions to avoid losses at all stages of the analysis. The efficiency of the separation process may vary with concentration. This is obviously true for precipitations, which are only quantitative when the solubility product of the precipitate is well exceeded, and so cannot be used at very low concentrations. Thirdly, the possibility of contamination by reagents must always be borne in mind. Although this is seldom important when major constituents are being determined, it is often a limiting factor in the analysis of trace amounts. These three factors, specificity, quantitative separation, and reagent contamination, govern the range of samples to which any given technique is applicable.

Activation analysis for trace elements is unique in that, at least in theory, none of these factors need be of major importance. The characteristic radiation and half-life of the activated elements can theoretically be used for specific identification, as discussed in Chapter 5, but a more or less selective chemical separation generally gives greater accuracy. Quantitative separations are no longer necessary, since any losses are allowed for by weighing the inactive carrier used before and after the separation, and the amount of carrier added initially can be adjusted so that precipitations are highly efficient. The only contamination from reagents that can affect the results is radioactive contamination, which is unlikely to be present and can readily be detected if it is. Despite its freedom from these restrictions on conventional analysis, activation has other limitations no less binding. These are radiation hazards to the analyst, and the time factor.

Radiation hazards to the analyst have not proved a major drawback to the technique, since with the neutron fluxes currently used for activation simple precautions in the form of lead screens and rubber gloves suffice to render them negligible. However if, as seems likely, the neutron fluxes available increase by several factors of ten, the hazards will increase in direct proportion and this will mean that initial stages of any separation process will have to be accomplished by remote handling techniques (Waldron, 1958). Time is a much more serious limitation, since it is impossible to alter the half-life of any radioactive nuclide. All chemical separations take time and it is virtually impossible to carry out even the simplest kind of separation in less than 30 seconds. If we restrict our attention to activation by neutron capture, this means that chemical separation is quite impossible for helium, lithium, and boron, which when activated have half-lives of less than 1 second. Separation would be extremely difficult, and has not been attempted in practice, for the elements nitrogen, oxygen, fluorine, and neon which give rise to activities with half-lives less than 1 minute. Useful nuclides with half-lives between 2 and 10 minutes are formed by neutron activation of magnesium, aluminium, titanium, vanadium, cobalt, niobium, rhodium, and thallium. Chemical separation is possible for some of these elements in the space of a few half-lives, but their determination depends on the swiftness and dexterity of the analyst. Finally, a few of the light elements (hydrogen, beryllium, and carbon) give rise to such long-lived nuclides that neutron activation can only be carried out with a very low efficiency in the analysts' lifetime. Fortunately the great majority of elements activate to nuclides with half-lives in a more convenient range (25 minutes–5 years).

TABLE 8.1

Characteristics and requirements of separation techniques

Method	Minimum time	Selectivity	Concentration dependence	Reagent contamination	Applicability
Volatilization . .	1 min	good–excellent	none	small	most non-metals
Solvent extraction .	1 min	moderate–good	usually none	v. small	most elements
Chromatography .	30 min	good–excellent	none	v. small	most elements
Precipitation . .	2 min	poor–good	exists	moderate	most elements
Electrodeposition .	30 min	moderate–good	none	moderate	some metals
Mass spectroscopy .	10 min	excellent	none	occasional	all elements
Requirement					
Conventional analysis	unimportant	necessary	none	important	all elements
Activation . .	may be vital	less vital	unimportant	unimportant	most elements

Methods of separation have been reviewed many times (e.g. Mellon, 1950; Garrison and Hamilton, 1951; Cook and Duncan, 1952; Finston and Miskel, 1955) and it seems remarkable that so few basic techniques are available. There is no space here to deal with the fundamental principles of separation, so the six most important methods will be treated in turn from the point of view of their applicability to activation analysis. These are volatilization, solvent extraction, chromatography (in the broadest sense), precipitation, electrodeposition, and mass spectroscopy. Certain characteristics of these methods are listed in Table 8.1, which also emphasizes the requirements of conventional analysis and activation.

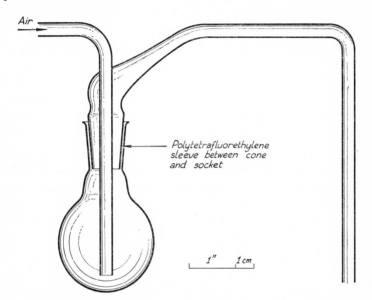

Air

Polytetrafluorethylene
sleeve between cone
and socket

1″   1 cm

Fig. 8.1. Apparatus for rapid distillation in a current of air.

Volatilization

Volatilization is a quick, simple, and efficient method of separation. It has one major drawback; the temperatures required to volatilize the majority of inorganic elements and compounds are too high for precise control. In practice its use is largely restricted to non-metals and the few metals which form volatile covalent compounds. The main practical difficulty is the prevention of spray or particulate matter coming over into the distillate.

Distillation techniques are legion (cf. Weissberger, 1951) and only a few will be described here. For rapid distillation a simple apparatus is that shown in Fig. 8.1, involving entrainment in a current of gas; quantitative distillation of halogens can be achieved in a few minutes using this equipment. The modified Bethge apparatus described by

Smith (1957) is invaluable for studying the efficiency of the distillation process, and for avoiding losses when wet-ashing biological material (Fig. 8.2). It is particularly suitable for distilling ruthenium, osmium, or the halogens from acid digests of activated samples. The distillation units devised by Conway (1940) are extremely simple, but since no heat is employed they are too slow for separating some elements, such as chlorine and iodine, which have short-lived isotopes. Flash volatilization, operating in 0·5 seconds, has been studied by Campbell and Nelson (1955) and Spiess (1954) for extremely short-lived materials. Thus astatine can be separated from polonium deposited on a platinum filament in 0·5 seconds. The sublimation of metals at high temperatures *in vacuo* requires a more elaborate apparatus such as those described by Treadwell and Frey (1944), Price (1945), Wahl and Bonner (1951), Geilmann (1958), and de Voe (1959), and takes minutes or even hours for completion.

Only a few elements are easily separated by volatilization. Prominent among these are the inert gases, which are released by simple dissolution of the sample (Garrison and Hamilton, 1951; Moljk, Drever, and Curran, 1955) and the halogens, which are volatile either as free elements or as the hydrides (Osmond and Smales, 1954; Bowen, 1959 c). Wahlgren (1959) has perfected a method of separating krypton and xenon from irradiated uranium in less than 20 seconds. Elementary phosphorus, arsenic, sulphur, or selenium could be distilled, but are more simply volatilized as their hydrides. Among the metals, mercury is unique in boiling at 356° C, and other elements such as silver, gold, zinc, cadmium, indium, thallium, bismuth, and lead have been separated from metals and ores by sublimation (cf. references above).

All the non-metals and a few metals such as germanium, tin, and antimony form volatile hydrides under strongly reducing conditions. Many of these hydrides are either difficult to prepare, somewhat unstable, or

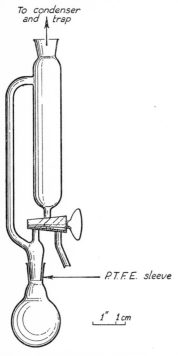

To condenser and trap

P.T.F.E. sleeve

1″   1 cm

FIG. 8.2. Modified Bethge distillation apparatus.

react with oxygen, and they have not been widely used for separation, though the Kjeldahl distillation of ammonia is an exception and Luke's separation of sulphur as hydrogen sulphide deserves to be better known (Luke, 1943, 1949). The same limitations have prevented the application of fractional distillation for separating B-group metals as their alkyls (Rochow, Hurd, and Lewis, 1957) or the transition metals as cyclopentadienyls (Fischer and Fritz, 1959) or carbonyls (Emeleus and Anderson, 1952). Acetylacetonates of such metals are more stable but less volatile *in vacuo* (Sidgwick, 1950; Truemper, 1960).

On the other hand, the volatile halides of many non-metals and a few metals have frequently been exploited for separation. Anhydrous chlorides of Al, As, B, Ga, Ge, Nb, P, Sb, Si, Sn, Ta, Ti, and V are all volatile below $250°$ C, but are often rendered involatile by the presence of water. The chlorides can generally be distilled in a stream of free chlorine (Meinke, 1949; Lowe *et al.*, 1959); similar remarks apply to bromides (e.g. Garrison and Hamilton, 1951; Smales and Pate, 1952 *a*). Higher fluorides of many elements are often extremely volatile (e.g. MoF_6, WF_6, and UF_6), but they are also sources of free fluorine and the technical difficulties of handling them have precluded their use in analysis.

One or two other compounds of unusual volatility have long been utilized. The tetroxides of ruthenium and osmium are readily distilled, that of osmium volatilizing from boiling nitric acid, while ruthenium tetroxide is only formed in the presence of a stronger oxidizing agent, e.g. sodium bismuthate or sodium periodate. The only other metal oxide which can be distilled easily is rhenium heptoxide which sublimes at $450°$ C. Chromyl chloride is unique in distilling at $117°$ C from strong sulphuric acid. The distillation of boron as the trimethoxide is only of academic interest, since no isotopes of boron have half-lives exceeding $0·5$ seconds. Aluminium alkoxides are much less volatile, as are the remarkable basic acetates of beryllium, zinc, and zirconium (Sidgwick, 1950). References to distillations commonly used in radiochemistry are given by Stevenson and Hicks (1953).

Solvent extraction

This is almost certainly the quickest and also one of the cleanest methods of separation. Theoretical and practical aspects have been well reviewed (Irving, 1951; Morrison and Freiser, 1957, 1959; Diamond and Tuck, 1960) and the field is expanding rapidly. The apparatus used consists of a tap-funnel of suitable size, preferably pear-shaped, though for difficult separations automatic extractors have been devised (Craig, 1957).

The few practical difficulties found in solvent extraction can be minimized by careful control of experimental conditions. Thus the extraction of ferric chloride into ether is critically dependent on the concentration of hydrochloric acid, and also depends on the concentration of ferric chloride, which is contrary to simple theory. Di-isopropyl ether seems to be a considerably better solvent (Irving, 1951). Perhaps the most serious difficulty, especially when the time for separation is limited, is emulsification. Fortunately conditions can often be worked out for breaking emulsions; an excess of neutral salt such as ammonium acetate is often effective. A powerful emulsifying agent is present in biological material which has been incompletely ashed with nitric acid. This is soluble in chloroform and so can be removed before chelating agents are added to render various metals soluble in this solvent.

Any inorganic substance which exists in aqueous solution as simple molecules is readily extracted by organic solvents. For example, bromine and iodine as the free elements can be extracted from water into carbon tetrachloride, as can the tetroxides of ruthenium and osmium. However, apart from these substances and a few halides of the weak metals (e.g. $HgCl_2$, $AsCl_3$, $GeCl_4$), there are very few cases known where inorganic substances exist as covalent molecules in solution. The vast majority of inorganic substances are ionized when dissolved in water. There are two general methods available for rendering ionized materials more soluble in organic solvents. The first, which is applicable to most of the transition metal ions, is the technique of chelation.

After chelation, the positive ion is surrounded by several molecules of a bulky organic anion. The chelated substance may be fully ionized in water, but exists as a covalent molecule in organic solvents. For example, the doubly charged zinc ion reacts with two singly charged dithizone anions to give a dithizonate which is soluble in chloroform.

Other well-known chelating agents include cupferron, 8-hydroxy quinoline, α-benzoin oxime, dimethyl glyoxime, thenoyl trifluoroacetone, and diethyl dithiocarbamate. So many metals form cupferrates soluble in chloroform, that exceptions like scandium, tungsten, and uranium can be radiochemically purified by solvent extraction of the impurities (cf. Chapter 13). Masking agents, such as fluoride, cyanide, or ethylene diamine tetra-acetic acid can be used to achieve much more specific separations (Moore et al., 1958).

The second method involves conversion of the substance to a uni-univalent salt in which one or both ions are large and bulky. In this way the ionic hydration energy is minimized and the ions are less diffi-cult to extract into a solvent of lower dielectric constant. Classic examples are tetraphenyl arsonium permanganate, pertechnetate, and perrhenate, which are soluble in chloroform. A clean separation is obtainable from chromates, molybdates, and other polyvalent anions.

As might be expected, the more electropositive metals are difficult to extract, but even the alkali metals form polyiodides which are soluble in nitromethane. Extensive data are available on the partition of the halides, thiocyanates, and nitrates of metals between aqueous solutions and organic solvents (Morrison and Freiser, 1957). Many of the separa-tions are not quantitative, but are quite adequate for activation analysis.

Chlorides have been particularly thoroughly studied. Gold and mer-cury chlorides can be extracted from weakly acid solutions into ether. When the hydrochloric acid concentration is increased to 18 per cent. (6N), many other elements are found in the ether layer, among them Sc^{III}, Nb^V, Mo^{VI}, Fe^{III}, Pt^{II}, Ga^{III}, Tl^{III}, Ge^{IV}, As^{III}, and Sb^V. Most of these appear to extract as univalent chloro anions, e.g. $SbCl_6^-$ and $FeCl_4^-$. Indium^{III} is unusual in that the bromide can be extracted into ether while the chloride is almost insoluble. Several additional elements (e.g. Cd^{II}, Sn^{II}, Pb^{II}) are extracted well as iodides but not as chlorides or bromides. Complex fluorides are much less readily extracted, possibly because the covalency maximum is reached and the complex ions are highly charged, e.g. FeF_6^{3-}. However, fluorides of Nb^V, Ta^V, and Re^{VII} partially extract into ether, while the extraction into certain ketones is more efficient.

If molar ammonium thiocyanate is present in the aqueous layer, a different set of elements (Ti^{III}, Fe^{III}, Zn^{II}, Ga^{III}, In^{III}, Sn^{II}, Mo^V, U^{VI}) are extracted into ether, and when excess thiocyanate is present Be^{II}, Co^{II}, Al^{III}, and Sc^{III} are also soluble in the ether phase. Separations using nitric acid and ether have been especially useful for concentrating some of the heavier polyvalent elements. Thus Au^{III}, Hg^{II}, Bi^{III}, Ti^{IV}, Th^{IV}, Pa^{IV}, and U^{VI} all extract into ether from nitric acid, together with some Fe^{III}, Sc^{III}, Ce^{IV}, and Cr^{VI}. Even more specific separations of tri- and tetravalent metals are obtained by replacing ether with tributyl phosphate. Unusual separations of high selectivity are those involving peroxychromic acid (H_3CrO_8), and dry phosphoric acid into ether.

Solvent extraction with metal amalgams shows promise as a selective method of separation for several elements, though it must be carried out in an inert atmosphere (de Voe *et al.*, 1960). The converse process, i.e. shaking a metal amalgam with an electrolyte in which trace impurities are preferentially soluble, has been described for bismuth by Faircloth (1959).

Chromatography and ion exchange

Chromatography has now become such a widely used method of separation that it is difficult to do more in a small space than to outline its possibilities, and to indicate which of the recent review articles and monographs are most pertinent to inorganic separations. Here the related methods of ion exchange and electrophoresis are included under the general heading.

Techniques used in chromatography can be classified as separations on columns or on paper. In column chromatography a solid adsorbent is packed into a glass or plastic column resembling a conventional burette. A solution containing the substances to be separated is then poured onto the top of the column, where it is fixed on the adsorbent, and eluted with a suitable solvent. The substances migrate down the column at different speeds and can be obtained pure either by dividing up the column, or by eluting them right through it and collecting fractions of the eluate. Simple devices can be used to maintain a constant head of eluant or to alter the pH or concentration of eluant continuously. The adsorbents used can either be substances with a large capacity for adsorption (aluminium oxide, activated charcoal), substances capable of holding large amounts of water from which the solutes can exchange with an immiscible eluant (silica gel, shredded filter paper), or ionic substances in which one ion is so polymeric that it is quite insoluble (alumino-silicate clays, sulphonated copolymers of styrene and divinyl benzene, etc.). In the last case the substances are known as ion exchangers and differ in properties according to whether the immobile polymer is the anion or cation (Samuelson, 1953; Hudgens, 1956; Kraus and Nelson 1956 and 1957; Kunin, 1958; Walton, 1959).

In one-dimensional paper chromatography the absorbent paper acts as its own support, or is sometimes enclosed between glass plates. Several samples can be eluted with the same solvent on a single wide paper strip. If a single solvent gives inadequate separation, two-dimensional chromatography can be employed. The sample is transferred to one corner of a square sheet of paper and the first solvent allowed to run down one side. The paper is then turned through 90° and a second solvent separates any unresolved components (Pollard and McOmie, 1953; Lederer and Lederer, 1955; Block, Durrum, and Zweig, 1955).

Alternatively the substance can be transferred to the mid-point of one side of the square of filter paper and the eluant allowed to flow perpendicular to a large potential gradient. If the substance is applied continuously its constituents form diverging bands, otherwise discrete spots are formed much as in two-dimensional chromatography. This modification is known as electrophoresis. (Parker, 1955; McDonald, 1955; Block et al., 1955, Lederer, 1955; Wieland and Dose, 1956.)

There are several limitations in the use of chromatographic methods. Care must be taken not to overload the column or filter paper with more ions than it can absorb, and this is not difficult in practice. Polyvalent elements may appear in more than one place on the chromatogram, but this can be eliminated by proper adjustment of solvents (Curry, 1953). The number of components which can be conveniently separated by one-dimensional chromatography seldom exceeds five. Hence when, as usually happens, the activated sample contains many different radioisotopes, it is best to fractionate it by precipitation reactions before applying chromatography. Thus Blasius and Gottling (1958) have divided the common cations into ten subgroups of two to five ions each and give practical details of chromatographic separation of each subgroup. Perhaps the most serious limitation of chromatographic separation is its slowness. Not much information is published on the speed of separation, but Pollard and McOmie (1953) mention that separations take at least 2 hours on filter paper using fast-moving solvents such as acetone, and up to 24 hours with more viscous solvents such as n-butanol. Samuelson (1953) states that flow rates in columns of ion exchangers should be from 0·2 to 1·2 ml/cm²/min and that the separation of sodium from potassium, for example, takes about 10 hours. Using shallow beds of resin, very rapid separations can be made. Campbell and Nelson (1956) have succeeded in separating 0·8-second lead 207 from bismuth and 4·9-second iridium 191 from osmium by this method.

Perhaps because of their inherent slowness, ion exchange techniques are not often used for separations after activation, and paper chromatography and electrophoresis have scarcely been employed at all (but see Winteringham et al., 1952). Hence the remainder of this discussion will consider only present and future applications of ion exchange resins. The theory of ion exchange has been fully treated by Glueckauf (1955), but most separations are still based on empirical methods. The speed of movement through a column depends on the size of the resin particles, but large particles, which give fast flow rates, yield relatively inefficient separations. The speeds at which different ions move depend on their weight, charge, and degree of hydration or chelation. The types of ion exchange resins available have been described by Hudgens (1956) and Kunin (1958). It appears that highly specific resins could be developed by incorporation of chelating agents such as EDTA, but these are not yet available commercially (Deuel and Hutschneker, 1955). Anion exchange resins in the hydroxide, iodide, or sulphide form can be used as specific precipitants (Kraus and Nelson, 1956; Komlev and Tsimbalista, 1953; Gaddis, 1942), and the separation of cations on anion exchange resins has been thoroughly studied as these are unusually rapid (Kraus and Nelson, 1956 and 1957). Thus selenium and tellurium, and also mercury, bismuth, and thallium are easily separated on De-Acidite FF (Schindewolf, 1960; Ehmann and Huizenga, 1959). Specific separations have been listed by several authors but no list can be said to be complete (Schindewolf, 1955; Kunin, McGarvey, and Farren, 1956; Hudgens, 1956). Applications in radiochemistry and activation analysis have been largely restricted to the alkali metals (Brooksbank and Leddicotte, 1953; Cabell and Smales, 1957), lanthanides (Cornish, 1956; Brooksbank and Leddicotte, 1953; Meinke, 1949; Ketelle and Boyd, 1947), and actinides (Kleinberg, 1958), though recent publications have added molybdenum, cadmium, and other elements to this list (Kleinberg, 1958; de Voe, 1959). It should be noticed that all these elements are difficult to separate by precipitation methods, and activate to isotopes with half-lives of 12 hours or more. Chromatographic methods are much less suitable for other systems. For example, alkaline earths require 16 hours for separation on filter paper (Magee and Headridge, 1955), by which time all activity from Ca^{49}, Sr^{87}, and Ba^{139} would have decayed away.

Precipitation

Precipitation is so well known as a method of separation and is so extensively described in analytical monographs that it will only be described briefly here. Suffice it to say that it is a rapid method, that success or failure are easily visible, and that its applicability is universal except for some gaseous elements. The main disadvantage of the technique is that all precipitates adsorb foreign elements to a greater or lesser extent, as described later under scavenging procedures. In practice, precipitation steps are employed in practically every chemical separation which has been described for use after activation.

Techniques of filtration and centrifugation are adequately discussed in numerous monographs (e.g. Vogel, 1954; Meinke, 1949; Faires and Parks, 1958). A modified Buchner funnel suitable for radiochemical work is shown in Fig. 8.3. Each technique has its advantages and disadvantages. Filtration is usually more quantitative except where the precipitate is very fine (e.g. $BaSO_4$), or tends to peptize on washing as does ammonium phosphomolybdate. Centrifugation is perhaps slightly quicker and contaminates less glassware, but leads to losses when voluminous precipitates, such as many organic derivatives of metals, are handled. It is certainly more widely used than filtration in radiochemistry. Scavenging precipitates are best filtered off, since it is important that they should not contaminate the liquid fraction.

Theoretically, precipitation after activation can be carried out under ideal conditions, since it is possible to control the concentrations of both ions forming the insoluble salt. In all other methods of analysis the solubility product of the precipitate determines the smallest amount of the ion sought which may be determined, but the addition of inert carrier nullifies this limitation. Most precipitations depend critically on the pH of the solution, and it is well known that the slower the rate of precipitation, the smaller the amount of impurities adsorbed on or occluded in the precipitate. Willard (1950) has shown that precipitation from homogeneous solution is the most efficient way of reducing co-precipitation, and Salutsky (1959) quotes numerous examples illustrating this point. Thus when aluminium hydroxide is precipitated by adding ammonia in the presence of Mn^{2+}, Co^{2+}, Ni^{2+}, Cu^{2+}, or Zn^{2+}, it may adsorb as much as 40 per cent. of the impurities. If the ammonia is produced in homogeneous solution, by boiling urea in the presence of ammonium succinate, the adsorption is reduced to well below 1 per cent. in all cases. If the time required to precipitate from homogeneous solution is not available, the ideal conditions are precipitation in the cold from supersaturated solutions, followed by boiling till the material becomes crystalline. Boiling causes local recrystallization which diminishes adsorption of impurities, but is obviously inapplicable if it dissolves the precipitate completely (Kolthoff and Sandell, 1952).

It is a well-known empirical generalization that far more substances are soluble in acid than in basic solutions. Hence the majority of specific or nearly specific precipitation reactions are carried out in acid solutions. Since many substances are brought into solution with the aid of strong nitric acid, it is useful to know that relatively few oxides and nitrates are insoluble in this reagent. However, the oxide of hexavalent tungsten, more or less contaminated with silica, niobium, and tantalum, is quantitatively precipitated from boiling nitric acid, while the dioxides of lead and manganese precipitate when sodium chlorate is cautiously added. Among nitrates, it is remarkable that only those of strontium, barium, and lead are insoluble in cold 80 per cent. nitric acid and many useful separations are based on these facts. Relatively few chlorides are insoluble in acids; these include thallium[I] as well as the better-known trio silver, lead, and mercury[I]. Barium chloride is specifically precipitated by concentrated hydrochloric acid containing 15 per cent. diethyl ether, and sodium chloride is insoluble in 12N hydrochloric acid. So many elements form sulphides insoluble in acids that more specific separations must be sought for them, and the same applies to elements with insoluble sulphates and fluorides.

A large number of metals can now be more or less selectively precipitated by suitable organic reagents, especially in the presence of chelating agents such as EDTA. Examples are the use of dimethylglyoxime for nickel and palladium, α-benzoin oxime for molybdenum and tungsten, salicylaldoxime for copper and gold, and rhodizonic acid for strontium and barium. It is even possible to find specific precipitants for the alkali metals (e.g. magnesium uranyl acetate for sodium or bismuth iodide for caesium) though no reagent is known which differentiates between rubidium and potassium. Treatises on organic and inorganic complexing reagents reveal that selective precipitants remain to be discovered for many of the rarer metals such as gallium, indium, scandium, and titanium (Finston and Miskel, 1955). Some of the least electropositive metals, such as tellurium, gold, platinum, ruthenium, rhodium, and indium are easily precipitated as the element by reduction of their aqueous solutions, and such steps are frequently used in their analysis. A section below describes electrolytic reduction, which can be made extremely specific in favourable cases.

Scavenging

Scavenging, or co-precipitation, is a relatively new technique which has not been studied in a systematic manner. Unlike the other topics discussed here, it is a method of removing unwanted impurities and is not a specific separation step. Short reviews have been published by Wahl and Bonner (1951) and by Kolthoff and Sandell (1952). According to the former authors, scavenging is best effected by highly

Fig. 8.3. Modified Buchner filtration apparatus for
use in radiochemistry.

insoluble gelatinous precipitates with a large surface area for adsorption. The ions adsorbed depend partly on the nature of the charge on the surface of the precipitate, which is positive for silver halides and negative for most sulphides. Broadly speaking, silver chloride acts as a scavenger for anions and copper sulphide as a scavenger for cations. Univalent ions are poorly adsorbed and cannot be removed efficiently by scavenging, but polyvalent ions can be adsorbed extremely effectively.

Since a large surface area is produced by rapid precipitation in the cold, and is reduced by warming with its possibility of local recrystallization, scavenging precipitates should not be boiled as should most other precipitates. As might be expected, the presence of carriers generally reduces the percentage adsorption on a scavenging precipitate of a given size (Sunderman and Meinke, 1957). Hence it is advisable to add only carriers of the elements required in the supernatant before a scavenging step. The scavenger removes a small percentage of the desired constituent, which reduces the chemical yield.

The most frequently used scavenging agents are hydroxides of tri- and tetravalent metals, sulphides of weakly electropositive metals, and silver halides. Data for percentage co-precipitation with ferric hydroxide are scattered throughout the literature (Bowen and Dymond, 1955; Bowen, 1956b, 1959a, b, etc.; Mashima, 1956; Shcherbov et al., 1956; Sunderman and Meinke, 1957) and some relevant data appear in Table 8.2.

Hydroxides of cobalt, yttrium, lanthanum, zirconium, and niobium have been less extensively used as scavengers. It is interesting that hydroxides of iron[III] and manganese[IV] are probably responsible for scavenging polyvalent ions from sea water in nature (Goldberg, 1954; Krauskopf, 1956). The charge on hydroxide precipitates is generally negative, but can be positive under certain conditions, in which case anions are scavenged (Calvet et al., 1953).

Co-precipitation with metallic sulphides has been extensively studied as a means of purifying reagents from biologically essential metals (Hewitt, 1952). Most sulphides form negatively charged colloidal precipitates with a more or less specific scavenging action. Thus copper sulphide collects molybdenum, lead, and zinc, while mercuric sulphide scavenges lead efficiently, but not copper or silver (Feigl, 1949). Sulphides of As, Bi, Cd, Cu, Hg, In, Mo, Pd, Re, Sb, and Te have all been employed as scavenging agents, and quantitative data are given for co-precipitation of a number of elements on indium sulphide by Sunderman et al. (1959) as shown in Table 8.3. This reaction was carried out in a sulphate/bisulphate buffer at pH 1·7. It should be noted that quite unexpected elements are often adsorbed—for example strontium sulphate on indium sulphide in Table 8.3, and phosphorus on copper sulphide (Kar and Rangan, 1957). Rudnev (1955) has shown that surface active agents can be used to reduce co-precipitation on sulphide precipitates.

TABLE 8.2

Percentage co-precipitation with ferric hydroxide

Element	With carrier	Without carrier
Antimony[III]	82	91·9
Barium	2·6	
Bromine	0·4	
Caesium	4·0	8·0
Cerium[III]	99·95	99·84
Chlorine	1·5	
Chromium[III]	99·70	99·74
Cobalt	17	77
Copper[II]	0·8	
Gallium	2·2	
Indium	99·88	99·79
Iodine	4·2	7·3
Iridium	85	96·1
Manganese[II]	5·0	
Molybdenum[VI]	5·0	
Phosphorus	99·84	
Ruthenium[III]	70	93·5
Selenium	29	64
Silver	8·7	8·6
Strontium	3·7	89
Tantalum[V]	99·97	99·92
Tin[II]	98·3	99·70
Zinc	1·4	
Zirconium	99·98	99·86

Silver chloride is sometimes used as an anion scavenger, as shown by the data of Table 8.3, taken from Sunderman and Meinke (1957). Few metals are co-precipitated apart from mercury, thallium (Gordon et al., 1955), and silver itself (Sunderman and Meinke, 1957). Co-precipitation of chlorine with silver iodide can be eliminated by carrying out the reaction in dilute ammonia solution instead of nitric acid (Bowen, 1959).

Other scavengers which have been used include barium sulphate, alkaline earth carbonates and phosphates, yttrium oxalate, and metallic tellurium. Many of these are crystalline precipitates and it is doubtful if they are more efficient than the colloidal types mentioned above. Recent Russian work on organic co-precipitants, including a monograph by Kusnetsov (1955), has been reviewed by Meinke (1958). A general technique of co-precipitation of metals with organic reagents has been developed by Mitchell and Scott (1947) and tested radiochemically by Pickett and Hankins (1958).

TABLE 8.3

Percentage co-precipitation with indium sulphide and silver chloride (carriers present)

Element	In_2S_3	AgCl
Antimony[III]	96	22
Caesium	1·0	0·5
Cerium[III]	20–70	0·5
Chromium[III]	2·0	0·5
Cobalt	1·7	0·5
Indium	91·8	0·5
Iodine	4·3	97
Iridium	4·9	27
Ruthenium[III]	96	2·5
Selenium	80	0·5
Silver	100	99
Strontium	100	0·7
Tantalum[V]	1·6	0·6
Tin[II]	97	0·8
Zirconium	8·7	0·4

Electrodeposition

Electrodeposition is a special case of precipitation, using electrons instead of chemicals as a precipitating agent. Several excellent reviews of techniques and applications in analytical chemistry are available (Schleicher, 1947; Ashley, 1950; Lingane, 1953). Since the range of voltage over which any given metal is deposited overlaps the range of many other metals, electrodeposition has not been used as a primary method of separation after activation, but is sometimes useful for the final precipitation of an element in a form convenient for weighing and counting.

For practical purposes, metals are usually plated onto platinum or stainless steel. Mercury has also been widely used (Bock and Hockstein, 1953), but is much less suitable for weighing and counting the deposit than is platinum. Typical experimental equipment is shown in Fig. 8.4. Many important practical details are discussed in the reviews mentioned above. These include the use of efficient stirring in the electrolyte to avoid depletion of the solution near the cathode, the control of cathode potential and pH, and the proper use of chelating agents, depolarizers, and surface active agents to prevent co-precipitation of impurities and to ensure a smooth coherent deposit.

Ashley (1950) gives a full discussion of the limitations of the method, of which the most serious is perhaps the small number of elements to which it can be applied successfully. These include most of the twenty-four elements in Group VIII and the B subgroups I to V, but reliable techniques have not been worked out in every case. The time required for electrodeposition varies from half an hour to many hours,

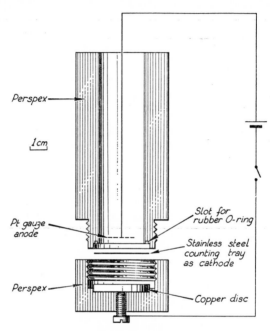

Perspex

1cm

Pt gauze anode

Slot for rubber O-ring

Stainless steel counting tray as cathode

Perspex

Copper disc

FIG. 8.4. Micro-electrodeposition cell.

which compares unfavourably with chemical precipitation. Reproducibility is not always obtainable, as small traces of impurities can alter the character of the metallic deposit. The friction caused by the evolution of hydrogen, or the occlusion of this gas or electrolyte, can result in a loose deposit which is partially lost on subsequent washing (Lingane, 1953). Despite these disadvantages, electrodeposition has often been used in radiochemical separations, since the pioneer work of Haissinsky (1935), mainly for the elements rhodium, copper, silver, tin, lead, antimony, and bismuth (Meinke, 1949; Kleinberg, 1958; Garrison and Hamilton, 1951; Stevenson and Hicks, 1953; Finston and Miskel, 1955).

Mass spectroscopy

Unlike all the methods of separation mentioned so far, mass spectroscopy does not depend on the chemical form of the element and is able to separate individual isotopes. Hence if it were used after activation, it would not merely separate all the elements concerned but would concentrate the active nuclides in a form admirably suited for counting. Techniques and applications have been reviewed by Duckworth (1958). The apparatus required would be expensive, but the time of separation is only of the order of minutes, which is better than the majority of multi-stage chemical processes. Kennett and Thode (1956) have used a mass spectrometer to determine fission yields of krypton and xenon isotopes after neutron fission of nuclides of uranium and plutonium.

It is, however, doubtful if activation will improve the sensitivity of the mass spectrometer as a tool in analytical chemistry. Using an electron multiplier as a detector, it is already possible to detect a mere 5×10^5 atoms of any xenon isotope (Reynolds, 1956). If the sample were to be activated before the analysis the electron multiplier could be replaced by a Geiger or scintillation counter. These detectors do not differ greatly in efficiency, and only for nuclides with half-lives of less than 2 hours would the radioactivity give an increase in sensitivity.

Summing up, it can be said that chemical separations after activation differ from other analytical techniques in that they need not be quantitative and that contamination by reagents is unimportant. In many cases, however, they have to be carried out under hurried conditions or at least with the minimum of delay, because of radioactive decay. In planning any radiochemical separation, it is as well to bear in mind the time required to carry out individual steps. Table 8.4, taken from

TABLE 8.4

Time taken for unit operations in radiochemical separations

Step	Minutes
Fusion of sample with Na_2O_2 and solution of melt .	3
Wet ashing biological material	1
Distillation	4
Solvent extraction	1
Ion exchange (10 ml)	10
Precipitation	1
Centrifugation	2
Filtration (100 ml)	2
Electrodeposition	30
Evaporation of water (10 ml)	3
Evaporation of volatile solvent	3
Plating and drying final precipitate . . .	2

our own experience and that of Kusaka and Meinke (1960), may be helpful in this respect. A combination of steps (frequently cyclical) involving precipitation and solvent extraction is generally found to give an adequate degree of radiochemical purity, and these can be tested using tracers of the element sought and its main impurities (e.g. de Voe and Meinke, 1959). For groups of very similar elements, such as the alkali metals or the lanthanides, the crucial part of the separation may depend on ion exchange, but this is a slower process than the other two. Volatilization and electrodeposition find limited use for particular elements only.

9

THE COLLECTION AND PREPARATION OF MATERIAL FOR ACTIVATION ANALYSIS

In any analytical problem, the method of collection of material is of fundamental importance for obtaining reliable results (Mitchell, 1960). It is obviously impossible to make satisfactory analyses of samples which have been contaminated or partially lost, yet such samples are frequently received in the laboratory without any indication of their history. In activation analysis the only major contamination and loss problems occur before the activation process, but the sensitivity of the method is often sufficient to detect traces of elements which no other technique would reveal. Hence extreme care must be taken to avoid contamination of samples for analysis, and some of the principles involved form the subject of this chapter. If possible, the analyst himself should carry out all processing of material, under controlled conditions. If this cannot be done, the analyst should at least be aware of the detailed history of the sample, so that he can take any necessary steps to remove surface contamination before or after activation is carried out.

Handling and sealing

Solid samples are best transferred using polythene or Perspex spatulas or forceps (Fig. 9.1), while liquids can be poured directly into containers for activation. Small polythene tubes (Fig. 9.2), and silica capillaries, can be sealed by the application of heat. Smales and Salmon (1955) recommend plugging silica tubes with aluminium foil if radiation produces gaseous decomposition products from solid samples. Aluminium tubes can be sealed by squeezing the ends in a vice; graphite tubes have to be plugged with a specially made cap of the same material. For short irradiations, especially for liquids, samples can be sealed in one polythene bag inside another to minimize the risk of leakage. The high temperatures found in most reactors may enlarge pinholes present in polythene tubes or bags, so it is worth while testing the seals by exposure to the temperature they will reach in the reactor before activation. Any type of sealed container for liquids should be tested in this way.

Dust contamination

It is almost impossible to handle any kind of sample without exposing it to the risk of contamination by laboratory dust. Dust itself is seldom analysed, and in any case its content is certain to vary from place to place. In chemical laboratories dust is liable to contain many more elements than usual (Sandell, 1959); industrial districts may also yield a heavy crop of dust of unusual composition; and districts near the sea will have dusts rich in marine salt with its associated trace elements. Cholak and co-workers (1950) have made a thorough survey of dust precipitation and content in Cincinnati, Ohio. They found that the rate of dust precipitation averaged over a period of three years was $2 \cdot 2 \times 10^{-9}$ g/cm^2/sec in an industrial area and $0 \cdot 18 \times 10^{-9}$ g/cm^2/sec in a suburb remote from industry. The composition of dusts in rural and industrial districts of Britain and North America are given in Table 9.1. The reasons for the differences in the two sets of results are not known.

TABLE 9.1

Composition of air in mμg/m^3 (after Cholak et al. (1950), Chambers et al. (1955) and Stocks (1960))

Element	Rural area (N. Britain)	Industrial area (N. Britain)	Rural area (N. America)	Industrial area (N. America)
Al			2200	5300
As	8	55	< 10	50
Be	0·1	0·5	0·1	0·3
Ca			5000	27,000
Cl				72,000
Co	0·5	1·5		
Cr	1	4		
Cu	7	60	190	300
F			260	210
Fe			2400	5200
K			30,000	60,000
Mn	7	35	70	70
Mo	0·25	2·5		
Ni	2	20		
Pb	170	610	400	2800
S			630	4900
Sb	2·5	10		
Sn			10	80
Ti	10	45	10	410
V	2	10	< 1	300
Zn	65	250	1300	2000

From this table the contamination caused by leaving samples exposed for different periods can easily be calculated. Thus if a 20-cm diameter

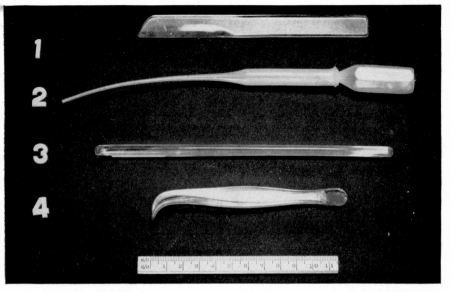

FIG. 9.1. Plastic apparatus used to reduce contamination.

1. Perspex knife.   2. Polythene Pasteur pipette.   3. Perspex spatula.   4. Perspex forceps.

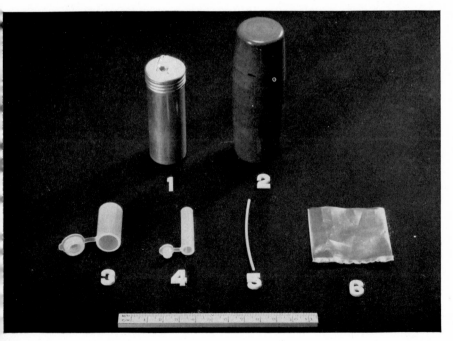

FIG. 9.2. Apparatus for neutron activation in BEPO.

1. Aluminium can.   2. Nylon rabbit.   3 & 4. Polythene tubes with captive cap.   5. Polythene capillary tube.
6. Thin polythene packet.

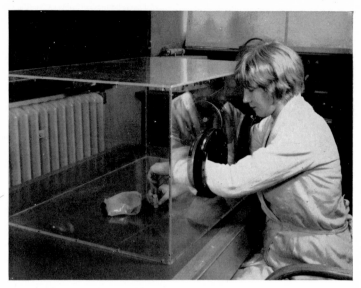

FIG. 9.3. Dust-proof box suitable for handling, storing, and sealing material prior to activation.

FIG. 9.4. Perspex mill for grinding biological tissue without metallic contamination.

evaporating basin was left overnight in the control area described by Cholak, it could pick up 4 mg of dust containing hundreds of microgrammes of elements such as K, Ca, Fe, and Al. Hence it is obviously important to keep all samples well covered or protected from dust at all stages of handling. A simple dust-proof box is shown in Fig. 9.3.

Canning materials

Since they have to satisfy a rather stringent set of conditions, only four materials have been widely used for canning samples for activation—aluminium (Brooksbank et al., 1956), graphite (Reiffel and Stone, 1957), silica (e.g. Brooksbank et al., 1953), and polythene (e.g. Bowen, 1956 b). All four can be made extremely pure, have a low cross-section for thermal neutrons, give little or no long-lived activity on activation and are resistant to radiation. Data on potential purity, cross-section, and radiation resistance are summarized in Table 9.2.

These data for aluminium, carbon, and silica do not apply to ordinary commercial materials, which are very much less pure; the polythene analysed was, however, an ordinary commercial sample. Each material has its advantages and disadvantages, e.g. aluminium cannot be made very pure and gives rise to sodium 24 by an (n, α) reaction, carbon has a low cross-section for neutrons but is difficult to fabricate, silicon becomes very active after irradiation, and polythene becomes brittle after a relatively short period in a reactor. Other possible canning materials such as beryllium, zirconium, and various plastics have no particular advantage over the four already mentioned.

Cleaning canning materials

Surface cleaning is carried out using specific reagents for each material. Aluminium is first degreased with benzene, then washed with distilled nitric acid and rinsed with water. Carbon is generally cleaned by machining off the surface layer (Slatter and Stitch, 1956). Silica and polythene can be cleaned with a warm 1:1 mixture of nitric acid and sulphuric acids (Thiers, 1957); chromic acid is best avoided since it can lead to serious contamination with chromium (Butler and Johnston, 1954). The acids are rinsed off with pure water, and the apparatus dried in a dust-free atmosphere as described by Thiers (1957). Polythene can also be cleaned by rubbing with alcohol or acetone. A jet of distilled water is a particularly effective cleaning agent, since it both washes off insoluble dust particles and dissolves any salts deposited from human perspiration. The latter is perhaps the commonest contamination of 'clean' materials. If one square centimetre of polythene

TABLE 9.2

Properties of extra pure materials suitable for canning samples for neutron activation

Property	Material			
	Al Zone refined	C Johnson Matthey	SiO$_2$ Thermal syndicate spectrosil	(CH$_2$)$_n$ Polythene commercial
n cross-section (barns)	0·23	0·0032	0·13	0·33
activation products {	2·3 min Al^{28} 15 hr Na^{24}	..	2·6 hr Si^{31}	..
n/cm^2 for breakdown	> 10^{20}	> 10^{20}	> 10^{20}	5 × 10^{17}
p.p.m. Ag	< 0·01	< 0·01		0·02
Al	10^6	< 0·1	< 0·02	0·3
As	0·001	< 2	< 0·0002	
Au	< 0·0001	< 0·1		
B	< 0·5	3	< 0·01	0·09
Ba		0·05		
Be		< 0·01		
Bi	< 0·1	< 0·1		
Ca	< 0·5	0·5	< 0·1	0·2
Cd	0·07	< 0·01		
Cl	< 0·01			
Co	< 0·01	< 0·2		
Cr	< 0·01	< 0·1		0·3
Cs	< 0·01			
Cu	0·08	0·01	< 0·0002	0·004
Dy	< 0·004			
Fe	< 0·2	0·03	< 0·1	0·6
Ga	< 0·04	< 0·05	< 0·004	
Gd	< 0·01			
Ge		< 0·05		
Hf	< 0·01			
Hg	< 0·01			
In	< 0·01			
Ir		< 0·1		
K	< 0·01	< 10	< 0·005	
La	< 0·001			
Li		< 0·01		
Mg	10	0·02		0·08
Mn	0·15	< 0·01	< 0·001	0·08
Mo	< 0·1	< 0·2		
Na	< 0·2	< 0·5	< 0·04	
Nb		< 0·5		
Ni	< 1	< 0·1		
P			< 0·001	
Pb	< 0·1	< 0·1		0·2
Pd	< 0·001	< 0·1		
Pt		< 0·3		
Rb	< 0·01	< 10		
Sb	0·002	< 2	< 0·0001	
Sc	0·2			
Se	< 0·01			
Si	< 0·01	0·1		2·0
Sm	< 0·0001			

TABLE 9.2 (*cont.*)

Property	Material			
	Al *Zone* *refined*	C *Johnson* *Matthey*	SiO_2 *Thermal syndi-* *cate spectrosil*	$(CH_2)_n$ *Polythene* *commercial*
Sn	< 0·1	< 0·1		
Sr	< 0·5	< 0·1		
Ta	< 0·01			
Ti	< 0·2		0·5	
Tl			< 0·1	
U	0·06			
V	< 5		0·5	
W	< 0·002			
Y	< 0·001			
Zn	0·6			
Zr	< 0·2			

Refs. Al Gaittet (1960); Johnson Matthey (pers. comm.); Mackintosh (1960); Jervis
  and Mackintosh (1958).
  C Johnson Matthey (pers. comm.).
  SiO_2 Thermal Syndicate (pers. comm.).
  Polythene Thiers (1957).

sheet is touched by human fingers it will pick up about 0·4 μg of sodium
(Bowen, unpublished). Since the composition of human sweat is known
(Spector, 1956) this corresponds to contamination with 2×10^{-3} μg
phosphorus, 2×10^{-5} μg manganese, and 3×10^{-6} μg iodine, to name
three elements with high cross-sections for thermal neutrons.

Massive solids

Massive solids can be analysed with less error by activation than by
any other technique. Only the surface layer is liable to contamination
before analysis, and this can generally be dissolved off after activation
and not used in the subsequent chemical procedure. All other methods
of analysis involve removal of surface contamination by abrasive
materials (e.g. hand filing or lathe turning), often followed by grinding
in a ball mill, which can lead to serious metallic contamination. Even
hand grinding in an agate mortar leads to detectable loss and transfer
of material. Finally, the reagents used to attack massive solids and
render them soluble in conventional analysis may contain an appreciable
concentration of the element sought. Hence activation is invaluable
for this type of sample and has been widely used for them.

Gels

Technically, fresh biological material is usually a gel if it is not fluid.
Such material can generally be cut with a quartz knife, or even with

a Perspex knife, and provided it is then handled with clean rubber gloves or plastic forceps in a dust-free atmosphere it should be suitable for activation, though before exposure to high temperature reactors it may need drying or even ashing.

Surface contamination can be removed after activation as described for massive solids. However, many biological objects exist in natural bags which are exceedingly convenient for activation. Examples are beans in a pod (Smales and Pate, 1952 c), kernels in nutshells, embryos in an egg or placental sac, and internal organs in small animals. The whole bag is activated and the contents dissected out after activation. This technique is one of the most elegant methods of avoiding contamination ever devised, but it is not suitable for elements which require long activation times since the tissues may break down under prolonged irradiation.

Cutting and grinding

These operations almost invariably give rise to contamination and should generally be avoided. Even if the cutting agent is very much harder than the material being cut, high local temperatures or pressures can develop during the cutting process and cause transfer of material. If massive brittle solids have to be split open this can sometimes be done by wrapping the solid in a polythene bag and hitting it with a hammer (e.g. Morris and Brewer, 1954). Metals have to be cleaned with hard steel tools containing a number of elements and it is best to dissolve off any surfaces touched by the tool after activation. Lowe et al. (1959) found very extensive contamination of silicon carbide after grinding in a boron nitride mortar, which made analysis of the ground material quite meaningless. Atkins and Smales (1960) record considerable contamination of minerals by tungsten and tantalum after grinding. Hard materials, including biological material frozen in liquid nitrogen, can be ground by hand in an agate mortar, but even this gives rise to a certain amount of contamination, notably by the element indium, which activates strongly (Ahrens, 1954). Hood et al. (1944) have shown that dry plant material can be quite heavily contaminated by comminution in different types of automatic mills, made largely of metal. Bowen (unpublished) has used a mill made entirely of Perspex for grinding dry biological material (Figs. 9.4 and 9.5); here the contamination is restricted to Perspex dust which has a low metal content. Other workers (Stitch, 1957; Gibbons, 1958) have used silica knives to carve up fresh biological tissue. Polythene screens and nylon net are now available which avoid the contamination associated with the use of brass or steel sieves.

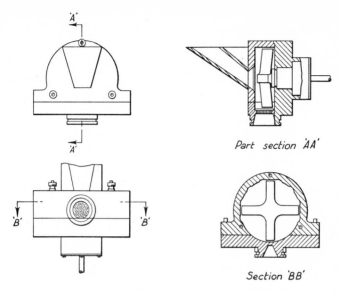

Part section AA'

Section BB'

Fig. 9.5. Diagram of Perspex mill.

Powdered solids

If the solids have been powdered by grinding, they are certainly more or less contaminated. However, very pure chemicals are produced in powder form by precipitation, recrystallization, or sublimation. Dry, stable powders are most likely to be contaminated by laboratory dust, and this can be avoided by sealing them in suitable containers immediately after preparation. While glass is suitable for normal storage, polythene, quartz, or aluminium ampoules are more suitable for activation for reasons described above.

Liquids

Liquids are especially susceptible to contamination and require great care in their collection. They tend to dissolve traces of material from the walls of their containers, and should therefore be handled as little as possible after collection. Alternatively, the container walls may adsorb materials from the liquid sample. The problems involved in collecting liquids can best be illustrated by two examples, sea water and human blood.

Sea water can be collected by evacuating quartz or polythene flasks and then opening them under water. In the case of polythene vessels, it is often possible to wash out the vessel several times by squeezing and releasing the pressure before taking the final sample. The composition of sea water varies with many factors such as depth, time of year, proximity to land and to large rivers. Even if great care is taken to prevent contamination during collection, trace elements may be lost by precipitation or adsorption on planktonic debris if the sample is not analysed soon after collection. Such debris should be centrifuged off in the stoppered container as soon as possible: filtering is not practicable without introducing further loss and/or contamination. Hummel (1957) has shown that gold in sea water is strongly adsorbed by polythene, though not by silica.

Blood is best collected by allowing it to drip from a scratch or venipuncture into a clean, weighed vessel of polythene or silica. The primary incision should be made through well-scrubbed skin with a sharp fragment of silica or a platinum needle. In the case of a venipuncture the blood can be led through a fine polythene tube. It is best to avoid the use of syringes or pipettes in handling blood, since these may introduce contamination or loss by adsorption; the amount of blood taken can easily be determined by weighing. The concentration of some elements in the blood may depend on local muscular contraction, time of day, certain pathological conditions, and peculiarities of diet or drugs, so all these factors should be borne in mind. Embryonic blood differs from adult blood, as does male blood from female blood, by its content of trace metals.

So far we have only considered methods of collecting samples which can be activated directly without prior concentration. In some cases it is inconvenient to activate samples for determining trace elements, because of the large volume required or the large amount of activity generated in other elements present in the material. For example, in the determination of barium in sea water by activation analysis it would be necessary to activate at least a litre of sea water for about 2 hours to obtain a reasonable count rate from the separated barium 139. Such a volume would be expensive in terms of reactor space, and after activation would present difficult handling problems, as it would contain about 1·2 curies of chlorine 38 and 0·3 curies of sodium 24. In this case the volume could be reduced to about 35 ml by evaporation of the water, but the sodium and chlorine would have to be separated without introducing barium contamination, before activation, if the laboratory was not equipped to handle curie quantities of activity. Any concentration procedure increases the risk of contamination.

Drying

Drying reduces the volume of biological material and liquids and so saves space in the reactor, but may lead to loss of certain elements and contamination from dust or the drying vessel. Several elements can be lost at temperatures of 100° C or even below this, notably arsenic (Satterlee and Blodgett, 1944), sulphur, selenium, and mercury (Gorsuch, 1959), the halogens, and the inert gases. When oxidizing acids are

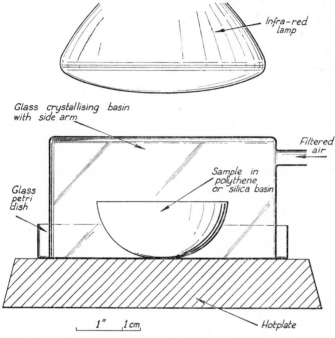

FIG. 9.6. Apparatus for drying material with the minimum of
contamination: after Thiers, 1957.

present, many other elements such as phosphorus (Thiers, 1957), chromium, germanium, osmium, rhenium, ruthenium, antimony, and tin (Hoffman and Lundell, 1939) may also be lost. Contamination is minimized by drying in the apparatus described by Thiers (1957), which is shown in Fig. 9.6. The sample is placed in a polythene basin inside a covered chamber through which filtered air is circulated, and is heated from above and below. Great care is needed in evaporating liquids to avoid losses by irregular ebullition or invisible sprays.

Ashing

This method of reducing the volume of biological material has been used prior to the determination of strontium, barium, and other elements by activation (Harrison and Raymond, 1955; Bowen and Dymond, 1955; Sowden and Stitch, 1956; Fukai and Meinke, 1959). If it is carried out in clean silica containers at a temperature not exceeding 500° C relatively few elements are lost; the recoveries of alkaline earth metals are particularly good. Losses by volatilization have been summarized by Thiers (1957) and further data are given by Gorsuch (1959). Large amounts of As, Br, Cl, Ge, Hg, I, and Se are lost during dry ashing and low recoveries of the following elements are recorded in the literature: Cd, Cr, Cu, Fe, Ga, In, Ni, Os, P, Pb, Re, Rn, Sb, Sn, Te, Tl, V, and Zn. Hence any ashing procedure used prior to determining these elements by activation or any other method of analysis should be tested for recovery, preferably using a radio-tracer technique. The high temperatures employed can lead to considerable retention of certain elements (Ag, Al, Cd, Cu, Cr, Cs, Fe, K, Mn, Na, Pb, Rb, Sb) on the crucible walls, and it may be impossible to dissolve these elements off again. Contamination from silica crucibles has often been noted, especially by zinc (Vallee and Gibson, 1948), and when heated in a muffle furnace for long periods samples are particularly liable to contamination by particles of the furnace wall and other dust. If dry samples are heated too rapidly they may ignite and lose large amounts of material in the resulting convection currents.

Ion exchange concentration

Smales and Salmon (1955) have concentrated rubidium and caesium from sea water by ion exchange prior to activation, and Bowen (1956 a) has used the same technique for strontium and barium. In the latter work several columns of resin were set up in polythene tubes and thoroughly washed with redistilled hydrochloric acid and purified ammonium chloride. The break-through volume for each element at a standard flow-rate was determined using radioisotopes, and a smaller volume of sea water was passed through a fresh column. After draining the resin was either activated in its tube and subsequently wet ashed, or dry ashed before activation. Brooks (1960) has concentrated gold, bismuth, and cadmium from 250 litres of sea water in the same way. Organic resins can be effectively freed from traces of metals if the cleaning agents used are themselves extremely pure. Methods of purifying acids, alkalis, and buffer solutions are described by Hewitt (1952), Thiers (1957), and Irving and Cox (1958). It is, of course, necessary to analyse blank samples of clean resin before carrying out a determination on an unknown solution.

Chromatography

This method of separation was first used as a preliminary step before activation by Winteringham, Harrison, and Bridges (1952) and Lissitzky and Michel (1952), in studying the separation of organic chlorides and bromides. The technique provides a useful method of detection of bands on a paper chromatogram, and has been used for the determination of Br, Cl, S (Schmeiser and Jerchel, 1953 a), Co, P, and V (Schmeiser and Jerchel, 1953 b; Benson, 1959). A disadvantage is that ordinary filter paper contains quite large quantities of most elements (Sandell, 1959). Benson (1959) showed that ashless filter paper contains about 1·5 μg sodium chloride/cm^2 by activation analysis, and that appreciable amounts of calcium 45 were also found in activated filter paper. Some of the sodium 24 found in activated paper may have derived from the (n, α) reaction of aluminium. Hence blanks are necessary, as in the method of concentration by ion exchange.

Precipitation

Harrison and Raymond (1955) used precipitation by oxalic acid to concentrate strontium and barium from urine prior to activation analysis. The large excess of calcium present provided an adequate scavenging agent, and the oxalic acid used contained only 0·5 p.p.m. strontium and 1·3 p.p.m. barium, which was negligible compared with the amounts in the sample. Leddicotte (1960) recommends a thallium sulphide precipitation step to collect manganese before determining this element in a solution containing excess iron, because of the interfering $Fe^{56} (n, p) Mn^{56}$ reaction. Before using a technique of this kind, it is obviously necessary to test the losses involved by tracer experiments, and to check contamination by measuring recovery of small amounts of the element under test. Centrifugation in stoppered polythene tubes is preferable to filtration, since the latter can lead to contamination by any of the elements normally present in filter paper or sintered glass. Reagents are also a potential contamination hazard (e.g. Butler and Field, 1956).

Solvent extraction

Uranium can be quantitatively extracted from sea water by shaking with 0·8 M tributyl phosphate in carbon tetrachloride. This procedure has been used by Stewart and Bentley (1954), prior to activation by the (n, f) reaction, and can obviously be applied with the minimum of contamination. Hudgens and Mayer (1956) have also purified uranium samples, by extraction of uranyl nitrate with diethyl ether, prior to activation with a low flux of neutrons.

Concentration techniques will probably be used increasingly to extend the sensitivity of determinations of rare elements in sea water and other materials which are too bulky for direct activation.

10

GEOCHEMICAL APPLICATIONS OF
ACTIVATION ANALYSIS

GEOCHEMISTRY, or the study of the distribution of elements in the earth's crust, has fascinating implications regarding the history of the earth and the whole solar system. In recent years the subject of geochemistry has undergone, and indeed is still undergoing, an explosive phase of development. New and precise methods of analysis have been major factors in this development, and activation analysis together with isotope dilution have played an important part, and become established techniques for the modern geochemist (Smales and Wager, 1960; Winchester, 1960). While it is most unlikely that they will oust the classical techniques of colorimetry (Feigl, 1958) and emission spectrometry (Ahrens, 1954), there is little doubt that the enormous sensitivity and freedom from interference enjoyed by the activation method will make it of outstanding importance for determining many rare elements in rocks and minerals. The fields which have benefited most greatly from its application so far are the study of meteorites (cosmochemistry), crustal rocks (lithogeochemistry), sea water (hydrogeochemistry), and the determination of geological age (chronogeochemistry). These, together with other miscellaneous applications, will be discussed in more detail below.

Practical difficulties

It is not a simple matter to obtain a fresh sample of rock since weathering processes may extend several hundred feet inside the earth's crust. Samples from deep mines are the best. Material from museum collections may have been varnished or coated with preservative, or contaminated by other minerals, and it is generally advisable to etch the surface with a suitable acid either before or after activation. Grinding is not really necessary as it introduces many contaminants, but it is a way of overcoming the inhomogeneous nature of most minerals. Such inhomogeneities can be extremely marked, as in iron meteorites, in which case it is useful to determine two related elements simultaneously. Although the absolute amount of each may vary throughout the sample, the ratio of the two should be approximately constant.

TABLE 10.1

Concentration in μg/g of elements in meteorites, rocks, sea water, and soils (typical values)

(after Mason, 1958; McDonald, in Abelson, 1959; Vinogradov, 1959; Stevens *et al.*, 1960)

Element	Chondrites	Iron meteorites	Terrestrial rocks	G-1 granite	W-1 diabase	Sea water	Soils
A	50		0·04				
Ac							
Ag	0·08		0·1	0·042	0·057	0·0002	0·1
Al			81,300	79,000	83,000	0·003	70,000
As		10	2	1	1·8	0·0025	5
At							
Au	0·2	1	0·005	0·005	0·007	0·00001	
B			3	4	9	4·6	10
Ba	4	< 0·001	400	1200	225	0·006	500
Be			2	3·3	0·8		6
Bi	0·002		0·2	0·2		0·0002	
Br			3			65	5
C			320			28	20,000
Ca	11,500		36,300	10,000	79,000	400	15,000
Cd			0·2	0·06	0·33	0·00005	0·5
Ce	0·51		46	600	70	0·0004	50
Cl			200	50		19,000	100
Co	5		23	2·2	51	0·0001	8
Cr	2200	100	200	22	120		200
Cs	0·058		1	1·5	1·1	0·0005	5
Cu	80	270	45	13	110	0·001	20
Dy	0·37		5				
Er	0·21		3				
Eu	0·083		1	0·8			
F			700	730	200	1·3	200
Fe		9×10^5	50,000	14,200	79,000	0·0034	40,000
Fr							
Ga		5	15	18	16	0·0005	30
Gd	0·34		6				
Ge		50	2	1	1·6		1
H			1400				
He			0·003				
Hf	1·2	0·02	5				6
Hg	0·05		0·5			0·00003	0·01
Ho	0·075		1				
I			0·3			0·05	5
In	< 0·001		0·1	0·026	0·064		
Ir	0·5		0·001	0·006			
K	800	1	25,900	45,000	5300	380	15,000
Kr							
La	0·32		18	130	30	0·0003	40
Li	10	< 0·01	30	24	12	0·1	30
Lu	0·36		0·8				
Mg			20,900	2400	40,000	1270	6000
Mn			1000	210	1300	0·001	850
Mo			1	7	0·5	0·014	2
N			46		24	0·5	1000
Na			28,300	24,000	15,000	10,600	6000
Nb			24	20	10		
Nd	0·63		24	80	50		
Ne							
Ni	10,000	10^5	80	1·2	82	0·0015	40
Np							
O			466,000				500,000
Os		2	0·001				

TABLE 10.1 (*cont.*)

Element	Chondrites	Iron meteorites	Terrestrial rocks	G-1 granite	W-1 diabase	Sea water	Soils
P			1180	390	5700	0·03	800
Pa							
Pb	0·2		15	50	10	0·004	10
Pd		5	0·01	< 0·01	0·0185		
Pm							
Po							
Pr	0·12		6				
Pt			0·005				
Pu							
Ra						3×10^{-11}	8×10^{-7}
Rb	2·5		120	220	22	0·12	100
Re		0·22	0·001	0·0007	0·0007		
Rh	0·2		0·001				
Rn							
Ru	1	7	0·001				
S			520			880	850
Sb		0·2	0·2	0·6	1·2	0·0002	
Sc	9	0·001	5	3	34	0·00004	7
Se	10		0·09			0·004	0·01
Si			277,000	337,000	244,000	0·01	330,000
Sm	0·22		7	11	5·1		
Sn			3	2·3	2·8	0·003	10
Sr			450	250	175	8	300
Ta	0·021	0·0024	2	1·6	0·47		
Tb	0·051		0·9				
Tc		< 0·0003					
Te	0·7		0·002				
Th	0·04	0·00003	10	52	2·4	0·000001	6
Ti			4400	1400	7400	0·001	4600
Tl	0·0004		1	1·3	0·17		
Tm	0·038		0·2				
U	0·01	< 0·001	2	3·7	0·52	0·0033	1
V			110	18	240	0·0024	100
W	0·14	1·7	1	0·12	0·43	0·0001	
Xe							
Y			40	21	35	0·0003	50
Yb	0·19		3	1	3		
Zn			65	40	82	0·015	50
Zr	35	0·35	160	210	100		300

Most minerals, especially igneous rocks, contain a great variety of elements and so constitute a particularly stringent test for the analyst. Moreover, the presence of elements with large cross-sections for thermal neutrons often makes self-shielding important, and may lead to dangerously large activities when a scarce element is sought. Finally, minerals as a class are not easily got into solution, though methods of dissolving them have been worked out in most cases.

Cosmochemistry

Meteorites appear to be fragments of a planet or planets in the solar system which broke up at some unknown period. Many different kinds of meteorites are known, but several of these are extremely rare and will not be considered here (Daly, 1943). The most abundant type are known as chondrites, which have a granular structure consisting largely of the iron magnesium silicate, olivine. Other siliceous meteorites are much rarer and are called achondrites. Iron meteorites consist largely of impure alloys of iron and nickel, and an intermediate group of stony-irons is known. Watson (1941) estimates the relative percentages of the different types by weight to be: chrondrites 89·3, achondrites 4·2, irons 5·0, and stony irons 1·5.

It is sometimes difficult to tell whether a given object is a meteorite or not. Fragments of impure native iron, some of which are known as terrestrial magnetic spherules, resemble iron meteorites more or less closely. Meteorites can be distinguished by their relatively high nickel content: they consistently have $Fe > Ni > Co > Cu$ (Smales et al., 1958). The same criterion has been used to show that ocean sediments (Ni/Cu ratio 0·4–1·6) contain negligible amounts of meteoritic material (Ni/Cu ratio 82–133) (Smales et al., 1957). The controversial objects known as tektites differ from known meteorite glasses in their low Ni/Fe ratio and are therefore supposed by Ehmann (1960) to differ in origin from chondrites.

The major constituents of meteorites have long been known and are tabulated in monographs (McDonald, in Abelson, 1959; Mason, 1958); Table 10.1 includes most of their data. Interest has been reawakened in the minor constituents since the discovery by Brown and Goldberg (1949) and Goldberg et al. (1951) that the gallium content of iron meteorites can be used to subdivide these into three groups. This fact, illustrated by the data of Fig. 10.1, was first revealed by activation analysis, and has been confirmed by spectrometric methods by Lovering et al. (1957), who also established that germanium resembles gallium in its meteoritic abundance, and determination of germanium by Smales et al. (1958) confirmed this point. Reed et al. (1960) divide chondrites into two independent classes distinguished by their contents of the chalcophile elements Pb, Bi, and Tl.

In reviewing earlier work on the abundances of elements in meteorites, Suess and Urey (1956) have pointed out how many of the analyses are of doubtful reliability, and that the accepted values for most of the rarer elements have decreased with time. In 1956 only four metals, gallium, palladium, rhenium, and gold, had been determined in meteorites by activation and nearly thirty elements had not been detected in them at all. In addition, the analytical data for the metals Ge, Ag, Cd, Sn, Sb, Te, Cs, W, Bi, Th, U, and the non-metals B, F, Cl, Br, I, S, and P were considered to be of doubtful quality. Since that time the activation results listed in Table 10.2 have been published, together with determinations by other methods. Figures for yttrium, ruthenium, cadmium, tin, hafnium, iridium, platinum, and bromine are needed to fill in the gaps in our knowledge, and the present sensitivity of activation should be adequate for all or most of these elements.

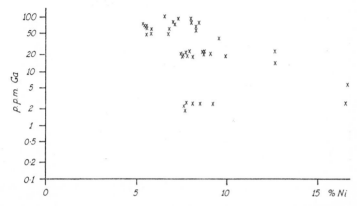

FIG. 10.1. Variation of gallium content (measured by activation) with nickel content of iron meteorites: from Goldberg, Uchiyama, and Brown, 1952.

The incompleteness of data in Table 10.2 makes it difficult to make profound deductions with regard to such fundamental questions as the origin of the elements. Where data for both chondrites and irons are shown, it is possible to confirm most of Goldschmidt's observations about the distribution of elements between different phases (1937). Thus Li, K, Sc, Ba, Ta, Se, Te, Th, and U are markedly lithophile; copper, a chalcophile element, can hardly be said to be more abundant in irons than in chondrites; and Atkins and Smales (1959) have shown that tungsten is siderophile, though Goldschmidt considered it lithophilic.

The chondrite figures in Table 10.2 should be compared with those given in Rankama and Sahama's monograph (1950) to show how many revisions have been made since its publication. Even such well-known elements as potassium, rubidium, and barium have been shown to be only half as abundant as was once thought. Rhodium is one-quarter as abundant as Goldschmidt found, but is much commoner than Suess and Urey estimated. Lanthanides, silver, tantalum, thorium, and uranium are at least ten times less common, and indium and tungsten 100 times less common than the figures quoted by Rankama and Sahama. In some cases these revisions are in accord with theoretical

Table 10.2

Elements and nuclides determined in meteorites by activation

Element	μg/g chondrites	μg/g achondrites	μg/g irons	μg/g stony irons	References
He³	0·1-9 μl/g		0·02-7 μl/g		{ Fireman & Schwarzer, 1957 / Stoenner & Zähringer, 1958
Li⁶	0·1-0·6		< 0·001		Fireman & Schwarzer, 1957
A⁴⁰			0·01-5 μl/g		Stoenner & Zähringer, 1958
A	30-80	< 0·6-40			{ König & Wänke, 1959 a / Wänke & König, 1959
K	800	< 10-340	0·006-2·2		{ Stoenner & Zähringer, 1958 / König & Wänke, 1959 a / Wänke & König, 1959
Ca	11,500	8000-77,000			Wänke, 1958
Sc	8·6	17-45	0·0004-0·002		{ Wänke, 1958 / Bate et al., 1960 / Kemp & Smales, 1960 a
V	67		< 0·2		Kemp & Smales, 1960 b
Cr	2200	1000-3200	6-185	< 5	{ Bate et al., 1960 / Smales et al., 1959
Co	150-900			1100	Smales, Mapper & Wood, 1957
Ni	5000-19,000			19,000	Smales, Mapper & Wood, 1957
Cu	75-100		120-430	140-230	{ Smales, Mapper & Wood, 1957 / Smales et al., 1959
Ga			0·4-100		{ Brown & Goldberg, 1949 / Goldberg et al., 1951
Ge			0·2-360	50	Smales et al., 1959
As			4-16	30	Smales et al., 1959
Se	6-13	0·002-6			Schindewolf, 1960
Rb	1-3				Cabell & Smales, 1957
Tc			< 0·0003		Boyd et al., 1956
Rh	0·2				Schindewolf & Wahlgren, 1960
Pd			1-10		{ Brown & Goldberg, 1949 / Goldberg et al., 1951
Ag	0·04-0·13				Schindewolf & Wahlgren, 1960
In	< 0·001				Schindewolf & Wahlgren, 1960
Sb			0·01-0·8	0·2	Smales et al., 1959
Te	0·5-0·9	< 0·007			Schindewolf, 1960
I	0·04-0·5				Goles & Anders, 1960
Cs	0·01-0·1				Cabell & Smales, 1957
Ba	3·5	44	< 0·001		{ Hamaguchi et al., 1957 / Reed et al., 1960
La	0·32				Schmitt et al., 1960
Ce	0·51				" "
Pr	0·12				" "
Nd	0·63				" "
Sm	0·22				" "
Eu	0·083	0·01-0·77			Schmitt et al., 1960; Bate et al., 1960
Gd	0·34				Schmitt et al., 1960
Tb	0·051				" "
Dy	0·37				" "
Ho	0·075				" "
Er	0·21				" "
Tm	0·038				" "
Yb	0·19				" "
Lu	0·36				" "
Ta	0·021		0·0024		Atkins & Smales, 1960
W	0·14		1·7		" "

TABLE 10.2 (cont.)

Element	$\mu g/g$ chondrites	$\mu g/g$ achondrites	$\mu g/g$ irons	$\mu g/g$ stony irons	References
Re			0·22		Herr et al., 1960
Os			2·0		Herr et al., 1960 Goldberg & Brown, 1950
Au	0·1–0·29		0·1–10		Goldberg & Brown, 1950 Goldberg et al., 1951 Vincent & Crocket, 1960
Hg	0·012–0·09	0·08			Reed et al., 1959 & 1960 Ehmann & Huizenga, 1959
Tl	0·0004	0·0007			Reed et al., 1960 Ehmann & Huizenga, 1959
Pb	0·16	0·5			Reed et al., 1960
Bi	0·003	< 0·001			Reed et al., 1960 Ehmann & Huizenga, 1959
Th	0·04	0·006–0·6	0·00003		Bate et al., 1957, 1958 & 1959
U	0·01	0·15	< 0·0001		Starik & Shats, 1956 Reed et al., 1955, 1958, 1959 & 1960 Hamaguchi et al., 1957 Hernegger & Wänke, 1957 König & Wänke, 1959 b

predictions. However, the extremely low values reported for indium, thallium, and bismuth in chondrites disagree markedly with Suess and Urey's estimates, and are not easily explained. These elements are all supposed to be chalcophile and should be looked for in meteoritic sulphides like troilite and in iron meteorites.

The methods employed for uranium and thorium merit some comment, as these elements exist in extremely small quantities in iron meteorites. Thorium was determined by activation of Th^{232} and counting the 27-day Pa^{233} formed after some hours' decay. Uranium has been measured by four independent methods, involving counting Np^{239} and the fission products Ba^{140}, Xe^{133}, and Xe^{135}, whach gave reasonable agreement.

No explanation has been put forward for the existence of three or four groups of iron meteorites with different ranges of gallium and germanium contents (Fig. 10.1). The elements appear to be siderophile in a manner inversely proportional to the nickel content of the metal phase. The hypothesis of preferential volatilization of these elements does not explain this relation, and is unlikely in view of the more constant value found for arsenic. Experiments on the retention of gallium and germanium during the crystallization of nickel-iron alloys might throw light on this unusual problem.

Fireman (1958, 1959) has made an ingenious use of his measurements of He^3 in large iron meteorites. From the distribution of this nuclide, which was assumed to be produced by spallation from iron, it was possible to estimate that the mean energy of cosmic radiation was roughly 6000 MeV, and also to determine the approximate size and shape of the meteorites before they met the earth's atmosphere. Neutron activation compares favourably with mass spectroscopy for determining He^3 in meteorites; the latter technique has been used by earlier workers (Paneth *et al.*, 1953).

Finally, the existence of cosmic ray-induced activities in meteorites should be mentioned. The possibility of activation by cosmic rays was first suggested by Bauer (1947), and since that time many activities have been detected by methods similar to those used for radiochemical isolation after artificial activation. The results are important in deciding how long meteorites have existed in space, notably in the case of tektites whose origin is unsettled, and are described in the last section of this chapter.

Lithogeochemistry

Very little use has been made of activation as a field method for prospecting for ores. The main reason for this is probably an economic one, since existing field methods are satisfactory for many elements.

Although both radium-beryllium sources and neutron generators are readily transportable by lorry, they are not cheap items, nor is a gamma spectrometer which is needed for detection. Brownell *et al.* (1957) used a 10 curie polonium-beryllium source to activate 300 g rock samples for short periods, and showed that sodium, aluminium, and silicon can be successfully determined under field conditions. Aluminium, silicon, and magnesium were also measured in cores from drilled shafts by Caldwell and Mills (1959); silicon and magnesium were measured by the (n, p) reaction, using fast neutrons generated from a van de Graaff machine, and interference by aluminium, sodium, and other elements was investigated. Laboratory studies by the Bradleys (1956) indicate that sodium and potassium, but not calcium, can readily be measured in felspars by activation and it is probable that their technique could be modified for field trials if required. More specific techniques for sodium and potassium are described by Salmon (1957 *a*) and by Winchester (1958, 1959). The use of charged particles for this kind of work has been fully investigated by Sippel and Glover (1960) who conclude that the sensitivity is adequate for sodium, magnesium, aluminium, phosphorus, and sometimes also carbon and fluorine in sedimentary rocks, but not for lithium, beryllium, boron, or silicon. There seems little doubt that several minor elements could also be detected, notably cobalt, manganese, silver, and vanadium, and Leipunskaya *et al.* (1959) give details of their techniques for determining these elements and several others in rocks and ore concentrates. Happ and Horwood (1952) found a 50 mc radium-beryllium source insufficient to assay uranium ore by the (n, p) reaction.

A simpler, but generally less specific, method of detection of an activated nuclide involves autoradiography. The first workers to use this technique for minerals were Goodman and Thompson (1943). Selected massive mineral specimens weighing 100–1000 g were ground flat on one face and exposed to neutrons for varying periods, and were then stood on top of photographic plates; the decay curve of the activity produced was measured and found to be exponential in most cases, indicating predominant activation of a single isotope. In this way the presence of barium in zinc ore, copper in chalcopyrite, gold in quartz, manganese in magnetite, willemite, etc., tungsten in wolframite, phosphorus in apatite, arsenic in arsenopyrite, and sodium and potassium in microcline was qualitatively demonstrated. Picciotto and van Styvandael (1951) have shown that the sensitivity of this technique for lithium, which yields tritons and alpha particles by the reaction

$$Li^6 + n^1 \to He^4 + H^3,$$

is 10^{-11} g if a flux of 10^{12} n/cm^2/sec is employed. Boron and nitrogen produce alpha particle tracks, but no tritons, in the photographic emulsion. The determination of uranium by neutron irradiation of ores followed by autoradiography of the fission fragments has been described by Curie and Faraggi (1951) and by Grace and Bates (1959). The autoradiographic method is qualitative or at best semi-quantitative, but could be valuable for locating elements in specific minerals in an inhomogeneous mass of rock.

Gaudin *et al.* (1952) tabulate the activities induced in a large number of minerals by exposure to a high neutron flux for 2·5 seconds, and give a limited amount of information on half-lives, which were believed to be caused by the decay of nuclides of aluminium, copper, fluorine, manganese, and silver, among other elements. The range of induced activities was so wide that these workers suggested that minerals might be sorted automatically by using β- or γ-ray operated sieves after activation. Thus crystals of beryl, which give off neutrons after photon activation, could be picked out from other material by a sorting device made sensitive to neutrons (Gaudin *et al.*, 1950). Galena, or lead sulphide, is scarcely activated by neutrons, but any silver it contains as an impurity activates, and this might be developed into a rapid test for silver in lead deposits.

The quantitative assay of ores for rare elements is an application of activation which will doubtless increase as facilities become more widespread. The light elements lithium, beryllium, and boron are all remarkably rare in nature; the determination of the former by the (n, t) reaction has already been discussed. Gaudin *et al.* (1950, 1951) and Mezhiborskaya (1959) have shown that as little as 1 p.p.m. of beryllium in ores can be detected by photon activation using the (γ, n) reaction and a portable berylometer has been designed for field work using this principle (Brownell, 1959). A few elements such as boron, cadmium, and gadolinium interfere by absorbing the neutrons produced before they reach the detector. Boron has been measured by counting the photons produced when the nuclide B^{10} absorbs neutrons, for which it has an extremely high affinity (Galuzo, 1958), though this is not strictly activation analysis. Methods and results for other elements not covered in other sections of this chapter are listed below.

Niobium, tantalum, and tungsten

Brownlee (1960) has developed a rapid chemical separation for niobium which makes it possible to detect 10^{-8} g of this element in activated rutile. The nuclide used, niobium 95m, has a half-life of only 6·6 minutes and can be detected by its 0·017 MeV photon activity. Tantalum gives a much longer-lived activity, and several workers have described the determination of this element in ores, where it always occurs with niobium, from which it is difficult to separate. Simple physical discrimination has been used to detect the tantalum in most cases (Long, 1951; Eicholz, 1952; Kohn, 1953 and 1954), but the only accurate results have been obtained using a chemical separation (Atkins and Smales, 1959; Morris and Olya, 1960). Tungsten has been measured in a number of rocks by the latter authors, and in ores by Leddicotte *et al.* (1958).

Silver and gold

Morris and Killick (1959 *a*, 1960 *a* and *b*) report an extremely sensitive activation assay for silver in ores and rocks. Gold has been shown to occur in certain diamonds by activation (Freedman, 1952), and has been measured in igneous rocks by Vincent and Smales (1956) as discussed below.

Gallium, indium, and thallium

These widely dispersed elements can be detected by activation more readily than by any other method of analysis. Morris and Brewer (1954) have shown that gallium can be accurately determined in 50 mg samples of blende (zinc sulphide) where it is sometimes concentrated above its normal abundance. The geochemistry of indium has also been extensively studied with the help of activation (Smales *et al.*, 1957; Irving *et al.*, 1957; Wager *et al.*, 1958), and thallium has been measured in some igneous rocks (Morris and Killick, 1960a and b; Brownlee, 1960; Kim *et al.*, 1960).

Selenium

Fineman *et al.* (1959) have shown that activation analyses for this element in ores and slags agree well with conventional determinations.

Technetium

Several workers have sought for this element without establishing its presence in nature. Technetium 97 and 99 have the longest half-lives (2×10^6 and 2×10^5 years respectively) and may yet be discovered in uranium minerals as fission products. Herr (1954) was the first to report negative results by activating various molybdenum-containing minerals with neutrons. Unfortunately the molybdenum 99 produced by activation decays to technetium 99 which must be allowed for. Anders *et al.* (1956) claimed to have found more technetium 99 in certain activated minerals than would have been expected from their molybdenum content. Boyd and Larsen (1956) used several methods of detection, of which the most sensitive was neutron activation, but found less than 3×10^{-10} technetium (the limit of detection) in molybdenum disulphide, potassium perrhenate, and numerous minerals. In addition Merz and Herr (1958) extracted ruthenium from various columbites, gadolinites, etc., but found its isotopic composition was normal by both activation and mass spectrometry, indicating that no technetium had occurred in these minerals.

Thorium and uranium

Thorium has been determined in ores by Leddicotte and Mahlman (1955) and by Rona (1957), and uranium has been found by neutron induced fission by many workers (Facchini and Orsini, 1949; Smales, 1952; Mahlman and Leddicotte, 1955; Rowland and Haskin, 1959). It is, however, doubtful if activation is superior to α-ray spectrometry or fluoroscopy for ore assays, though its great sensitivity makes it useful for rocks containing amounts of these fissionable elements far below those required for economic extraction. For example, Hamilton (1959) has confirmed earlier findings that the uranium content of granite is closely related to its potassium content (see Fig. 10.2).

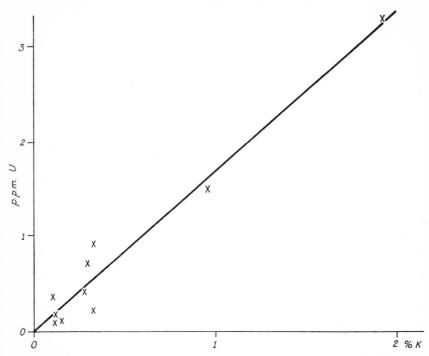

FIG. 10.2. Association of uranium and potassium in rocks from the Skaergaard intrusion: uranium determined by activation analysis (Hamilton, 1959).

Abundances of the elements in the lithosphere

The abundances of the vast majority of the elements in the lithosphere are now tolerably well known, and as yet activation has added little to our knowledge of them. According to Rankama and Sahama (1950), the only elements whose abundances have not been established are ruthenium and osmium, the rare gases krypton, xenon, and radon, and the short-lived nuclides of technetium, promethium, astatine, francium, and the transuranic elements. The first four of these are suitable for study by activation. However, a large number of the earlier determinations of other elements may be erroneous, as was pointed out in the section on meteorites, and this is further illustrated by the data for two rocks chosen as standards by the United States Geological Survey, a granite G-1, and a diabase W-1. Gamma spectra of these rocks are given in Figs. 10.3 and 10.4: sodium, potassium, and manganese constitute the bulk of the initial γ-ray activity. Table 10.3 summarizes determinations of certain elements by activation, largely by Smales and co-workers, and comparative determinations by spectrometric methods. The values reported in Table 10.3 may not represent the

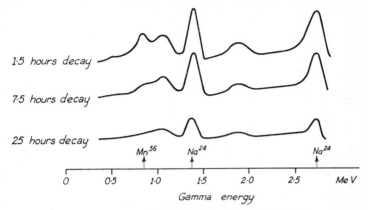

FIG. 10.3. Gamma spectra of granite G-1 activated with neutrons for 15 hours, showing peaks due to Mn^{56} and Na^{24}.

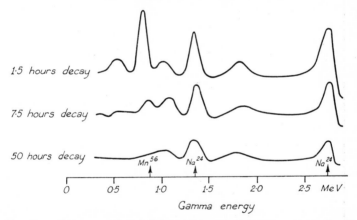

FIG. 10.4. Gamma spectra of diabase W-1 activated with neutrons for 15 hours, showing peaks due to Mn^{56} and Na^{24}.

true values for the rock as laid down because of contamination during handling. For example, in the preparation of G-1, Fairbairn (1951) states that two jaw crushers, a roller crusher, an Abbe mill with mullite balls, two metal sieves, and a porcelain mixing mill containing flint pebbles were employed. However, the prepared rock samples make very convenient standards for comparing analytical results from different laboratories.

TABLE 10.3

Elements determined in standard rocks by activation

Element	p.p.m. in G-1 by activation	p.p.m. in W-1 by activation	Reference	p.p.m. in G-1 by spectrometry, etc.	p.p.m. in W-1	Reference
Sc	2·8	34	{ Kemp & Smales, 1960 a / Hamaguchi et al., 1961 }	3	27	Ahrens, 1954
V	13	246	Kemp & Smales, 1960 b	18	240	Ahrens, 1954
Co	2·1	48·9	Smales, Mapper & Wood, 1957	4	36	Ahrens, 1954
Ni	1·2	73·1	" "	5	90	Ahrens, 1954
Cu	9·5	111·5	" "	11	110	Ahrens, 1954
Ga	20·9	18·0	Morris & Chambers, 1960	19	17	Ahrens, 1954
As	0·67	2·2	Hamaguchi et al., 1961	1·0	1·8	Stevens et al., 1960
Rb	219*	21·3*	Cabell & Smales, 1957	205	22	Goldich & Oslund, 1956
Sr	252*	172*	Loveridge, et al., 1960	287	172	Turekian et al., 1957
Pd	< 0·01	0·0185	Vincent & Smales, 1956			
Ag	0·042	0·057	Morris & Killick, 1960 b			
Cd	0·06	0·33	Vincent & Bilefield, 1960			
In	0·0255	0·0645	Smales, Smit & Irving, 1957			
Sb	0·28	0·95	Hamaguchi et al., 1961	0·6	1·2	Stevens et al., 1960
Cs	1·5	1·1	Cabell & Smales, 1957	2·5		Ahrens, 1954
La	122	27	Hamaguchi et al., 1961	150	30	Stevens et al., 1960
Sm	11	5·1	" "			
Eu	0·8		" "			
Ta	{ 3·0† / 1·3 }	0·93†	Morris & Olya, 1960 / " "			
W	0·12	0·48†	Atkins & Smales, 1960			
Re	0·0007	0·43†	Atkins & Smales, 1960			
Au	0·0045	0·0084	Morris & Fifield, 1961 / Vincent & Crocket, 1960 b			
Tl	1·3	0·17	Morris & Killick, 1960 a			
U	3·55	0·53	Hamilton, 1959 a	3·5	0·53	Larsen, cf. Hamilton, 1959

* Confirmed by isotope dilution technique. † Possibly contaminated by grinding.

Many determinations made by classical methods earlier than those reported in Table 10.3 gave much higher figures (e.g. Mitchell, in Turekian *et al.*, 1957, and Ahrens, 1954) for Rb and Sr. Hence abundances of a large number of elements, especially those in the second and third long periods, may be revised if they are studied by the new technique. Table 10.1 summarizes what is known of the composition of terrestrial rocks, G-1 and W-1, and may be used to calculate activities generated under specified conditions.

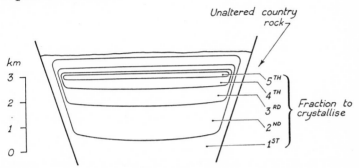

FIG. 10.5. Diagrammatic section across the Skaergaard intrusion, showing successive stages in the solidification of the original pool of molten magma: after Wager and Mitchell, 1951.

Magmatic crystallization

It is well known that igneous rocks vary widely in chemical constitution, whereas the original molten magma was presumably homogeneous. The chemical differentiation must have been brought about by fractional crystallization, but the detailed process is extremely complicated and occupies much space in textbooks (Rankama and Sahama, 1950; Mason, 1958). Grossly simplified, the process involves the primary deposition of ultrabasic silicates (dunites) together with oxides and sulphides, followed by the bulk of the silicates, which become more and more acidic as they crystallize out, leaving a mother liquor which crystallizes in the remaining cracks and gaps to form veins of pegmatite. The behaviour of many rare elements in this process is not known completely, but a recent series of studies has thrown more light on it.

These are the studies of Wager and co-workers on the rocks of the Skaergaard intrusion in east Greenland. The area has been described by Wager and Deer (1939) as originally consisting of a pool of basic magma, in the form of an inverted cone, which crystallized from its outer edges inward, so that pegmatites form the central layer and undifferentiated magmatic materials surround the exterior (Fig. 10.5).

The behaviour of nineteen rare elements has been studied spectrographically by Wager and Mitchell (1951), and their data have been
supplemented by activation analyses in a number of papers by Smales's
group (see references below). These should be consulted for further

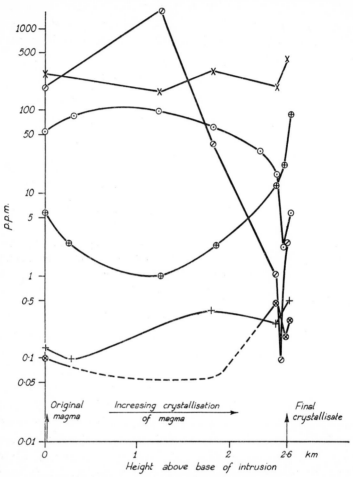

FIG. 10.6. Amounts of Sr (×), Co (⊙), V (⊘), Rb (⊕), Cs (⊗), and Cd (+)
determined by radioactivation in rocks from the Skaergaard intrusion: after
Wager et al., 1957, Cabell and Smales, 1957, Loveridge et al., 1960, Vincent
and Bilefield, 1960, and Kemp and Smales, 1960 b.

details, but some of their results are represented graphically in Figs.
10.6 and 10.7. These figures plot p.p.m. in rocks as a function of height
above the base of the intrusion, which can be related to the percentage
solidification of the whole magma. It will be seen that nickel appears
in the first fractions, followed by cobalt and vanadium, while copper,

tungsten, caesium, and indium crystallize late but are lost before the final solidification. Uranium, rubidium, and to a lesser extent tantalum are concentrated in the last portion of the melt to crystallize. Strontium, cadmium, scandium, gold, and, as far as the limited data allow

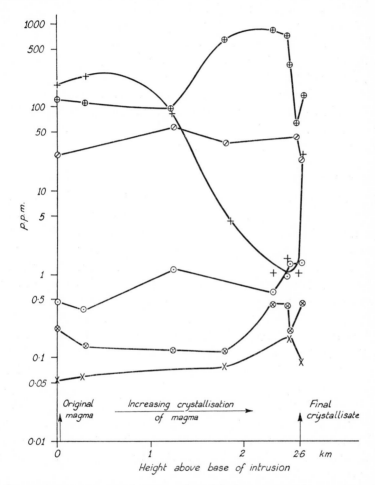

Fig. 10.7. Amounts of Ni (+), Cu ($\oplus$), Sc ($\oslash$), Ta ($\bigcirc$), W ($\otimes$), and In ($\times$) determined by radioactivation in rocks from the Skaergaard intrusion: after Wager *et al.*, 1957, Wager *et al.*, 1958, Atkins and Smales, 1960 *a*.

generalization, palladium are not greatly concentrated in any particular fraction. These findings are supported by the data of Table 10.3, where G-1 represents a late and W-1 an early stage of magmatic crystallization, except in the case of tungsten, where the W-1 results may be in error through contamination. The data for cobalt, nickel, and copper

(Wager *et al.*, 1957), vanadium (Kemp and Smales, 1960 b), and strontium (Loveridge *et al.*, 1960) agree qualitatively, though in general not quantitatively, with those of Wager and Mitchell (1951). These authors could detect rubidium in only a few of the rocks by spectrography, whereas it was readily determined by activation together with caesium (Cabell and Smales, 1957). The remaining elements, indium (Wager *et al.*, 1957, 1958), scandium (Kemp and Smales, 1960 a), cadmium (Vincent and Bilefield, 1960), palladium and gold (Vincent and Smales, 1956; Wager *et al.*, 1957; Vincent and Crockett, 1960 a), tantalum and tungsten (Atkins and Smales, 1959), and uranium (Hamilton, 1959 b) could not have been determined spectrographically at their existing concentrations. Only in the case of uranium were other methods of analysis equally sensitive and satisfactory.

Sedimentary rocks

The processes of sedimentation have been widely studied, but activation analysis has contributed relatively little to our knowledge of this subject. Rubidium and caesium have been determined in sediments from the Atlantic ocean, where it was shown that caesium is markedly enriched with respect to rubidium over its value in sea water (Smales and Salmon, 1955); potassium was not determined in these samples.

Bowen (1956) has measured calcium (by flame photometry) and strontium and barium (by activation) in recent and fossil corals of different ages. Barium was enriched by a mean factor of 5·5 and strontium by 1·4 as compared with calcium in recent corals. No significant trends were observed for the barium content of fossil corals, but strontium was found to decrease regularly as the geological age increased, though the oldest specimens studied did not fit in with this simple picture (Fig. 10.8). This suggests that strontium has been steadily accumulating in the ocean during geological time, which would explain the fact that the Sr/Ca ratio in sea water is much larger than in any common igneous rock.

The contents of cobalt, nickel, and copper in marine sediments have been reported by Smales and Wiseman (1955) and Smales *et al.* (1957). Copper and nickel occur in approximately equivalent amounts (10–300 p.p.m.) in globigerina ooze, radiolarian ooze, and red clays, while cobalt is always less abundant by a factor of 2 to 5, with the exception of radiolarian ooze. Manganese nodules, which are mixed hydrous manganese and iron oxides supposed to act as scavengers as they precipitate from the ocean, contain more nickel than copper and quite large amounts of cobalt. Clearly all three elements are effectively scavenged by the nodules, as they are at least ten times more abundant there than in the other sediments. The cobalt, and especially the copper contents of all the sediments are much too high relative to that of nickel for there to have been appreciable amounts of meteoritic material present, though this conclusion has been disputed by Pettersen (1959). Current problems

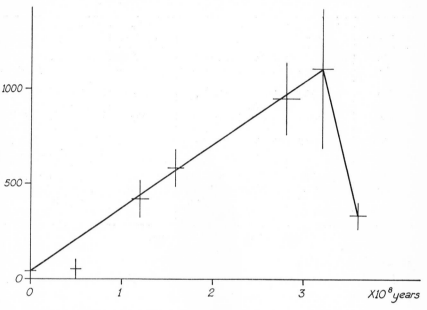

Fig. 10.8. Ca/Sr in corals as a function of geological age; after Bowen, 1955.

in sedimentation to which activation could well be applied are described by Keith and Degens (in Abelson, 1959) and by Goldberg and Arrhenius (1958).

Activation has also given useful information about rubidium and caesium in coals (Smales and Salmon, 1955) and about cobalt, iron, nickel, phosphorus, potassium, and vanadium in oils (Brooksbank et al., 1953; Leddicotte et al., 1959).

Soils have received relatively little study, though Leddicotte et al. (1959) briefly report figures for aluminium, manganese, potassium, scandium, sodium, thorium, and uranium in soils. Bowen and Dymond (1955) measured strontium and barium in a number of soil extracts made by shaking soils with very pure ammonium acetate solution. Normal soils contain 0·5–10 p.p.m. of extractable strontium and barium, but in the vicinity of strontium mines strontium may become a major element in the soil. Vinogradov (1959) has pointed out how little information is available concerning the amounts of the heavy elements in soils, except for the metals which have so far been proved to be essential for plants and animals. His data on soils are summarized in Table 10.1.

TABLE 10.4
Content of certain metals in sea water in µg/litre

Element	Activation values	Reference	Older values	Reference
Mn	1	Rona *et al.*, 1960	1–10	cf. Harvey, 1957
As	1·7–3·65	Smales & Pate, 1952 *b*	1–1000	cf. Smales & Pate, 1952 *b*
Rb	120	Smales & Salmon, 1955	35–1000	cf. Smales & Salmon, 1955
Sr	8300	Bowen, 1956; Hummel & Smales, 1956	13,000	cf. Harvey, 1957
Cs	0·5	Smales & Salmon, 1955	0·4–10	Wattenburg, 1938; Ishibashi & Hara, 1959
Ba	6·3*	Bowen, 1956	30–90	von Engelhardt, 1936
Au	0·01–0·5*	Hummel, 1957	< 0·0005–2	cf. Hummel, 1957
U	2·5*	Stewart & Bentley, 1954	0·15–3·4	Harvey, 1957

* Coastal surface water.

Hydrogeochemistry

Table 10.4 summarizes the contribution of activation analyses to the chemistry of sea water, and also shows the values obtained by other methods (cf. Table 10.1 for other elements in sea water).

Among the many elements whose abundance in sea water has never been satisfactorily measured, the activation method might provide data for Hf, In, Ir, Pd, Re, Ta, and Tl. The main difficulty is that the two major elements in sea water, sodium and chlorine, both have rather large cross-sections for neutrons and if large volumes of sea water have to be irradiated their activity can become too large for convenience of handling. Dyrssen and Nyman (1955) have calculated the theoretical activities generated in sea water by exposure to neutrons.

The work of Hummel (1957) in particular emphasizes the importance of careful collection of sea-water samples. The gold content of sea water varies markedly with proximity to land, and also to some extent with depth. Gold, and probably many of the rarer elements in sea water, exists largely in the colloidal state, and can readily be precipitated by adsorption onto larger colloidal particles, plankton, or the walls of the sampling vessel. Gold is unusual in having a stronger affinity for polythene than it has for glass or silica when it is present in low concentration. All these points should be studied for other rare elements in order to obtain reliable analyses. Lyon and Reynolds (1955) and Blanchard *et al.* (1959) have shown that at least twenty elements can be determined in tap water by neutron activation, but so far no studies of natural fresh waters have been made by this method.

Chronogeochemistry

The only absolute method of determining the age of a mineral is to measure the amount of a naturally occurring radioactive nuclide and its daughter product present in a sample. Such determinations are generally difficult both to perform and to interpret, since the amount of radioactivity present is generally small and the daughter product may not all be radiogenic in origin. The majority of measurements have been made using mass spectrometers of high sensitivity, but recently it has been shown that neutron activation may be equally convenient for determining some of the nuclides involved.

Table 10.5 lists some of the long-lived nuclides of interest for determining mineral ages, together with their daughter products, half-lives, mode of decay, and possibilities for activation.

Several useful reviews of absolute age determination are available (e.g. Faul, 1954; Ahrens, 1955; Abelson, 1959), and it is not proposed to deal with difficulties of analysis and interpretation here, other than those involving activation analysis.

The potassium-argon method has been widely used, since potassium is much the most abundant element with a long-lived nuclide. Use of activation for determining the argon 40 content of minerals was first suggested by Curran (1952, 1953) and subsequently applied by Moljk *et al.* (1955), who extracted the argon from potassium minerals by fusion in evacuated silica apparatus before activating it. Later workers adopted the more reliable procedure of extraction after activation. In a study of the age of iron meteorites, Stoenner and Zahringer (1958) determined both argon 40 (by activation to 1·8-hour argon 41) and potassium (by activation to 12-hour potassium 42). The potassium content of these meteorites was extremely low (1 p.p.m. or less) and was distributed most inhomogeneously. However, although the potassium content varied by a factor of 300 within one specimen of a meteorite, the argon/potassium ratio did not change by more than a factor of 2. Two corrections were found to be necessary. Firstly there could have been a loss of argon by diffusion which was not easy to estimate.

Secondly argon 40 might have been produced by processes other than the decay of potassium 40. It is unlikely that much argon 40 was produced from potassium 39 since the neutron flux in outer space is less than 1 neutron/cm^2/sec (see below). However, spallation reactions from cosmic rays could produce some argon 40, and this was allowed for by measuring the spallation-produced helium 3 in the samples. A number of meteorites had negligible helium 3 contents, and all gave ages in the range 5–13 × 10^9 years. Similar determinations on five chondrites and two achondrites by Wänke and König (1959), where potassium is about a thousand times as abundant and spallation-produced argon is no problem, gave ages of 2·8–4·2 × 10^8 years. Neither of these figures agree with results from Pb^{207}/Pb^{206} ratios determined by mass spectrometry, which give an age of 4·5 × 10^9 years for chondrites (Patterson, 1956), but the latter method is inconsistent with the uranium determinations of Hamaguchi et al. (1957), Hernegger and Wänke (1957), and König and Wänke (1959).

Herr, Merz, and co-workers (1954, 1955, 1958 a and b, 1960) have pioneered the use of activation in studying three rare long-lived nuclides in nature: lutecium 176, tantalum 180, and rhenium 187. Since ytterbium is much more abundant than lutecium, it is unlikely that measurements of lutecium 176 and ytterbium 176 in rare earth minerals will yield useful age data. However, after isolating a few hundred microgrammes of hafnium from rare earth minerals and zircons by ion-exchange methods, and determining the specific activity of 19-second hafnium 179 and 45-day hafnium 181 after neutron activation, the former samples showed lower specific activity, indicating a greater percentage of radiogenic hafnium 176 (Herr et al., 1958).

In the same way, excess tungsten 180 in tantalites was indicated by measurements of the specific activity of 24-hour tungsten 187. In the case of osmium, rhenium minerals contain only 1 p.p.m., but this must be almost pure radiogenic osmium 187 judging by the low specific activity of the activated element (Herr and Merz, 1958 b). Normal osmium activates to 1·3-day osmium 193 and other active products. The rhenium/osmium 187 ratio could be used to calculate the ages of iron meteorites if the primordial abundance of the latter nuclide were known (Herr et al., 1950).

Unfortunately activation analysis is not a very sensitive method for determining lead isotopes, but it is more sensitive than a mass spectrometer for estimating the heaviest members of the three alpha decay chains. Rona (1957) has used measurements of thorium 232 in uranium minerals for calculating their age, and Reed *et al.* (1958) give figures for lead 208 (the final decay product of thorium) in five chondrites. If these two nuclides were determined in the same sample they could give accurate ages. Reed (1960) has also measured Pb^{204}, by fast neutron activation to Pb^{203}, in several meteorites. Many workers have devised techniques for measuring uranium 235 and 238 by activation (Macklin and Lykins, 1951; Seyfang, 1955; Wänke and Morse, 1955, etc.). Reed (1960) has shown that the ratios Ba^{130}/Ba^{134} and Hg^{196}/Hg^{202} are identical in terrestrial and meteoritic samples.

TABLE 10.5
Long-lived radioactive nuclides

Nuclide (I)	Decays by	Daughter (II)	$t_{\frac{1}{2}}$ of I $\times 10^9$ yr	(n, γ) on I	(n, γ) on II
K^{40}	β^-	Ca^{40}	1·3	stable K^{41}	10^5-yr Ca^{41}
K^{40}	K	A^{40}	1·3	stable K^{41}	1·8-hr A^{41}
V^{50}	K	Ti^{50}	4×10^5	stable V^{51}	5·8-min Ti^{51}
Rb^{87}	β^-	Sr^{87}	43	18-min Rb^{88}	stable Sr^{88}
Cd^{113}	β^- ?	In^{113}	$> 3 \times 10^6$	stable Cd^{114}	49-day In^{114}
In^{115}	β^-	Sn^{115}	6×10^5	54-min In^{116}	stable Sn^{116}
Sb^{123}	β^- ?	Te^{123}	$> 10^4$	60-day Sb^{124}	stable Te^{124}
Te^{130}	$2\beta^-$	Xe^{130}	10^{12} ?	25-min Te^{131}	12-day Xe^{131}
I^{129}	β^-	Xe^{129}	0·017	12·6-hr I^{130}	stable Xe^{130}
La^{138}	β^-	Ce^{138}	200	stable La^{139}	140-day Ce^{139}
La^{138}	K	Ba^{138}	200	stable La^{139}	85-min Ba^{139}
Nd^{144}	α	Ce^{140}	2×10^6	stable Nd^{145}	32-day Ce^{141}
Nd^{150}	$2\beta^-$	Sm^{150}	$> 10^7$	15-min Nd^{151}	80-yr Sm^{151}
Sm^{147}	α	Nd^{143}	130	stable Sm^{148}	long-lived Nd^{144}
Lu^{176}	β^-	Hf^{176}	30	6·8-day Lu^{177}	stable Hf^{177}
Lu^{176}	K	Yb^{176}	30	6·8-day Lu^{177}	2-hr Yb^{177}
Ta^{180}	β^-	W^{180}	$> 10^2$	stable Ta^{181}	140-day W^{181}
W^{180}	α	Hf^{176}	$1·1 \times 10^4$	140-day W^{181}	stable Hf^{177}
Re^{187}	β^-	Os^{187}	50	17-hr Re^{188}	stable Os^{188}
Pt^{190}	α	Os^{186}	10^3 ?	3-day Pt^{191}	stable Os^{187}
Bi^{209}	α	Tl^{205}	3×10^8	5-day Bi^{210}	4·2-min Tl^{206}
Th^{232}	6α	Pb^{208}	13·9	27-day Pa^{233}	3·3-hr Pb^{209}
U^{235}	7α	Pb^{207}	0·71	fission	stable Pb^{208}
U^{238}	8α	Pb^{206}	4·51	2·3-day Np^{239}	stable Pb^{207}

N.B. For attempts to detect radioactivity in the nuclides Ca^{48}, Zr^{96}, Mo^{100}, Cd^{113}, Sb^{123}, Te^{123}, Te^{130}, and Pb^{204} see Kohmann (1953).

Inspection of Table 10.5 shows that many possibilities of age determination in minerals remain to be investigated. It is to be hoped that activation will prove useful in studying some of them. For example, measurements of bismuth 209 and thallium 205 in meteorites might reveal specimens with ages very much greater than 10^9 years, which would raise interesting problems concerning the age of the universe.

Terrestrial and cosmic activation

The high-energy proton flux in outer space is of the order of 0·3 protons/cm²/sec and this generates secondary neutrons, electrons, muons, etc., when it meets with matter. Many of the electrons and some of the protons are trapped in special regions round the earth called Van Allen belts (Ogilvie, 1959). In the outer part of the earth's atmosphere, cosmic radiation activates a number of nuclides, notably carbon 14 by the (n, p) reaction on nitrogen; tritium is also produced by the (n, t) reaction of nitrogen and gives rise to the rare nuclide helium 3 by decay. Libby (1955) estimates the integrated neutron flux per cm² of the earth's surface to be 2·6 neutrons per second. This neutron flux decreases markedly through the atmosphere from its maximum at 12,000 metres until the surface of the earth is reached, when a further burst of neutrons is produced by various nuclear reactions, and the flux then decreases with depth. The flux at the surface of the ocean is about 0·007 n/cm²/sec, and is about ten times as high at an altitude of 3000 metres.

Terrestrial neutrons are produced by (α, n) reactions and by spontaneous fission, especially where there are local concentrations of uranium and thorium. Schaeffer and Davis (1956) have calculated the neutron flux produced in this way for various minerals, and Thode (in Faul, 1954) considers that the two processes are about equally important as sources of neutrons. Both are generally small compared with the flux induced by cosmic radiation, but Cherdyntsev and Suvarova (1958) have shown that in certain pegmatite veins, containing both uranium and beryllium in unusual amounts, neutron fluxes as high as 0·16 n/cm²/sec can be found.

Although these fluxes sound extremely small, they have been operating for a long period of time and have given detectable amounts of activated materials. Thus in addition to carbon 14 and tritium, beryllium 7, phosphorus 32, sulphur 35 (Reed, in Abelson, 1959), silicon 32 (Lal et al., 1960), and chlorine 36 (Davies and Schaeffer, 1955) have been found in terrestrial materials, and beryllium 10, aluminium 26, and cobalt 60 in meteorites (Ehmann and Kohmann, 1958; Anders, 1960). Fireman and Schwarzer (1957) determined helium 3 and lithium 6 in meteorites by activation and worked out the neutron flux to which they had been subjected, and Wänke (1958) has argued that scandium 45 in chondrites may be the end product of an (n, γ) reaction on calcium 44, while 90 per cent. of that in iron meteorites comes from spallation of iron (Herr, 1960). Care must be taken in interpreting activation analyses of elements from rocks containing unusual amounts of uranium and thorium, since normal isotope ratios may have been disturbed by (α, n) or (n, γ) reactions, as has been found for neon, argon, and xenon, for example (Wetherill and Ingram, 1953; Duckworth, 1958).

An understanding of the theory of neutron capture is necessary to formulate hypotheses on the origin of the elements. According to Burbidge *et al.* (1957), all elements in stars are synthesized from hydrogen at high temperatures. The majority of heavier nuclides appear to have been synthesized by (n, γ) reactions by one or other of two mechanisms, one slow enough to allow time for beta decay, and the other very fast with enormous neutron fluxes. The latter process terminates in fission, the former in alpha decay. It can be concluded that the neutron fluxes existing in stars are far higher than any yet achieved in terrestrial experiments.

11

BIOLOGICAL APPLICATIONS OF ACTIVATION ANALYSIS

ALTHOUGH the geochemical applications of activation analysis to date may be judged unsystematic and haphazard, the biological applications are even more difficult to fit into a coherent pattern. This is the more lamentable because there are no reliable published data on the content of more than half the known elements in organisms. Both plants and animals possess the ability to discriminate between elements to a marked extent, and so have a remarkably constant elementary composition when grown in a wide range of environments. A good example of this discriminatory power is the accumulation of potassium as the commonest alkali metal in marine organisms, despite the overwhelming preponderance of sodium in the ocean. Thus biological material is much less variable in composition than geological material, and contains far less of many of the rarer heavy elements.

Practical problems in handling biological materials

Methods of collecting biological material with the minimum of contamination have already been described, and it must be emphasized how important it is to take all possible precautions in handling samples. External organs (skin, hair, nails, carapaces, shells, roots, leaves, etc.) are always more or less contaminated by their environment, and internal organs can easily have impurities introduced into them during dissection. With small organisms it is possible to carry out dissection after activation, though it must be remembered that the intense radiation inside a reactor may break down cell walls and disrupt internal membranes. In this connexion it is worth remembering that an exposure to a flux of 10^{12} n/cm^2/sec for 1·5 hours delivers a dose of approximately 10^6 rads. Such a dose would kill everything except a few bacterial and fungal spores, but would not induce much chemical breakdown. Cell walls would begin to break down after about five times this exposure, and after a hundred times this dose (6 days in the reactor) about 50 per cent. of the organic molecules would have decomposed.

Another problem when collecting biological material is the frequent occurrence of commensalism and symbiosis. Large marine algae, for example, are almost invariably found to have smaller species of algae, bryozoa, and invertebrates adhering to them, and in mammals the rumen, stomach, and intestine are heavily infested with many species of bacteria. Bowen and Sutton (1951) found that some specimens of the sponge *Dysidea crawshayi* contained unusual amounts of nickel: they attributed this to an unknown constituent of the microflora growing within the tissues of the sponge.

From a biogeochemical point of view, the most important organisms for which analyses are required are those which are most abundant. It is difficult to obtain reliable estimates for a quantity so subject to temporal variation as the total mass of organisms existing on the earth. However, it would appear that the greatest weight of biological matter is concentrated in the marine plankton, with relatively small contributions from multicellular algae (sea weed), fish, and other phyla. Terrestrial organisms are nearly as important, but mammals and even arthropods have an insignificant biomass compared with the higher plants. Thus Borchert (1952) estimates 98·7 per cent. of all organic carbon is plant material and only 1·3 per cent. is of animal origin. So far the number of papers dealing with activation analysis of biological material varies inversely with the biomass concerned. The proportions are roughly: mammals 72 per cent., higher plants 10 per cent., marine algae 8 per cent., and plankton no analyses. It is to be hoped that this situation will be remedied in the future.

Composition of biological material

Soft tissues and fluids contain large quantities ($> 0\cdot1$ per cent.) of only eleven elements, H, C, N, O, Na, Mg, P, S, Cl, K, and Ca. The remaining elements are known as trace elements and can be further subdivided into those known to be essential for life (B, V, Mn, Fe, Co, Cu, Zn, Mo, I) and the rest. Certain exceptional species, families, or phyla have the capacity to accumulate specific elements to a remarkable degree, but it is not yet known whether this accumulation represents a specific need for the element concerned. Despite the extraordinary power of discrimination shown by living material, the environment does affect their composition to some extent. This can be shown by comparing the analyses of terrestrial and marine organisms, as is attempted in Tables 11.1 and 11.2. These tables are based on limited data much of which is in need of revision, but it will be seen that marine organisms are generally richer in boron, sodium, and the halogens, while terrestrial

TABLE 11.1

p.p.m. dry weight of elements in terrestrial organisms

Element	Bacteria		Fungi		Angiosperms		Arthropods		Mammals	
Ag			0·1*	26	0·2	26			0·03	56
Al			30	21	70	42	100	46	11	56
As					0·2	43			0·2	56
Au					0·001	52				
B			13*	26	20	46			0·5	3
Ba					10	11				
Bi					0·06	42				
Br			20	37	15	37			12	56
C	450,000	46	500,000	46	450,000	3	380,000	24	480,000	3
Ca			350	31	20,000	46	500	24	35,000	3
Cd			12*	26	1·5	42				
Cl			10,000	31	1000	31	1200	24	4500	3
Co			1*	26	0·3	33			1·3	56
Cr			0·14	40	0·3	33				
Cs					0·2	53				
Cu			75	31	10	46	50	46	7·5	56
F					0·5	34			100	3
Fe			120	31	100	33	200	46	130	3
Ga			2·5*	26	0·03	42				
H	75,000	46					31,000	24		
Hg					0·015	34			0·04	56
I					0·5	22	0·9	46	2·5	3
K			55,000	31	20,000	46	11,000	24	5500	3
La–Lu					0·4	21				
Li					0·1	33			0·08	3
Mg			1500	31	3000	46	750	24	1000	3
Mn			10	31	15	46	10	46	0·5	56
Mo			2*	26	3	33	0·6	2	0·5	3
N	100,000	46	90,000	46	130,000	3	100,000	24	130,000	3
Na			1000	31	100	31	3000	24	6500	3
Ni			4*	26	2	33	9	46	0·9	56
P	15,000	46	16,000	46	15,000	46	17,000	24	16,000	3
Pb			110*	26	14	42	7000	24	2	56
Ra					$0·1 \times 10^{-8}$	51			$0·9 \times 10^{-8}$	56
Rb					10	33			20	3
S	5000	46	4000	31	2000	46	4000	24	16,000	3
Se			2	41	0·5	34				
Si					1500	21	6000	46	60	3
Sn			7*	26	0·3	42			2·5	56
Sr					20	11				
Ti					8	33	160	46		
U					0·1	34			0·02	56
V			0·3	3	0·5	33	0·15	3	0·07	3
W					0·07	10				
Y			1·5*	26	0·05	21				
Zn			30	31	30	46	400	46	130	56
Zr			10*	26	1	26				

* Lichens.

organisms are, rather surprisingly, no richer in aluminium, silicon, and titanium.

The main constituents of biological tissue are elements of the first short period (hydrogen, carbon, oxygen, and nitrogen). Nitrogen, hydrogen, and boron are particularly important in that they absorb 99 per cent. of the thermal neutrons which react with biological tissue, by the reactions $N^{14}(n, p) C^{14}$, $H^1(n, \gamma) H^2$, $B^{10}(n, \alpha) Li^7$.

Hence the nuclear reactions with trace elements on which activation analysis depends are caused by an insignificant proportion of the total number of reacting neutrons.

Using the data in Tables 11.1, 11.2, and 11.3, it is possible to calculate the amount of activity induced in the tissues listed there after a specified exposure to neutrons. For example, Curtis and Teresi (1946) have made such a calculation for vertebrate tissues. These and many other calculations imply that at least 99 per cent. of the initial induced radioactivity in irradiated biological material is made up of only four or five nuclides. These are 37-minute chlorine 38, 2·6-hour manganese 56, 12-hour potassium 42, 15-hour sodium 24, and 14-day phosphorus 32. Their relative proportions depend on the tissue analysed, the length of the irradiation, and the subsequent cooling period.

References for Tables 11.1, 11.2, 11.3

1. Beharrell, 1942. *2.* Bertrand, 1942. *3.* Bertrand, 1950. *4.* Black and Mitchell, 1952. *5.* Bowen, 1956 *a.* *6.* Bowen, 1956 *b.* *7.* Bowen, 1959 *a.* *8.* Bowen, 1959 *b.* *9.* Bowen, 1959 *c.* *10.* Bowen, 1960. *11.* Bowen and Dymond, 1955. *12.* Brooksbank and Leddicotte, 1953. *13.* Chilean Iodine Educational Bureau, 1952. *14.* Cholak and Hubbard, 1948. *15.* Fukai and Meinke, 1959. *16.* Fore and Morton, 1952. *17.* Gibbons, 1958. *18.* Hamaguchi *et al.*, 1960. *19.* Hill and Smith, 1959. *20.* Hulcher, 1960. *21.* Hutchinson, 1943. *22.* Johnson and Butler, 1957. *23.* Kehoe, Cholak, and Story, 1940. *24.* King, 1957. *25.* Koch *et al.*, 1956. *26.* Lounamaa, 1956. *27.* Lux, 1938. *28.* Mackle, Scott, and Treon, 1939. *29.* Maillard and Ettori, 1936. *30.* Matsumura *et al.*, 1955. *31.* McCance and Widdowson, 1960. *32.* Meinke, 1959 *a.* *33.* Mitchell, 1944. *34.* Monier-Williams, 1950. *35.* Mullin and Riley, 1956. *36.* Muth *et al.*, 1960. *37.* Neufeld, 1936. *38.* Newman, 1949. *39.* Regnard and Schlösung, 1897. *40.* Saint-Rat, 1948. *41.* Schwartz and Foltz, 1958. *42.* Shimp *et al.*, 1957. *43.* Smales and Pate, 1952 *c.* *44.* Smales and Salmon, 1955. *45.* Sowden and Stitch, 1957. *46.* Spector, 1956. *47.* Stitch, 1956. *48.* Stock, 1940. *49.* Tobias *et al.*, 1952. *50.* Turner *et al.*, 1958 *a.* *51.* Turner *et al.*, 1958 *b.* *52.* Warren and Delavault, 1950. *53.* Yamagata, 1950. *54.* Yamagata, 1960. *55.* Young and Langille, 1958. *56.* Calculated from text and data of Table 11.3.

TABLE 11.2

p.p.m. X in dry marine organisms (Vinogradov (1953) et. al.)

X	Unicellular Cyanophyceae	Multicellular Phaeophyceae	Diatoms	Porifera	Coelenterata	Mollusca	Echinodermata	Crustacea	Pisces
Ag	25	0·3 [4]		1	5	50 [15]	2	15 [15]	10 [15]
Al		60		5	30	0·005	0·09	0·08	10
As		50		0·01	0·007	0·008	0·03	0·0005	0·30
Au		0·01 [15]		100		20	40	15	0·0003
B		100		0·6	0·3	3	0·15	0·2	20
Ba		10 [5]		100*	1000		60		
Bi									0·04
Br		1000* [5]			1000	1000		400	400
C	330,000	350,000	200,000	200,000	400,000	400,000	180,000	400,000	500,000
Ca	9000	9000	8000 [35]	7000	1300	1500	30,000	10,000	1200
Cd		0·2	2	1000	1	3		0·7	3
Cl		60,000				50,000		6000	6000
Co		1		0·5	4	0·7	0·5	0·8	0·5
Cr		0·1		0·2	1·3	2		2	0·2
Cs		5				20 [35]			
Cu	700	10 [44]		35	50	700	15	50 [35]	8
F									4
Fe		500 [4]	1500	2500	400	60,000 [30]	150	20	30
Ga		0·2 [55]		0·2	1·5	1	0·3		0·15
Ge				0·3		4			0·15
H	40	50,000	40,000	10,000*	40,000	25,000	6	60,000	70,000
Hg		0·03			15				0·3
I		1000* [46]	300	2000	30	1		1	1
K		30,000	3200	3500		5000	10,000	13,000	12,000
Li		6				10	15		
Mg	15,000	1300		60	10		1·5	2000	1200
Mn	0·35	50			26			280	0·8
Mo		0·4	0·5			2		0·6	1
N	80,000	18,000	25,000	80,000	14,000	90,000	40,000	100,000	120,000
Na		45,000		8000	20,000	25,000		4000	3000
Ni		1·5 [55]			35	4	3	0·4	1
P	10,000	4000 [4]	6000	3000	23	6000	4000	9000	8000
Pb		2		5		0·7	18	0·3	0·5
Ra		10×10⁻⁷ [44]				15×10⁻⁸ [50]	4×10⁻³	0·7×10⁻³ [15]	1·5×10⁻³ [50]
Rb		12				20	0·2	0·0005	0·0008
Re		0·01				0·006 [15]			
S	1300	18,000		2000		2000	6	7000	100,000
Sb		1		0·08		1000	0·003	300	0·2
Sc							5		
Si		1500	200,000	65,000		1000		300	70
Sn		1·5 [5]		1·7		15	2	0·2	3
Sr		800 [1]		8		60		500	
Th						20		17	
Ti		15		1·7	0·03	0·7		0·8	0·2
V		0·3 [4]		2 [3]	7	0·05 [15]		0·0005	0·15
W					2				0·0014
Zn		30 [15]		150	1500	200	20	200	80
Zr		3 [1]							

TABLE 11.3

Elements in mammalian tissue (p.p.m. dry weight except for blood); from Spector (1956) et al.

Element	Bone	Hair	Muscle	Brain	Liver	Kidney	Heart	Spleen	Lung	Blood
A	0·01 [23]		0·04 [23]	0·12 [23]	0·2 [23]	<0·04 [23]	<0·04 [23]	0·04 [23]	0·16 [23]	0·75 [39]
Ag	7·5 [23]	30	12 [25]	12 [25]	18 [47]	14	8	11 [47]	100	0·15
Al	0·3 [43]	0·4 [43]	0·2 [43]	0·1 [43]	0·6 [43]	0·6 [43]	0·5 [43]	0·2 [43]		0·45
As					<0·0001 [17]				0·001	0·2 [19]
Au										<0·0001 [14]
B	2 [45]				<0·1 [37]					3 [9]
Be										
Ba	7 [37]	5	14	3 [37]	10	20 [37]	10 [37]	20 [37]	30 [37]	3
Br										
C	8000	200								
Ca	260,000	20,000	350 [25]	350 [25]	330 [25]	300 [25]	330 [25]	350 [25]	440 [25]	100
Cd		15	0·1	0·04	8 [47]	40 [47]		0·3 [47]	0·08 [47]	0·04 [25]
Cl	2700 [25]	2	2800	8000	4800	9000	6000	7500	12,000	2700 [9]
Co	5	2	0·1	0·04	0·04	0·12	0·4	0·03	0·05	0·001 [6]
Cr			0·01	0·6	0·03	0·03	0·05	0·07	0·6	
Cs				7	17	9	8			
Cu	0·14 [54]	70	0·08	0·03	0·05	0·03		0·04	0·04	0·75 [7]
F	6		8		4	9	2	4	6	0·3
Fe	1500	130	1200	400	550	240	35	1300	500	480
Ga	200									
Hg										0·0005 [8]
I	0·1 [48]		0·02 [48]	0·4 [13]	0·2 [13]	0·25 [13]	0·02 [48]	0·03 [48]	0·1 [48]	0·003 [48]
K	900		15,000 [13]	20,000	8500	8000	11,000		7000	1900
La–Lu	10 [12]				0·0015					
Li										0·02 [6]
Mg	4000 [16]	1 [16]	1200 [16]	1700 [16]	700 [16]	1000 [16]	700 [16]	650 [16]	350 [16]	38
Mn	0·3		0·6	1·6	8	5	1·3	0·2	0·6	0·025 [8]
Mo			0·1	0·04	5	0·7		0·2	0·6	0·014
N	45,000		140,000	100,000						
Na	5000 [25]	6	4000 [25]	10,000 [25]	5500 [25]	8000 [25]	4500 [25]		1200 [25]	1900 [25]
Ni	2·5	800	0·3	0·15	0·3	1	0·25	0·2	0·5	0·3
P	120,000 [47]	20	8500 [36]	20,000 [36]	8500 [36]	8000 [36]	8000 [36]	17,000 [36]	5000 [36]	400 [6]
Pb	6 [36]		0·8	0·4	4	1	0·25	2·5	4	0·2 [34]
Ra	0·6×10⁻⁸		1·0×10⁻⁸		0·8×10⁻⁸	0·4×10⁻⁸		0·7×10⁻⁸	0·6×10⁻⁸	
Rb			7 [47]	5 [47]	14 [47]	13 [47]	13 [47]	11 [47]	10 [47]	
S		38,000		10,000		600				40
Sc	0·001 [27]									
Se	6				3 [32]					2·5 [23]
Si	6 [25]	3	1·5 [25]	2 [25]	500		75	600 [25]	1400	0·14 [6]
Sn	30 [45]	0·1			5 [34]		0·9	1	8	0·03 [29]
Sr					2	0·8 [25]				0·03 [38]
Ti	0·016 [38]		0·3 [29]	0·2 [29]	0·2 [29]	0·2 [29]	0·3 [29]	0·07 [38]	9	0·03 [3]
U	1 [20]		0·02 [38]		0·05 [38]	0·04 [38]	0·3 [38]		0·05 [38]	0·017
V			0·25 [20]		0·2 [3]	0·02 [3]				0·001 [10]
W										
Y	0·04 [12]									
Zn	150 [34]	150	120 [25]	40 [25]	150	110 [25]	70 [25]	40 [49]	10	8 [7]

Some examples will help to emphasize this point. The gamma spectra of activated vertebrate blood or bone is essentially that of sodium 24 (Spencer *et al.*, 1957; Druyan *et al.*, 1958; Hutchinson, 1960; Figs. 11.1 and 11.2). The predominance of sodium has been used to obtain auto-radiographs of this element in activated bone sections (Vincent, 1959)

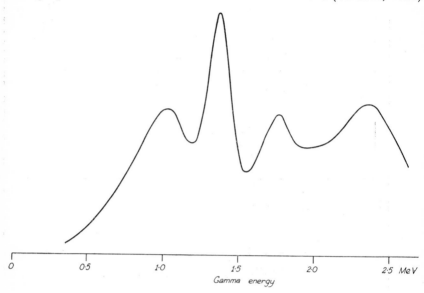

FIG. 11.1. Gamma spectrum of whole blood activated with neutrons for 15 hours, after one hour's decay. The spectrum is that of sodium 24.

and fingerprints (Yamamoto, 1959). Vegetable tissues, which contain much more manganese than animal tissues, give gamma spectra with peaks due to manganese 56 (Figs. 11.3 and 11.4). The sodium 24 peaks are generally prominent, but are not seen when certain fruits are activated. An example is the fruit of the hazel (*Corylus avellana*) (Fig. 11.4) which contains large amounts of potassium but negligible sodium. Roughly speaking, sodium activates ten times as readily as potassium. Hence marine organisms, which contain approximately equal amounts of sodium and potassium, give a gamma spectrum due to sodium 24, but, with terrestrial plants and vertebrate soft tissues, in which potassium generally exceeds sodium by a factor of ten, the elements contribute equally to the gamma spectrum. The chlorine 38 γ-ray contribution is both short-lived and difficult to resolve from the 1·39 MeV peak of sodium 24, though it has been determined in muscle by gamma spectrometry (Bergstrom, 1959). Phosphorus 32 is a pure beta emitter, but its presence is readily demonstrated by plotting decay curves for

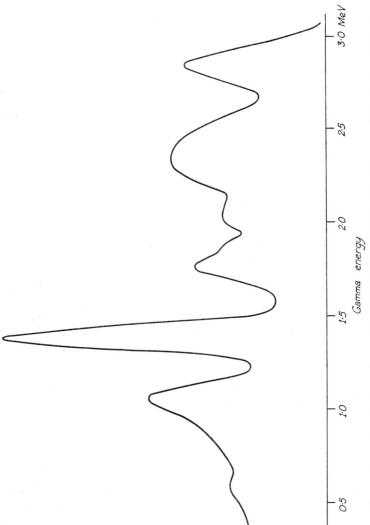

FIG. 11.2. Gamma spectrum of bone ash activated with neutrons for 24 hours. The spectrum is that of sodium 24.

irradiated biological material (Fig. 11.5). After about 4 days, the decay curve of activated soft tissues shows the characteristic 14-day half-life (Tobias and Dunn, 1948; Odeblad and Tobias, 1954).

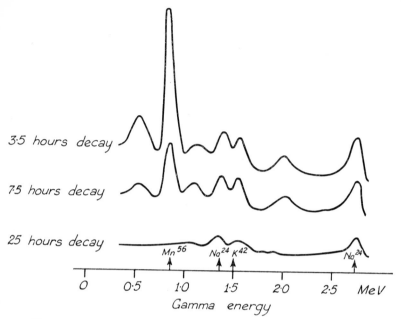

FIG. 11.3. Gamma spectra of tomato seeds activated with neutrons for 15 hours. Peaks due to Mn^{56}, Na^{24}, and K^{42} can be seen.

Actual and potential applications

The actual elements which have been studied reveal conspicuous gaps in our knowledge (Tables 11.1, 11.2, 11.3). A large number of workers have used activation to analyse biological material for arsenic, cobalt, copper, gold, and strontium for a variety of reasons, but the elements scandium, chromium, germanium, palladium, indium, antimony, tantalum, and iridium, all of which have large cross-sections for thermal neutrons, have not been looked for at all. Again, it is surprising how few workers have used the very great sensitivity provided by activation for determining manganese, rubidium, and bromine. Essential trace elements such as manganese, copper, zinc, and molybdenum have been exhaustively studied by conventional methods of analysis, some of which are extremely sensitive. It is probable that the technique will make its greatest contribution to inorganic biochemistry in studying elements for which no other analytical methods are available.

Despite the very great sensitivity of activation analysis, it is quite inadequate to determine elements in individual cells or parts of cells, apart from a few exceptional cases. This is because of the very small size of most cells. For example, a typical yeast cell is a spherical object of diameter 10^{-3} cm. Since most biological material has a density of

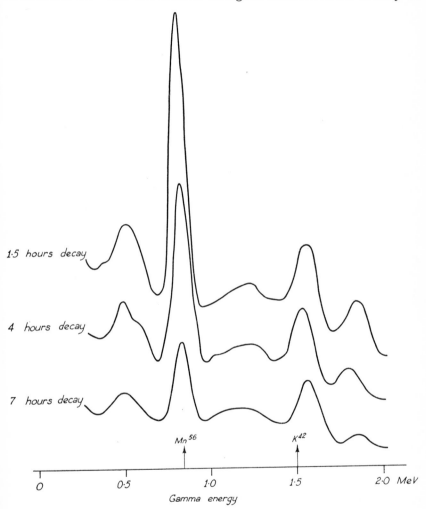

FIG. 11.4. Gamma spectra of hazel nut activated with neutrons for 15 hours. Peaks are due to Mn^{56} and K^{42}.

nearly unity, this cell will weigh only 5×10^{-10} g, and its potassium content will be of the order of 5×10^{-12} g. While such a trace quantity of potassium might be detected after activation, the remaining elements, present in far less abundance, certainly would not. Much larger cells are known, as in the Characeae, but these are highly atypical. In the same way it is doubtful if even the largest chromosomes known weigh more than 10^{-9} g, so that it would be extremely difficult to determine any element in a single chromosome, with the possible exceptions of potassium and phosphorus.

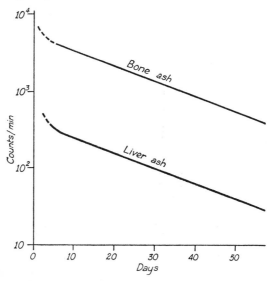

FIG. 11.5. Decay curves of neutron-activated tissues showing 14-day half-life due to P^{32}: after Tobias and Dunn, 1948.

Vertebrate tissues

According to the International Commission on Radiological Protection (1951), a 70 kg man contains 7 kg of bone (moisture content 20 per cent.), 5 kg of blood (moisture content 83 per cent.), and 58 kg of soft tissues, mostly muscle (moisture content 75 per cent.). If the amounts of elements present in muscle, blood, and bone (Table 11.3) were all known it would be possible to calculate roughly the elementary composition of man, but data (not all reliable) are only available for about 30 elements at present (Table 11.1). Activation has filled a number of gaps in our knowledge already, but most data are fragmentary or unsystematic. Published data are classified below according to the periodic table. Note that the chemical composition of the matrix (bone or soft tissue) is unimportant, both with regard to ultimate sensitivity and interferences, which is not true for spectrometric methods. Where activation analysis gives very different results from spectrometry this is pointed out below, and the necessity for further work should be understood.

Hydrogen

Hydrogen cannot be determined by neutron activation, but Haigh (1953) used the (γ, n) reaction of deuterium to determine the percentage of heavy water in biological fluids. One curie of sodium 24 was used as a source of photons, and by counting the prompt neutrons Haigh could determine 4 μg of deuterium. Odeblad (1956) wrapped his samples in indium foil and counted the indium 115 produced by secondary activation, and found the limit of detection to be 15 μg D. Improvements in technique are needed if the method is to compete with established procedures for deuterium assay.

Group I

(a) *Lithium.* Lithium 6 has a very large cross-section for thermal neutrons, and reacts with them in a unique manner by the $Li^6 (n, t) He^4$ reaction. If the samples are activated in contact with nuclear emulsions, the α-particle and triton tracks can be counted under a microscope. The technique has been used to locate lithium in amphibian embryos (Ficq, 1951 and 1954; Dent and Sheppard, 1957) with a sensitivity of 10^{-8} g.

(b) *Sodium and potassium.* Most workers have used simple beta or gamma spectrometry to determine these elements, which produce the bulk of the induced radioactivity in neutron-activated material (cf. Curtis and Teresi, 1946; Reiffel and Stone, 1957; Spencer *et al.*, 1957; Druyan *et al.*, 1958; Leddicotte *et al.*, 1958). Odeblad (1954) used α-particle activation to show that sodium can be determined in blood, urine, and liver by the (α, n) reaction to give 6·5-second aluminium 26. Deuteron activation has also been employed to determine sodium in cervical mucus (Odeblad *et al.*, 1958). The ultimate sensitivity of the neutron activation technique is at least equal to that obtainable by flame photometry.

Rubidium and caesium. These elements follow potassium closely in the body, but activate to much longer-lived nuclides than potassium 42. Hence potassium need not interfere with their estimation as it does in conventional analysis. Wolfe *et al.* (1949) describe preliminary work on separating rubidium and caesium from activated tissue, using similar methods to those later perfected by Smales and Salmon (1955). The caesium content of 1–10 p.p.m. in animal tissue mentioned by Leddicotte *et al.* (1958) seems rather high, but the limits of detection are very low (6×10^{-10} g Rb; 10^{-10} g Cs). Yamagata (1960) has made an extensive study of caesium in human tissues, with results summarized in Table 11.3. Caesium is much enriched in bone compared with potassium, which concentrates in the soft tissues. Muscle contains only about 0·08 p.p.m. (dry weight), much less than Leddicotte's figure mentioned above.

Group II

Beryllium. This element is not very suitable for activation analysis. Odeblad and Nati (1955) could not determine beryllium in tissues by the $Be^9 (\alpha, n) C^{12}$ reaction, although the sensitivity was 5 μg using a 130-millicurie polonium 210 source.

Magnesium and calcium. There are no reports of the determination of these elements by activation. The sensitivity is poor, the half-lives of the neutron-activated products unsuitable, and the elements are readily determined by other methods (cf. Bowen and Cawse, 1959).

Strontium and barium. Although the sensitivity of activation analysis is not particularly good (10^{-7}–10^{-6} g) for these elements, it has been extensively used for metabolic studies (Harrison and Raymond, 1955), and for establishing the concentration of strontium in bone (Brooksbank et al., 1953; Tipton et al., 1954; Sowden and Stitch, 1957; Savchuk, 1959; Loveridge et al., 1960). The greatest single advantage of the technique is probably its freedom from interference by calcium, which can be serious in arc and flame spectrometry. Most workers have employed 2·8-hour strontium 87m and 1·4-hour barium 139, as the slightly greater sensitivity obtainable by using longer-lived nuclides is offset by the greater length of time needed for the analysis, but both methods agree with one another. A noteworthy result is the concentration of barium in the iris, ciliary body, and choroid of the mammalian eye (Sowden and Pirie, 1958; Garner, 1959): otherwise the elements follow calcium and are not known to be essential.

Group III

Boron. Boron 10 has an enormously large cross-section for thermal neutrons, and the prompt alpha particles can be detected by autoradiography in a nuclear emulsion, with a sensitivity of 10^{-9} g (Mayr et al., 1953; Edwards, 1956). If mice are fed on a diet enriched in boron 10 the distribution of boron in the tissues can be followed by this technique; it has been shown, for example, that boron accumulates in brain tumours. The main drawback is the background of proton tracks in the emulsion caused by the $N^{14} (n, p) C^{14}$ reaction, but the method is promising.

Aluminium. The neutron-activated product, aluminium 28, has a half-life of only 2·3 minutes and has not been used for analysis. Odeblad (1954) has used α-particle activation of the $Al^{27}(\alpha, n)$ 2·5-minute P^{30} reaction to determine the element in rat tissue.

Yttrium and lanthanides. These elements have been determined in bone after activation using an ion exchange separation (Brooksbank and Leddicotte, 1953). The method is extremely elegant, but gives much higher results than the spectrometric method of Lux (1938). It seems unlikely that this group serves any function in the body. Scandium should be looked for by activation.

Group IV

Carbon (with nitrogen and oxygen). In one of the earliest reports of activation by photons of approximately 20 MeV, Mayneord *et al.* (1949) showed that 2-minute oxygen 15 and 20-minute carbon 11 were the major activities generated in mammalian tissue. Later work by Baldwin *et al.* (1953), who irradiated blocks of yeast with 100 MeV X-rays, showed that 10-minute nitrogen 13 must also be taken into account when analysing decay curves. The activities are small, and are not improved by substituting $(n, 2n)$ for (γ, n) activation (Meinke, 1959). Neutron activation gives nuclides with half-lives too short or far too long for convenience.

Other Group IV elements. These seem to occur only as contaminants in the body, where they are adsorbed on bone. The short half-life of titanium 51 makes it difficult to measure less than 6×10^{-7} g in biological ash (Kim, 1960). Leddicotte *et al.* (1958) quote 1–10 μg Zr/g found in animal tissue: there are no comparable figures in the literature.

Group V

Phosphorus. This gives rise to one of the major activities after neutron activation, and is one of the simplest elements to determine in this way. For example, Reiffel and Stone (1957) determined phosphorus in muscle without any chemical separation, by measuring the beta activity of the sample after 8 days' decay. Such a procedure is justified by the results of Tobias and Dunn (1948) which are shown graphically in Fig. 11.5. The only systematic work on this element is the early study of Curtis and Teresi (1946) on mouse tissues. These workers found approximately 0·04 per cent. P in blood, 0·4 per cent. in soft tissues (liver, kidney, spleen, and lungs), and 5 per cent. in bone; Bowen and Cawse (1961) have shown that the sensitivity can be as little as 10^{-10} g. Deuteron activation has also been recommended for locating phosphorus in 20 μ tissue sections by autoradiography (Odeblad and Tobias, 1954), and for human cervical mucus (Odeblad et al., 1958).

The abundance of phosphorus 32 in activated tissue frequently hinders the radiochemical purification of rare elements. It has a long half-life and a strong tendency to adsorb on all kinds of precipitates. Hence in all radiochemical separations of biological material it is advisable to insert specific chemical steps; for example, precipitation of ferric phosphate or magnesium ammonium phosphate will remove the bulk of this nuclide.

Arsenic and antimony. Both elements are highly poisonous and arsenic is also carcinogenic. After administration, arsenic appears rapidly in hair and nails. Following Griffon and Barbaud's (1951) discovery that arsenic could be detected by activation in a single hair, several workers (Griffon, 1955; Dewar and Lenihan, 1956; Heyndrickx and Schanvliege, 1958; Lenihan and Smith, 1959; Smith, 1959) have investigated the medical and toxicological status of the element. Others have measured arsenic in bone (Kohn-Abrest, 1956; Michon, 1956) and teeth (Gotte and Hattemer, 1955), and surveys of the element in other tissues have been carried out by Smales and Pate (1952) and Dale (1959). The sensitivity is about 10^{-10} g, which is far lower than that attainable by any other method. Leddicotte (1960) mentions that antimony has been measured recently in biological material.

Group VI

Oxygen. This is a difficult element to determine by activation. Photon activation is inefficient (see under carbon above), but proton activation of oxygen 18 to 1·9-hour fluorine 18 looks much more promising; a possible technique is suggested in Chapter 13, and an interesting application is discussed under the section on activated chromatograms.   '

Sulphur. No satisfactory method has been worked out for determining this element by neutron activation, partly because the sensitivity is not good but largely because so much sulphur 35 is produced by the (n, p) reaction of chlorine 35.

Selenium and tellurium. Both elements are highly toxic. Certain parts of the world, notably regions of North Dakota, Columbia, Israel, Queensland, and Eire, possess a high concentration of selenium in the soil, which is transmitted to grazing animals and local inhabitants via the plants. Thus selenium reaches high levels in some human livers from Dakota (Leddicotte, 1960). Figures of 10^{-6}–10^{-5} g Se and 10^{-5} g Te per g animal tissue seem unusually high (Leddicotte *et al.*, 1959). Meinke (1959) describes attempts to utilize 17-second selenium 77m and 3·9-minute selenium 79m in the analysis of rat liver.

Group VII

Fluorine. The only method tested, the $F^{19}(\alpha, n)Na^{22}$ reaction, could not detect less than 10^{-4} g of fluorine and so is quite unsuitable for analysing biological material (Odeblad, 1954).

Chlorine, bromine, and iodine. Chlorine is essential to vertebrates where its main function appears to be to maintain ionic balance. Bromine is universally present but is not thought to be of any importance in animal tissue. Iodine, on the other hand, is essential for thyroid function, and the determination of protein-bound iodine in blood is not easy. Early work by Brues and Robertson (1947, 1950) showed that iodine in activated thyroid is determinable without chemical separation. Once the halogens have been isolated, for example by distillation, chlorine 38 and iodine 129 can be separated or simply allowed to decay before bromine 80 or 82 are counted. The limits of detection are roughly 10^{-8} g for Cl, 10^{-9} g for Br, and 10^{-10} g for I, but chlorine is so much more abundant than the other halogens that it contributes the largest activity. Determinations in blood (Bowen, 1959; Leddicotte *et al.*, 1958) agree with those made by other methods.

Transition elements

Vanadium. This element is probably essential, and recent studies have emphasized its importance in the formation of teeth. Despite Brues and Robertson's (1947) report of a 3·8-minute activity in irradiated thyroid, there have been few attempts to measure vanadium in vertebrate tissues. Brownlee (1959) and Bowen and Cawse (1959) have reported rapid procedures for determining vanadium 52 in activated biological material with sensitivities of $2·5 \times 10^{-9}$ and 10^{-7} g respectively, so the element should be detectable in tissue samples of 1 g dry weight. Niobium and tantalum should be looked for, as the former may be essential for certain ascidians.

Molybdenum and tungsten. Molybdenum is an essential co-enzyme, but no function has been assigned to tungsten. The respective sensitivities are 10^{-7} g and 10^{-11} g. Bowen (1959, 1960) has determined the elements in mammalian blood, where the Mo/W ratio is about 10:1, as it appears to be in most soils and rocks.

Manganese. This is an important enzyme activator, which is probably essential in the mammalian diet: deficiencies lead to bone disorders. Keynes and Lewis (1951) made one determination of manganese in invertebrate nerve tissue. It is readily determinable by activation, as shown by Bowen's (1956) work with single drops of blood and single hairs. Bowen's mean value for human blood (0·025 g/ml) is considerably lower than that found by spectrometric methods though supported by the most recent work (Cholak and Hubbard, 1960). Borg (1958) has shown that physical methods of discriminating the photons from manganese 56 are generally inadequate for detecting the low concentrations in animal tissue. However, if the sample is activated by epithermal neutrons with energies near to a resonance peak in the cross-section for manganese, it may be possible to detect manganese 56 by gamma spectrometry even in mammalian tissues. If a chemical separation is used the sensitivity may be 10^{-12} g.

Iron. The first determinations, using a chemical separation, were made by Wolfe, Dunn, and Tobias (1949) on the dry ash produced by evaporating 1 g wet tissue with nitric acid and hydrogen peroxide, and later work has not been described in much detail (Koch *et al.*, 1956; Leddicotte *et al.*, 1958). Activation has not been used to determine less than 200 μg of iron, and there seems little doubt that colorimetric techniques are best for low concentrations of this essential trace element.

Cobalt. Early work by Wolfe *et al.* (1949) and Tobias *et al.* (1952) achieved a sensitivity of 5×10^{-9} g for soft tissues using 5-year cobalt 60. Subsequent work (Brooksbank *et al.*, 1953; Schonken, 1959; Dale, 1959) has not improved on this, and Kaiser and Meinke (1960) have shown that the sensitivity is only 5×10^{-8} g if 10-minute cobalt 60m is used instead. The minute traces of cobalt existing in animal tissues make it desirable to use the long-lived isotope with its greater sensitivity. Koch *et al.* (1956) have used the method extensively for human tissues, and found much more cobalt in blood (0·04 μg/ml) than other workers have found by spectrometry (Haerdi *et al.*, 1960). The element is apparently essential to sheep, and it is a constituent of vitamin B_{12}. Tobias *et al.* (1952) found somewhat increased uptake by nuclei of tumour cells.

Nickel. Leddicotte *et al.* (1958) reported 0·5–2 μg/g in animal tissue, but gave no further details. The sensitivity of activation for this element is not very good, and it is not known whether the element has any importance in nutrition.

Copper and zinc. As little as $4 \times 10^{-10} \mu g$ Cu and $5 \times 10^{-8} \mu g$ Zn can be determined by activation, and since copper 64 and zinc 69 have similar half-lives and zinc is about ten times as abundant as copper in biological material the two metals can be conveniently determined together. Wolfe *et al.* (1949) first measured these elements in mouse liver, kidney, spleen, and lung, and other tissues have been investigated by Koch *et al.* (1956), Leddicotte *et al.* (1958), Seal *et al.* (1957), Banks *et al.* (1959), and Bowen (1959). The activation results agree with those obtained by other methods, but use smaller samples of tissue. Use of the method has established the low zinc content of leucocytes of leukaemic subjects (Dennes *et al.*, 1960). The elements are essential, and both their analysis and metabolism have been studied extensively.

Silver and gold. Tobias *et al.* (1952) claimed to have detected nuclides of silver and gold in active tissue ash but gave no details. Leddicotte *et al.* (1958) found $0 \cdot 1 - 1$ $\mu g/g$ Ag and Dale (1959) found $0 \cdot 01 - 0 \cdot 5 \mu g/g$ Au in animal tissue: both these figures seem remarkably high compared with upper limits derived from spectrometry, and Gibbons (1958), using a reliable method, found an upper limit of $0 \cdot 0001$ $\mu g/g$ Au in animal liver. Colloidal gold 198 is often used in medicine, and Tobias and Dunn (1948, 1949), Muller (1958), and Purser *et al.* (1959) have studied the distribution and blood clearance of orally administered gold by activation. Such studies are useful for calculating the radiation dose given to different tissues by the active isotope.

Cadmium and mercury. These elements are generally regarded as toxic, and are known to combine with proteins and to concentrate in the kidney. Leddicotte's (1958) quoted value of $1-5$ μg Cd per g animal tissue seems high. Tobias *et al.* (1952) claim to have detected mercury isotopes in active tissue. This has not been confirmed, but Hamaguchi *et al.* (1960) have found about 1 p.p.m. Hg in soft tissues of molluscs and fish. Westermark and Sjöstrand (1960 *a* and *b*) have measured these elements in tissues from individuals suffering from heavy metal poisoning.

Gallium and thallium. Neither of these has any claim to be essential, and thallium is markedly toxic. The only data available for gallium are those of Bowen (1959) who showed that the limit of detection was 3×10^{-10} g. The element was just detectable in rat blood at a concentration of about $0 \cdot 0005$ $\mu g/ml$. Heyndrickx and Schanvliege (1958) showed that thallium could be detected in viscera at 10^{-7} g/g.

Other elements

Taylor and Havens (1956) quote a report of Brooksbank, Leddicotte, and Strain (1955) demonstrating the presence of Cr, Pd, Re, and Pb in a dilute enzyme solution by activation. It is probable that these elements were only contaminants, though they should be sought in more biological samples.

Mammalian blood

A number of elements have now been determined in mammalian blood by activation, and some of the results are compared with determina-

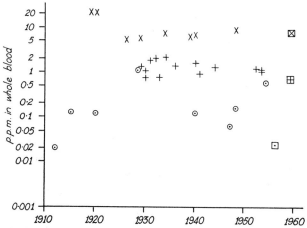

FIG. 11.6. Determinations of zinc (×), copper (+), and manganese (⊙) in blood during the last fifty years: results obtained by activation are boxed.

tions made by other methods in Figs. 11.6 and 11.7. These show selected data from the literature for zinc, copper, manganese, bromine, arsenic, and molybdenum in whole blood. It will be seen that those elements which occur in blood at concentrations of 1 p.p.m. and above (Zn, Cu, Br) give reasonable agreement and little scatter. For the remaining elements, the scatter is tremendous and there are no reliable data with which to compare the results obtained by activation.

Marine organisms

The composition of marine organisms has been fully discussed by Vinogradov (1953), whose conclusions are summarized in Table 11.2. Most marine organisms contain large quantities of sodium, and they may need handling behind lead shielding after activation because of the γ-ray activity of sodium 24.

The results of Keynes and Lewis (1950, 1951) form a particularly elegant demonstration of the changes in electrolytes occurring when muscle is stimulated. They used single cephalopod axons weighing approximately 300 μg for determinations of sodium, potassium, chlorine, and phosphorus. Chlorine was determined by the (n, p) reaction to sulphur 35, and no correction was made for interference by the $S^{34}(n, \gamma) S^{35}$ reaction. Their results are summarized in Table 11.4.

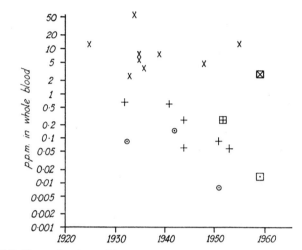

Fig. 11.7. Determinations of bromine ($\times$), arsenic ($+$), and molybdenum ($\odot$) in blood during the last forty years. Activation results are boxed.

TABLE 11.4

Elements in resting and stimulated cephalopod axons

(all figures are mg/g fresh weight)

Element			Na	K	P	Cl
Resting axon	.	.	0·92	13·0	0·78	2·6
Stimulated axon	.	.	3·00	9·7	0·90	3·2

It can be seen that stimulation of the axon results in a gain in sodium and a loss of potassium from the tissue, in agreement with tracer experiments.

Keynes and Lewis (1951) also first demonstrated the potentiality of the technique for trace elements by determining copper, manganese, and arsenic in material from the nerve of the crustacean *Carcinus maenas*. They showed that these elements gave very little activity compared with sodium, potassium, and phosphorus but that they could be determined after a chemical separation. The values quoted for these three elements (1·8, 0·4, and 0·2 p.p.m. wet weight respectively, or about 9, 2, and 1 p.p.m. dry weight) agree with the wide range reported by other methods (Vinogradov, 1953).

Smales and Salmon (1955) and Bowen (1956 a) have used chemical precipitation methods to determine the rare alkali and alkaline earth metals respectively in marine algae and other organisms. Rubidium was determined as 19-day rubidium 86, so there was no interference from 12-hour potassium 42, nor from the traces of caesium 134. Determinations of caesium were made using both the 3-hour and the 2·3-year isomer of this last nuclide, which gave equivalent results. Strontium and barium were determined using 2·8-hour strontium 87 and 1·3-hour barium 139 respectively, so a rapid chemical separation was necessary. Apart from caesium, which had not previously been found in algae, the results agreed with those obtained by other methods in order of magnitude. They are interesting in showing a pronounced discrimination by organisms for both caesium and barium with respect to potassium and calcium; in addition it appears that the brown algae (Phycophyceae) accumulate strontium, whereas mollusc shells discriminate against this element (see Table 11.5).

TABLE 11.5

Alkali and alkaline earth metals in sea water and marine organisms

Element	p.p.m. in sea water	p.p.m. in dry brown algae	p.p.m. in gastropod shells	Reference
K	390	38,000	..	Young and Langille (1958)
Rb	0·12	12	..	} Smales and Salmon (1955)
Cs	0·0005	0·10	..	
Ca	403	9200	375,000	
Sr	8·5	820	190	} Bowen (1956 a)
Ba	0·0062	22	..	

These figures may be compared with those for the halogens, where it has long been known that the rare element iodine is concentrated far more efficiently than either chlorine or bromine by brown algae and other marine organisms. It would be worth investigating comparable series of elements such as scandium, yttrium, and lanthanum or sulphur, selenium, and tellurium to see if the same effect holds good.

Smales, Mapper, and Wood (1957) give figures for cobalt in five brown and two red algae which agree with spectroscopic determinations. Using 5-year cobalt 60, they were able to estimate 2×10^{-8} g cobalt in seaweed ash. Fukai and Meinke (1959), also using ashed samples, have determined arsenic, gold, molybdenum, rhenium, vanadium, and tungsten in green and red algae, a mollusc, a crustacean, and a fish.

Their work provides the first data on rhenium and tungsten in biological material, and it is greatly to be hoped that similar and more extensive studies will be carried out with other neglected elements. Copper, mercury, and arsenic have been determined in four molluscs and a fish by Hamaguchi *et al.* (1960), and uranium in algae and fish bones by Das (1960).

Higher plants

A number of elements have been determined in seeds, where the great sensitivity of activation is useful. Seeds can be activated inside intact fruits, which prevents contamination, as described by Smales and Pate for arsenic in beans (1952). Bowen (1959 *a, b,* and *c*, 1960) has measured the elementary content of tomato seeds from plants grown in sand culture on known nutrients, and has shown that several trace elements are stored in seeds in amounts greatly in excess of those required for satisfactory germination. It is possible to cut down the excess by growing the plants under conditions of mineral deficiency, as shown in Table 11.6.

TABLE 11.6

Elements in tomato seeds determined by neutron activation

Element	$\mu g/g$ in normal seed	$\mu g/g$ in deficient seed	g seed needed per analysis
Ba	0·9	..	1·0
Br	1·3	..	0·05
Cl	70	25	0·05
Cu	7	1·8	0·01
Ga	0·014	0·003	0·5
I	0·4	..	0·5
K	7000	..	0·001
Mn	55	10	0·01
Mo	2·5	0·09	0·5
Na	190	..	0·002
P	7700	..	0·001
Sr	0·75	..	1·0
V	0·06	0·005	1·0
W	0·14	0·02	1·0
Zn	56	20	0·05

Bowen and Dymond (1955, 1956) determined strontium and barium in plants, soil extracts, and nutrient solutions in an attempt to find out whether growing plants discriminate between the alkaline earth metals. No wholly satisfactory method of extracting these metals from soils was found, but plant roots were shown to absorb strontium preferentially from nutrient solutions with Ca/Sr > 5. No discrimination between calcium and strontium was found in the shoots. Leddicotte *et al.* (1959) have reported analyses for cobalt, copper, iron, and molybdenum in sugar cane and cereals by activation, but give no details either of samples or methods employed.

Radioactivation of chromatograms

The increasing importance of chromatography in biochemical research has led several workers to employ radioactivation as a developmental technique after activation (Chapter 9). Although great care must be taken not to introduce impurities in either the eluant or the solid phase used for chromatography, the method can prove exceedingly useful. It was first introduced by Winteringham *et al.* (1952) to detect chlorine and bromine in metabolic products from insects treated with insecticides containing these halogens. Subsequently Schmeiser and Jerchel (1953 *a* and *b*) used fast neutrons from a cyclotron to activate chlorine, bromine, phosphorus, and sulphur on paper chromatograms. Born and Stärk (1959), who determined iodine by thermal neutron activation, discuss the impurities which give rise to background activity in the filter paper. Many commercial papers contain aluminium, calcium, chlorine, silicon, and sodium which interfere. Benson (1959) has reported excellent sensitivity for phosphatides and other phosphorus-containing compounds, which are not easily developed by spray reagents, and also for cobalt and vanadium. After a few days' decay one can detect $0.05 \ \mu g \ P/cm^2$ by autoradiography of a paper chromatogram (Strickland and Benson, 1960). A particularly interesting application is the proton activation of photosynthetic products labelled with oxygen 18, which activates to 1.9-hour fluorine 18. Unfortunately filter paper contains too much oxygen for direct proton activation, and the separated metabolic products have to be eluted onto tantalum foil for activation (Fogelström-Fineman *et al.*, 1957). Neutron or γ-ray activation of nitrogen-containing substances spotted on filter paper leads to the production of brown colours which might be useful for identification (Bowen *et al.*, 1960).

12

INORGANIC AND PURE CHEMICAL APPLICATIONS OF ACTIVATION ANALYSIS

THE inorganic applications of activation analysis present the most random picture of all. The range of materials analysed, combined with the different elements determined, makes the number of different analyses seem limitless. In the inorganic field the majority of applications are on individual materials, usually, but not always, as a check on purity. These analyses are more often made as a matter of expediency, rather than as part of any detailed survey. It is therefore difficult to give an overall picture of the results so far published, or of their significance. For example, Leddicotte *et al.* (1959) have listed some fifty-three elements which have been determined during their activation programme. The range of matrix materials is so wide that over 130 different analyses are represented. Unfortunately, only very sketchy details of these analyses are presented, and although the majority involved radiochemical separations, the methods of separation are not given. However, the tabulation is of interest in showing the types of analyses which have been successfully completed. These analyses only represent the scope of one group; although other workers may not have such extensive interests, the total number of combinations must be considerable.

One type of application which must be singled out for discussion is the activation of trace impurities in high-purity materials, particularly in the semiconductor industry. It is probably true to say that this industry would never have developed so rapidly had it not been for activation analysis. The impurity levels which are sufficient to render semiconductor materials useless are so low, in many instances, as to be orders of magnitude below the level of detection by conventional methods of analysis. The semiconductor material silicon, which gives rise to a short-lived and pure beta-emitting matrix activity, lends itself very well to non-destructive analysis by direct γ-ray spectrometry. Others, such as germanium, give rise to high levels of induced activity, necessitating the most rigorous and detailed radiochemical purification procedures.

High-purity materials are also of extreme importance in nuclear reactor construction, where the presence of trace impurities with high neutron capture cross-sections results in the excessive absorption of neutrons with a lowering of reactor efficiency, and the production of radioactivity in the structural materials which can make reactor maintenance extremely difficult if not impossible. In connexion with the latter problem, it can be truly said that neutron activation analysis has come into its own, for it is just those impurities which are the most easily determined in this way. In fact, many reactor engineers are not really interested in the true trace element content, but only in the amount of induced activity attributable to any one impurity. Such answers can be obtained without genuine analysis, in that no reference standard need be irradiated. Nevertheless, most other techniques of the method are involved, particularly gamma spectrometry and radio-chemistry. In this field, the types of material analysed vary from simple elements such as aluminium, with its very short-lived induced activity, to complex zirconium alloys and stainless steels.

In the preparation of high-purity materials, activation analysis is frequently associated with the technique of zone-refining. This method of analysis is often sufficiently sensitive for the determination of the very low impurity content in small sections of materials purified in this way, so that impurity gradients can be plotted and the optimum conditions for the purification readily determined (Gibbons, 1960 a).

The neutron activation technique is often used in inorganic analysis for determinations which do not require anything like its full sensitivity. In fact determinations have frequently been made at levels which, at first sight, are well within the sensitivity limits of more conventional methods of analysis. It is here that other advantages of the activation technique become more important, as the analysis may perhaps be accomplished more easily and more quickly, without interference from other components, or even non-destructively, or on very small samples.

Analysis of high-purity materials

Aluminium and its oxide have probably been analysed more often than any other material, since they are eminently suitable for the application of the activation technique. After a few minutes decay, all of the residual activity is caused by impurities, apart from some sodium 24 produced by the reaction $Al^{27}(n, \alpha) Na^{24}$. The impurities can be identified, in many cases, by direct γ-ray spectrometry, or determined by radiochemical separation methods.

Jervis and Mackintosh (1959) examined three grades of high purity aluminium, designated IS, super-pure, and zone-refined respectively. Cr, Cu, Dy, Fe, Ga, Hf, La, Se, Sm, and Zn were determined and the levels shown to decrease from the IS grade to the zone-refined grade. For Co and W, however, the level in the zone-refined grade was higher than that in the IS grade. The maximum limits of many other impurities were also calculated. In addition the impurity content of aluminium spectrographic standard samples, as analysed by activation analysis, were compared with the best estimates obtained by spectrographic analysis. Although, at first sight, there was some variation between the two sets of results, 'the general agreement was within the dispersion of the less precise spectrographic results'.

Gaittet and Albert (1958) made an extensive study of the impurity content of aluminium and developed a radiochemical separation scheme for Ag, As, Bi, Ca, Cd, Ce, Co, Cs, Cu, Fe, Ga, Hf, Ho, K, Mn, Mo, Na, Ni, Pd, Pr, Rb, Sb, Sc, Se, Sm, Sr, Ta, Te, U, W, Y, Zn, and Zr, all of which could be determined with a sensitivity of at least 0·1 p.p.m. in a 1 g sample. The isotopes were initially separated into about nine groups and full radiochemical procedures were then employed for the individual members of the different groups. A similar separation scheme was also used for the determination of the same impurities in iron.

The analysis of zirconium and its alloys is much more difficult because of the γ-ray-emitting zirconium activities produced. Jervis and Mackintosh (1959) showed that ion exchange techniques coupled with γ-ray spectrometry largely eliminated this difficulty and facilitated the determination of Cu, Cr, Fe, Hf, Mn, Sb, and W. The levels formed were again compared with those obtained by conventional methods, and the agreement was within the limits of precision except for Cr. Maximum limits were also calculated for Cd, Co, Hg, Ir, Os, Pt, Ta, and Zn. A rapid, non-destructive method was developed for the determination of Hf in zirconium and its alloys, which obviated some of the difficulties of the conventional approach (Mackintosh and Jervis, 1958). This procedure involved activation of Hf to 19-second Hf^{179m}, which was detected by means of a gamma spectrometer focused on the 0·22 MeV γ-ray and coupled to a high-speed logarithmic ratemeter/recorder. Analysis of the resultant decay curve enabled less than 70 p.p.m. Hf to be determined and it was estimated that the method was capable of determining hafnium contents as low as a few parts per million before interference from other γ-ray emitting impurities would become appreciable.

Smales (1956a) analysed sodium-potassium alloys by activation analysis in case spectrographic techniques were not sufficiently sensitive for some of the impurities which would be important when the alloys were used as reactor coolants. He found the following impurity contents (in p.p.m.): Hg < 0.5, Cr < 0.2, Rb 77, Cs 0.15, Ag < 0.02, Sb < 0.001, Sr < 0.5, Co 0.02. The advantages of the activation technique can be seen in this case over the emission spectrographic method, where although Rb was found, and said to be about 50 p.p.m., neither Cs nor Co could be detected. By radioactivation analysis, all three elements are determined readily, and γ-ray spectrometry showed that other elements are unlikely to be significant in terms of induced activity. Activation is therefore the logical approach for this investigation as impurities which are of most concern are the easiest to detect.

Analysis of semiconductor materials

The purity requirements of semiconductor materials are even more stringent than those for reactor materials, so that the highly sensitive activation technique becomes almost indispensable. Smales (1955) compared various methods for the determination of trace impurities in semiconductors. These methods included emission spectroscopy, mass spectroscopy, polarography, colorimetry, fluorimetry, and various radioactive techniques including activation analysis (Table 12.1). It will be seen that in general the activation method is superior. Some authors (e.g. Kant et al., 1956) use activation analysis exclusively in the analysis of semiconductor materials, even though the sensitivity for some elements may be worse than by conventional methods. They argue that a standard method of analysis is preferable to several of widely differing principles, particularly where separation schemes can be developed to enable several elements to be determined on one sample, thereby reducing the total amount of sample used and the cost of reactor irradiations.

For the determination of impurities in silicon, γ-ray spectrometry is most useful, provided that the impurity levels are high enough, because of its speed and non-destructive possibilities. Several authors have therefore used this method of analysis. Thus Jakovlev et al. (1959) determined As, Cu, Fe, Ga, K, Mn, Na, Sb, Sm, Ta, and Zn, and Morrison and Cosgrove (1955) determined As, Fe, K, Na, W, and Zn. The latter claimed an accuracy of better than ± 2 per cent. by the analysis of

TABLE 12.1

Comparison of methods of analysis of semiconductors (Smales, 1955)

Method	No. of elements per analysis	Sensitivity	Specificity	Accuracy	Freedom from contamination blanks, etc.	Possibility of avoiding surface contamination
Emission spectroscopy Direct . . .	Several	1 p.p.m.	Good	Doubtful	Good	Good
After chemical concentration	Several	0·01 p.p.m.	Good	Reasonable	Bad	Bad
Mass spectroscopy Vacuum spark. .	Several	0·01 p.p.m.	Good	Doubtful	Good	Good
Isotope dilution .	One	Very high	Good	Reasonable	Bad	Bad
Polarography . .	A few	0·01 p.p.m.	Reasonable	Good	Bad	Bad
Vacuum fusion . .	Oxygen, nitrogen, and hydrogen	1 p.p.m.	Reasonable	Reasonable	Good	Bad
Colorimetric Fluorimetric } . .	One	0·1 p.p.m.	Reasonable	Good	Bad	Bad
Radiotracers . .	One	High	Good	Doubtful	Good	Bad
Radioactivation .	A few in some cases	Very high	Good	Good	Good	Good

standard samples whereas the former claimed only ± 10–30 per cent., particularly where the technique was employed to control the quality of silicon in pilot plant production.

Smales (1956 b) has pointed out that if the impurity levels are so high that analysis is possible by γ-ray spectrometry, the material will, in general, be too impure for ultimate use in semiconductor work. When highly purified material has to be analysed, it is generally necessary to use radiochemical separations after irradiation, and it is then preferable to use simpler and more accurate methods of determining the activity.

James and Richards (1955 a and b) used the radiochemical separation technique for the separate determination of arsenic and phosphorus in silicon. On the other hand, Jakovlev et al. (1959) determined As, Cu, Eu, Ga, Mn, Ni, Sb, and Zn simultaneously in a single sample. The errors for a series of samples cut from one specimen of silicon were within 30–40 per cent.: this variation was attributed to the inhomogeneity of the specimen. Rather more ambitious schemes were put forward by Kant et al. (1956) and Cali et al. (1957) involving separations for Ag, As, Bi, Cd, Cu, Fe, Ga, In, P, Sb, Tl, and Zn. The activation method was compared with spectrographic analysis by preparing silica standards containing known amounts of added indium (Table 12.2). Where both methods could be used, they were equally precise, but the spectrographic method was more accurate. Below the limit of the spectrographic method, however, activation analysis still gave reasonable precision and accuracy. In our experience activation is generally more accurate than spectrography.

Germanium is also an important semiconductor material and, since the early work on arsenic by Smales and Pate (1952 a), other impurities have been determined by the activation technique. Since germanium itself forms γ-ray-emitting nuclides on activation, it is not possible to use non-destructive γ-ray spectrometry for the analysis of germanium and its compounds. Chemical separations are therefore necessary to remove germanium and arsenic activities before attempting to analyse the remaining activities on the spectrometer. Both Morrison and Cosgrove (1956) and Jakovlev et al. (1959) used a distillation method as the basis of this separation. The latter compared the determination of Ga, In, and Sb with results obtained using electrophysical methods. Earlier, Jakovlev (1956) had used a full radiochemical method for the determination of Cu, Eu, Mo, Sb, and Zn in germanium and germanium dioxide.

TABLE 12.2

Comparison of spectrographic and activation methods in the determination of indium in silicon

(Kant, Cali, and Thompson, 1956)

Sample no.	Theoretical (1) p.p.m.	Spectrographic p.p.m.	Activation p.p.m.
1	1640	1640 ± 160	1565 ± 157
2	164	164 ± 16	147 ± 15
3	16	Faint line	15 ± 2
4	1·6	Not detected	$3·9\pm0·4$ (2)

Notes

(1) The samples were prepared by doping silicon dioxide with weighed amounts of indium oxide.

(2) The high value by activation for sample 4 is attributed to a blank value of about 2 p.p.m. indium impurity in the silicon dioxide used.

Water analysis

Neutron activation analysis has been used fairly extensively for the determination of low levels of impurities in water, both sea water and drinking water, to study the uptake of these impurities by marine organisms and to broaden and extend knowledge of the types and quantities of elements being consumed by man.

Blanchard, Leddicotte, and Moeller (1959) have made a detailed study of the impurity content of drinking water, analysing for A, As, Ba, Br, Cl, Ca, I, K, Mn, Mg, Na, Rb, Sr, Th, and Zn. They used a chemical separation scheme to divide the elements into six main groups, the radioactivity of each group being analysed by gamma scintillation spectrometry. Where mutual interference occurred within a group further radiochemistry was necessary, particularly for Na^{24}, K^{42}, and Rb^{86}. Special stages were also necessary for Mg^{27}, I^{128}, and A^{41}.

These workers put forward neutron activation analysis as a valuable method for sanitary engineers and geochemists in their study of water, especially as the limit of detection is so much more favourable than by conventional methods. Several elements (A, As, Ba, Br, I, Mn, Th) were detected and analysed quantitatively in drinking water in which they had not previously been determined. A comparison was also made between activation analysis and conventional analysis for elements which could be determined by both methods. Good agreement was obtained in most cases.

Determination of elements in inorganic materials other than those of geochemical interest

ALUMINIUM

Aluminium is a difficult element for determination by activation analysis because of its short half-life (2·3 min). Nevertheless, Chauvin and Leveque (1956) have determined as little as 1 μg with a flux of 10^{11} n/cm²/sec. They claimed a precision of 1–5 per cent. using non-destructive γ-ray spectrometry. In order to obtain an activation product with a longer half-life, other workers have used other activation processes. Thus, Odeblad and Odeblad (1956) used alpha particle activation, by means of a polonium 210 source, to give phosphorus 30, while Turner (1956) used 14 MeV neutrons to produce sodium 24. This reaction had previously been used by Stephens and Lewis (1946) for studying the distribution of aluminium in silicon using autoradiographic detection of the induced sodium 24 activity.

ANTIMONY

Although Süe (1951) described a non-destructive method for the determination of antimony in lead, most other workers have used radiochemical separation methods. Hudgens and Cali (1952) and Kant, Cali, and Thompson (1956) used a separation based on distillation and solvent extraction for the determination of antimony in zirconium oxide and silicon. Smales (1956 b) used precipitation methods for antimony in sodium-potassium alloys and a similar procedure was used by Smales, Mapper et al. (1957) for antimony in silicon. Jakovlev (1956) also used a radiochemical method for the determination of antimony in germanium and its oxide. Lowe, Thompson, and Cali (1959) determined antimony in silicon carbide.

ARGON

The only worth-while published method in the inorganic chemical field seems to be that of Woodman (1954) for the determination of argon in carbon dioxide. As little as 0·1 p.p.m. of argon could be determined in a 10 ml sample, using air as a reference standard.

ARSENIC

The majority of analyses for arsenic have been made in biological materials, possibly because of the toxicological implications. Nevertheless extensive determinations have been made in the inorganic field, particularly on semiconductor materials. The radiochemical distillation method of Smales and Brown (1950) and Smales and Pate (1952 a) for the analysis of germanium dioxide has been used by many later workers with slight modification. Thus Smales, Mapper *et al.* (1957), James and Richards (1955 *a*), and Kant, Cali, and Thompson (1956) determining arsenic in silicon, and James and Richards (1956 *b*) determining arsenic in tungsten, all used distillation methods of purification. On the other hand, Morrison and Cosgrove (1955) used non-destructive γ-ray spectrometry for the determination of arsenic in silicon. Radiochemical distillation techniques have also been used for the analysis of high-purity sulphur (Salmon, 1952) and of platinum/alumina catalysts (Shipman and Milner, 1958).

BARIUM

The only published method in this field seems to be that of Bowen (1956 *a*) who found 6·2 μg/l in sea water by a radiochemical separation method. This was lower than values previously reported from conventional methods of analysis.

BERYLLIUM

Beryllium has only been determined by measurement of the prompt radiations emitted during the activation process. Thus, Gaudin and Pannell (1951) and others used γ-ray activation, measuring the prompt neutrons with a boron trifluoride counter. Similarly, Gold (1957) measured the prompt γ-ray produced on alpha particle activation, and Keomley (1956) used a similar technique but with deuteron activation. It could be argued that these techniques are not strictly activation analysis in the normally accepted sense, since the activated product is not itself determined.

BISMUTH

Bismuth has been determined in silicon (Kant, Cali, and Thompson, 1956) using a radiochemical purification method. The procedure was based on precipitation reactions.

BORON

Odeblad (1954) used alpha particle activation, and Süe (1956) used deuteron activation for the determination of boron, nitrogen 13 being produced in each case. More recently, Gill (1958) has used proton irradiation, together with radiochemical separation of the resulting carbon 11, to determine boron in silicon down to 10^{-9} g. The phosphorus 30 activity produced from the silicon matrix was used for flux monitoring.

BROMINE

Cosgrove, Bastian, and Morrison (1958) used a full radiochemical separation method for the determination of as little as 0·001 μg of bromine in the presence of other halogens in zinc sulphide. A less-refined technique was used by Daudel (1944) for the analysis of mixed alkali halides. Very little purification was used, reliance being placed on the longer half-life of the induced bromine activity compared with the other halogens. An unusual separation was used by Winteringham (1950). This involved exchange between the irradiated compound and a gas such as methyl bromide, which was then separated, decomposed and converted to silver bromide. The activation method has been used in polymer chemistry (Pfann, Salley, and Mark, 1944) to measure the number of bromine atoms per polymer chain in styrene polymerized with p-bromobenzoyl peroxide. The method gave good agreement with chemical analysis. Agreement was also obtained between mass spectrometry and activation analysis by Cameron, Herr *et al.* (1956) in the determination of bromine 79 in lead bromide.

CADMIUM

Cadmium was determined in silicon by Kant, Cali, and Thompson (1956) using a radiochemical separation procedure. Gibbons (1960 a) found that additional specific stages were necessary to overcome contamination due to radio-zinc when determining cadmium in super-pure zinc. The separation scheme gave a product which contained less than 1 per cent. of detectable impurities from 0·001 p.p.m. cadmium. Cadmium has also been determined in resins (Brooksbank, Leddicotte, and Mahlman, 1953).

CAESIUM

Smales and Salmon (1955) determined caesium in sea water using a radiochemical separation based on cobaltinitrite and bismuth iodide precipitations. A similar scheme was used by Smales (1956 a) for the determination of caesium in sodium-potassium alloys, and the method was extended by Cabell and Thomas (1955) to include cation exchange chromatography, so that caesium could be determined in the presence of large quantities of rubidium.

CALCIUM

Although calcium is not an easy element to determine by neutron activation, since only a weak beta emitter is produced, Atchison and Beamer (1952) obtained a sensitivity of 10^{-6} g for the determination of calcium in high-purity magnesium. Shvangiradze and Mozgovaya (1957) used activation analysis to check the uniformity of distribution of calcium in silicon standards for spectrographic analysis.

CARBON

Riezler (1949) first determined carbon in iron by deuteron irradiation. It was shown that 4 MeV deuterons gave the optimum sensitivity, and that the 10-minute nitrogen 13 could be distinguished easily from the 18-hour cobalt 55 (produced from iron) by decay measurements. This method was further developed by Curie (1952) and Süe (1956). Point (1958) preferred activation by 600 keV protons, nitrogen 13 again resulting. Simple Geiger counting gave a detection limit of 20 p.p.m., while coincidence scintillation counting enabled this to be reduced to 4 p.p.m.

CHLORINE

Relatively high levels of chlorine were determined by Lbov and Naumova (1959) in graphite and polymethacrylates using 14 MeV neutrons, by Leveque and Goenvec (1955) in chlorotrifluorethylene by slow neutron irradiation, and by Daudel (1944) in mixed alkali halides. Little or no separation was made. Lower levels of chlorine were determined in titanium, its alloys and compounds by Brooksbank, Leddicotte, and Reynolds (1956). A radiochemical separation method was used by Bancie-Grillot and Grillot (1953) for the detection of 1 p.p.m. of chlorine in zinc sulphide. The procedure was claimed to be five times as precise as the usual nephelometric method. Cosgrove, Bastian, and Morrison (1958) used a more detailed purification procedure, involving distillation of hydrochloric acid, for this analysis and measured 1 p.p.m. of chlorine in the presence of bromine and iodine to within 3·5 per cent. A similar distillation procedure, coupled with decay curve analysis, was used by Gibbons (unpublished) for the determination of a range of concentrations of chlorine in nickel.

CHROMIUM

Jervis and Mackintosh (1959) used direct activation and γ-ray spectrometry to determine chromium in high-purity aluminium, a similar procedure being used by Morrison and Cosgrove (1955) to determine chromium in aluminium alloys and silicon. A radiochemical separation method, giving a sensitivity of 10^{-6} g, was used by Atchison and Beamer (1952) for the analysis of magnesium metal. Smales (1956 a) also used a radiochemical method, involving extraction of the blue chromium-peroxy complex, for the determination of chromium in sodium-potassium alloys.

COBALT

The most popular matrix for the determination of cobalt has been steel, presumably because of its extensive use in reactor construction. A radiochemical separation method was used by Cornand and Gillis (1955) for cobalt at the 0·1–1 per cent. level. A similar method was used by Albert, Caron, and Chaudron (1953) for the analysis of 1–10 p.p.m. cobalt in iron. Monnier, Haerdi, and Vogel (1960) pointed out that such methods did not distinguish between cobalt 60 and cobalt 58 produced from nickel. γ-ray spectrometry was therefore used, but a radiochemical separation was still necessary because iron 59 has almost the same γ-ray energies as cobalt 60. This interference by iron was overcome by Salmon (1957 b) by means of coincidence spectrometry, while Westermark and Fineman (1959) used a method involving a short irradiation time and counting of cobalt 60m. A chemical separation was necessary for manganese contents more than forty times the cobalt content. Smales (1956 a) used the radiochemical purification method to determine traces of cobalt in sodium-potassium alloys, and Grand, Baus et al. (1959) determined the solubility of cobalt in molten sodium by a similar method. Cobalt has also been determined in silicon (James and Richards, 1957) and in nickel alloys (Debiesse, Challansonnet, and Neyret, 1951), but no correction was made for cobalt 58 produced by fast neutron activation of nickel. However, the concentrations of cobalt measured were relatively high.

COPPER

Albert, Caron, and Chaudron (1952) have used radiochemical separation methods for the determination of 1–250 p.p.m. copper in high-purity aluminium. Brooksbank, Leddicotte, and Dean (1958) analysed aluminium alloys by a similar method and obtained an accuracy of 5–7 per cent. The results had a positive bias, which was attributed to contamination by zinc 69m. Non-destructive analysis by γ-ray spectrometry was used by Jervis and Mackintosh (1959) for copper in aluminium, and by Morrison and Cosgrove (1955) who also used this technique for traces of copper in silicon. γ-ray spectrometry was used by Smales, Mapper et al. (1957) for some silicon samples, but a radiochemical separation was necessary for others. The latter technique was also used by Kant, Cali, and Thompson (1956) for traces of copper in silicon. Radiochemical methods were also necessary for the analysis of germanium and its oxide owing to the interfering activity of the matrix. Both Jakovlev (1956) and Alimarin, Jakovlev, and Zhabin (1955) determined 10^{-8} g copper by this method, while Szekely (1954) determined 10^{-10} g with an uncertainty of 10^{-10} g. Radiochemical methods have been used to determine copper in iron (Albert, Caron, and Chaudron, 1953), in beryllium (Brooksbank, Handley et al., 1957), in magnesium (Atchison and Beamer, 1952), in silicon carbide (Lowe, Thompson, and Cali, 1959), in titanium (Brooksbank, Leddicotte, and Reynolds, 1956), and in phosphorus (Grillot, 1952). Finally, activation by particles other than neutrons has also been used. Seaborg and Livingood (1938) determined copper in nickel by deuteron activation, and King and Henderson (1939) determined copper in silver by alpha particle bombardment.

DEUTERIUM

Deuterium has been determined by measurement of the prompt neutrons emitted when water samples containing deuterium are exposed to γ-rays from sodium 24 (Haigh, 1953).

FLUORINE

Fluorine 20, produced by neutron activation, has a half-life of only 12 seconds, but has been determined successfully by Atchison and Beamer (1956) using a van de Graaff neutron generator and an automatic timing device for the irradiations and subsequent counting. Leveque (1956) used a 'rabbit' system and an automatic counter to achieve the same end. Odeblad (1954) used alpha particle activation to obtain a radionuclide with a longer half-life. Plaksin, Smirnov, and Starchik (1959) also used alpha particle activation, but measured the prompt neutrons instead.

GALLIUM

Jervis and Mackintosh (1959) determined gallium in aluminium by direct γ-ray spectrometry, while Brooksbank, Leddicotte, and Mahlman (1953) used a radiochemical method. Radiochemistry was found to be necessary by Kant, Cali, and Thompson (1956) in the determination of gallium in silicon, the separation being based on solvent extraction. Seaborg and Livingood (1938) used deuteron activation of iron to establish the presence of 6 p.p.m. of gallium.

GOLD

Although gold has been determined extensively in geochemical and biological materials, few analyses have been reported in the inorganic field. A radiochemical separation method was used by Hummel (1957) to determine gold in sea water and by James and Richards (1957) to measure the segregation coefficient of gold in silicon. Freedman (1952) used non-destructive beta-activity decay-curve analysis to establish the presence of 10–20 p.p.m. of gold in certain diamonds.

HAFNIUM

Aten (1943) first determined hafnium in zirconium by neutron irradiation, counting the resulting short-lived hafnium 179. Getoff (1959) showed the method to be applicable at the p.p.m. level. Leveque (1956) used γ-ray spectrometry to make the method more selective for hafnium and found that the sensitivity depended on the sodium content. Nakai, Yajima et al. (1959) studied the experimental conditions for this analysis and found the coefficient of variation to be less than 2 per cent. in the 5–20 μg range. Combined γ-ray spectrometry and decay-curve analysis was used by Mackintosh and Jervis (1958) who also developed a radiochemical separation method involving the longer-lived hafnium isotopes for use when counting equipment is not available at the reactor site. Finally, Feldman (1949) considered the use of activation analysis as a check on spectrochemical methods of determining hafnium/zirconium ratios.

HELIUM

Coon (1949) compared the helium 3 content of well helium and atmospheric helium by neutron irradiation and determination of the resulting tritium in a proportional counter.

INDIUM

Hoste and van den Berghe (1956) determined micro amounts of indium in zinc and gallium by activation with a radium-beryllium neutron source, using a simple radiochemical separation scheme. More rigorous purification of the indium activity was used by Kant, Cali, and Thompson (1956) for the determination of traces of indium in silicon. Both methods involved solvent extraction.

IODINE

Iodine was determined in mixed alkali halides by Daudel (1944) using neutron irradiation and carbon tetrachloride extraction of the iodine. A similar, but improved, technique was used by Cosgrove, Bastian, and Morrison (1958) to determine traces of iodine in zinc sulphide. It was possible to determine 1 μg iodine with an accuracy of ± 3.5 per cent.

IRIDIUM

Combined radiochemistry and γ-ray spectrometry were used by both Miller (1959) and Jowanovitz, McCarley, and Martin (1958) for the determination of iridium. The latter workers determined iridium in platinum and used the activity induced in the platinum as a measure of the neutron flux. A similar method was used by Airoldi and Germagnoli (1957) who also measured the iridium activity after the complete decay of the platinum activity. An independently measured value of the neutron flux was then used in the calculation of the iridium content. More recently, Jowanovitz, McNatt et al. (1960) determined iridium down to 0·04 p.p.m. in platinum with no evidence of interference due to the (n, p) reaction. A purification based on the precipitation of iridium (IV) hydroxide was used.

IRON

Although the sensitivity of the activation method for iron is no better than the o-phenanthroline method at neutron fluxes less than $10^{12} n/cm^2/$ sec, iron has been determined in a variety of materials since the early work of Seaborg and Livingood (1938) who used deuteron activation to demonstrate the presence of iron in cobalt. Radiochemical separation methods have been used by Lowe, Thompson, and Cali (1959) for the determination of iron in silicon carbide and by James and Richards (1957) and Kant, Cali, and Thompson (1956) for the determination of iron in silicon; while Shvangiradze and Mozgovaya (1957) used activation analysis to check the standards used in the spectrographic determination of iron in highly pure silicon. Combined radiochemistry and γ-ray spectrometry was used by Miller (1959), while Morrison and Cosgrove (1955) used non-destructive γ-ray spectrometry for iron in silicon. This non-destructive technique was also used by Jervis and Mackintosh (1959) for iron in aluminium. Brooksbank, Leddicotte, and Dean (1958) compared the determination of iron in aluminium base alloys with average certificated values. Iron has also been determined in magnesium (Atchison and Beamer, 1952).

LITHIUM

Methods for the determination of lithium are based on the reaction $Li^6 (n, t) He^4$. Both Brooksbank, Handley et al. (1957) and Kaplan and Wilzbach (1954) used this reaction and measured the activity of the tritium produced. The latter workers state that the only significant interference is from lithium impurity in the irradiation container. On the other hand, Keinberger, Greene, and Voss (1957) determined the lithium by measuring the helium produced in a fission counter. Coleman (1960) allowed the tritium to react further with oxygen (the sample was irradiated in solution in water) and the resulting fluorine

18 was measured in a positron counter to give an error of only 1–2 per cent.

MAGNESIUM

Odeblad (1954) used alpha particle activation for the determination of magnesium in pure chemical compounds by conversion to aluminium 28.

MANGANESE

Activation of ferromanganese alloys with a low-level neutron source and direct Geiger counting of the induced activity enabled Kusaka (1957) to determine 3–8 per cent. of manganese to within 5 per cent. Fisher and Beydon (1953) used a simple separation of the manganese activity with potassium bromate to overcome the interference of silicon 31 and scandium 49. A rigorous radiochemical purification was used by Albert, Caron, and Chaudron (1953) for the determination of 1–10 p.p.m. manganese in highly purified iron, and by Lowe, Thompson, and Cali (1959) for manganese in silicon carbide. Jervis and Mackintosh (1959) were able to determine manganese in high-purity aluminium by direct γ-ray spectrometry, a similar technique being used by Brooksbank, Handley et al. (1957). Brooksbank, Leddicotte, and Dean (1958) studied the determination of manganese in aluminium alloys, and Brooksbank, Leddicotte, and Reynolds (1956) determined manganese in titanium, and in its alloys and compounds.

MERCURY

A radiochemical separation method, based on the sublimation of mercurous chloride, was used by Smales (1956 a) for the determination of mercury in sodium-potassium alloys. Westermark and Sjöstrand (1960) used a non-destructive γ-ray spectrometric method for the determination of mercury in aluminium and its corrosion products, in addition to a wide range of biological and organic materials. They discussed the errors associated with this technique and pointed out that mercury can be lost by volatilization at reactor temperatures. They recommended that both samples and standards should be irradiated in sealed silica ampoules, which are then allowed to decay for 2 days before measurements are made.

MOLYBDENUM

Direct γ-ray spectrometry was used by Jervis and Mackintosh (1959) for the determination of molybdenum in high-purity aluminium. Interference from germanium activity necessitated the use of rigorous purification, however, when determining molybdenum in germanium and its oxide (Alimarin, Jakovlev, and Zhabin, 1955; Jakovlev, 1956). A separation method was also used by Lowe, Thompson, and Cali (1959) for the analysis of silicon carbide, the sample being decomposed first with chlorine and oxygen at 1250° C.

NICKEL

Albert, Caron, and Chaudron (1953) determined traces of nickel in high-purity iron using a full radiochemical method. Brooksbank, Leddicotte, and Dean (1958) compared activation analysis results for nickel in standard aluminium base alloys with the average certificated values. The results had a positive bias which was attributed to contamination of the nickel fraction with silicon 31 activity. Lowe, Thompson, and Cali (1959) also used a radiochemical method to determine nickel in silicon carbide. Nickel has been determined in zirconium metal by Leddicotte (1956) and in titanium by Brooksbank, Leddicotte, and Reynolds (1956). Miller (1959) has discussed the determination of nickel, describing a chemical separation and giving the γ-ray spectrum.

NIOBIUM

Grandjean, Lerch, and Monnier (1960) determined niobium by activation and γ-ray spectrometry. Recently, Brownlee (1960) has used a radiochemical separation method with a moderate amount of success, despite the short half-life (6·6 min) of niobium 94m.

NITROGEN

Süe (1955b, 1956) used deuteron activation to determine about 1 p.p.m. of nitrogen to ± 20 per cent. in metals, 2·1 min oxygen 15 being produced. Broda and Rohringer (1953) used neutron activation followed by chemical separation of carbon 14 to determine traces of nitrogen.

OSMIUM

The determination of osmium by neutron activation has been discussed by Miller (1959).

OXYGEN

Osmond and Smales (1954) determined oxygen in beryllium by mixing with lithium fluoride and irradiating with neutrons. Fluorine 18, produced by $Li^7 (n, \alpha) H^3$; $O^{16} (H^3, n) F^{18}$, was chemically separated and counted. Other activation reactions have been used, without chemical separation. Coleman and Perkin (1959) used fast neutrons to give nitrogen 16, Fineman, Hansen *et al.* (1957) used protons to give oxygen 15, Süe (1956) used deuterons to give fluorine 17, while Leveque (1956) used γ-rays to give oxygen 15.

PALLADIUM

Palladium has been determined extensively in geochemical samples, but no procedures appear to have been published for the inorganic chemical field.

PHOSPHORUS

Since the early work of Seaborg and Livingood (1938), who used deuteron activation to demonstrate the presence of phosphorus in various substances, phosphorus has been determined in a variety of matrices by neutron activation analysis. These have all involved radiochemical purification since phosphorus 32 emits only beta particles. The analyses include phosphorus in aluminium (Foster and Gaitanis, 1955; Plumb, 1956), phosphorus in magnesium (Atchison and Beamer, 1952), and phosphorus in silicon (Kant, Cali, and Thompson, 1956; James and Richards, 1955 *b*). James and Richards (1956 *b*) have also determined phosphorus in iodine.

PLATINUM

Miller (1959) has discussed the determination of platinum.

PLUTONIUM

McKay (1957) discussed the determination of plutonium 239 by neutron irradiation, and measurement of fission products, rather than by direct alpha counting.

POTASSIUM

The determination of traces of potassium in tungsten have been discussed by Schonken (1959). Atchison and Beamer (1952) have used a radiochemical separation method for potassium in magnesium, and Brooksbank, Handley *et al.* (1957) have described a separation method involving chloroplatinate precipitations. The determination of potassium in silicon by direct γ-ray spectrometry has been described by Morrison and Cosgrove (1955).

RARE EARTHS

Rare earths, in general, have very high neutron activation cross-sections and are therefore easily detected even with low neutron fluxes.

Low-flux neutron sources have been used, mainly for the determination of individual rare earths in small samples of mixtures of rare earths. Activation analysis was founded when Hevesy and Levi (1936) determined dysprosium in yttrium, and europium in gadolinium oxide (1938). Goldschmidt and Djourkovitch (1939) determined dysprosium in rare-earth mixtures and Meitner (1940) discussed the analytical possibilities of these techniques. The contamination of certain rare earths by other rare earths was examined by Kohn and Tomkins (1949) who measured samarium in cerium, dysprosium in ytterbium, neodymium and cerium in praseodymium, and cerium in lanthanum. Similarly, Phillips and Cornish (1953) determined dysprosium in holmium oxide, while Born, Vaiss, and Kobaladze (1956) determined gadolinium and dysprosium in yttrium, samarium in cerium and gadolinium, and europium in samarium. Süe (1951) used absorption-curve methods in the determination of cerium and yttrium in mixtures of the two. Activation analysis of the rare earths with a low-flux neutron source was compared with photometric methods by Meinke and Anderson (1954). Neutron-activation techniques have been described by Nelson (1956) and by Leveque (1956) for the determination of europium, dysprosium, and samarium in mixtures. Albert, Caron, and Chaudron (1951) estimated the total rare-earth content of aluminium using a simple separation scheme. A more detailed separation was used by Alimarin, Jakovlev, and Zhabin (1955) to determine rare earths in germanium. Only europium was actually measured; the other rare earths were found by calculation. This procedure was extended by Jakovlev (1956) to the analysis of graphite, beryllium, bismuth, and lead. Both europium and samarium were measured prior to calculating the remainder. Cornish (1953) described a full radiochemical ion-exchange separation method for the determination of all the rare earths except promethium. Microgram quantities of carriers were used and the chemical yields were determined by reactivation.

RHENIUM
Rhenium has been determined only in geochemical samples.

RHODIUM
Meinke and Anderson (1953) have analysed mixtures containing rhodium by means of a low-flux neutron source. Gauthier (1955) determined 5–10 per cent. rhodium in platinum-rhodium alloys with a precision of 5 per cent. The determination of rhodium has also been discussed by Miller (1959).

RUBIDIUM

The rubidium content of sea water was measured by Smales and Salmon (1955) using a separation based on cobaltinitrite precipitations. The same procedure was used by Smales (1956 a) for the determination of rubidium in sodium-potassium alloys and the scope of the method was extended by Cabell and Thomas (1955) by the introduction of a step involving the separation of the alkali metals by cation-exchange chromatography. The new procedure was also applied to the determination of rubidium in potassium chloride and hydroxide.

RUTHENIUM

The determination of ruthenium has been discussed by Miller (1959).

SCANDIUM

Iredale (1957) detected the presence of scandium in aluminium by radioactivation and γ-ray spectrometry.

SELENIUM

Putman and Taylor (1958) determined selenium in glass using a double crystal γ-ray spectrometer. One crystal counted the sample, the other crystal counted a similar glass sample which was selenium-free. Automatic subtraction of the two outputs enabled the selenium spectrum to be recorded free from interference. Direct γ-ray spectrometry, of the normal type, was used by Jervis and Mackintosh (1959) to determine selenium in aluminium, and by Erion, Mott, and Shedlovsky (1960) to determine selenium in sulphur. The latter application was only satisfactory if a neutron flux with a high thermal/fast neutron ratio was available, otherwise interference by the $S^{32}(n, p)P^{32}$ reaction necessitated a radiochemical separation.

SILICON

Neutron activation analysis has been used by Short and Williams (1958) to determine silicon in high-purity iron, and by Brooksbank, Leddicotte, and Reynolds (1956) to determine silicon in titanium. Riezler (1949), on the other hand, used deuteron activation, while Turner (1956) and Lbov and Naumova (1959) used 14 MeV neutrons.

SILVER

Kusaka (1959) and Meinke and Anderson (1953) used low-flux neutron sources to determine silver in mixtures, without chemical separation. Okada (1960) used direct γ-ray spectrometry to determine microgramme quantities of silver and obtained a coefficient of variation of only 2·8 per cent. at this level. Chemical separation schemes have been used by Bancie-Grillot (1956) to determine silver in cadmium sulphide, by Kant, Cali, and Thompson (1956) for silver in silicon, and by Smales (1956 a) for silver in sodium-potassium alloys. A rigorous separation scheme enabled Morris and Killick (1959 b) to determine 0·22 p.p.m. silver in platinum sponge. A novel application of the activation technique was developed by Berlman (1953) for the determination of silver grain density in exposed photographic film.

SODIUM

A precision of 1–5 per cent. was obtained by Chauvin and Leveque (1956) for the determination of 1 μg sodium by direct γ-ray spectrometry. This technique was used by Morrison and Cosgrove (1955) to determine sodium in silicon, and by Smales and Salmon (1955) to determine sodium in sea water. The determination of sodium in aluminium has been reviewed by Plumb (1956) and studied in detail by Albert, Caron, and Chaudron (1952). Salmon (1954) has studied the fast neutron reaction on aluminium and shown this to give the equivalent of 81 p.p.m. sodium in the centre of the Harwell reactor BEPO. Aluminium alloys have been analysed by Plumb and Silverman (1954) with a precision of 1 per cent., a limiting accuracy of 0·0001 per cent., and an average standard deviation of 0·0024 per cent. over the range 0·01–0·04 per cent. sodium. Brooksbank, Handley et al. (1957) used a chemical separation method and discussed the interference of uranium if the sodium was precipitated as zinc uranyl acetate. Sodium has also been determined in magnesium (Atchison and Beamer, 1952), in lead (Fisher, 1956), in lithium (Smales and Loveridge, 1955), and in tungsten (Schonken, 1959). Finally, deuterons have also been used for the determination of as little as 0·001 per cent. of sodium in aluminium (Sagane, Eguchi, and Shigeta, 1942) with an error of 0·001 per cent. (Riezler, 1949).

STRONTIUM

Radiochemical separation methods have been used by Atchison and Beamer (1952) for strontium in magnesium and by Smales (1956 a) for strontium in sodium-potassium alloys. Hummel and Smales (1956) compared two radiochemical methods (via strontium 87 and strontium 89) with the isotope dilution method for strontium in sea water. Bowen (1956 a) also measured strontium in sea water using a different counting technique and obtained reasonable agreement.

SULPHUR

Early work by Seaborg and Livingood (1938) using deuteron activation was supported by Süe (1956). Atchison and Beamer (1952) used slow neutron activation to sulphur 35 for the determination of sulphur in magnesium, a chemical separation being necessary. Fast neutron activation to phosphorus 32 has been used by Leddicotte, Mullins et al. (1959) for sulphur in nickel, lithium, and fluoride salts, and by Lbov and Naumova (1959) for sulphur in graphite and polymethacrylates. The latter drew attention to the interference of the $P^{31} (n, \gamma) P^{32}$ reaction, which was overcome by Gibbons and Simpson (1960 a) by means of a double irradiation technique.

TANTALUM

Non-destructive analysis has been used for the determination of tantalum in alloys and niobium/tantalum oxides by gross counting and also by γ-ray spectrometry. Thus, Kohn (1953) determined tantalum in ferroniobium to 5 per cent., while Beydon and Fisher (1953) determined tantalum in niobium pentoxide to 10 per cent. by direct counting. γ-ray spectrometry was used by Grandjean, Lerch, and Monnier (1960), and by Milner and Smales (1954) for the analysis of the mixed oxides. Gibbons and Simpson (1960 b) also used γ-ray spectrometry for tantalum in ferroniobium and drew particular attention to errors arising from self-shielding during irradiation. Barker (1958) has determined the tantalum content of glass, and Grand, Baus et al. (1959) have used a radiochemical separation method to determine the solubility of tantalum in sodium.

THALLIUM

Radiochemical separation methods have been used by Kant, Cali, and Thompson (1956) for the determination of thallium in silicon, and by Delbecq, Glendenin, and Yuster (1953) for thallium in thin crystals of potassium iodide. Both methods involved solvent extraction.

THORIUM

Chauvin and Leveque (1956) used direct γ-ray spectrometry, and Peirson (1956) used a two-crystal Compton Subtraction spectrometer for the determination of thorium. Leddicotte and Mahlman (1956) used a combined radiochemical and γ-ray spectrometer method based on protoactinium 233, while Jenkins (1955) used a full radiochemical method for the purification of thorium 233.

TIN

A neutron activation method was developed by Williams (1959) for the determination of tin down to 1 p.p.m. in alloy steels and 0·5 p.p.m. in iron.

TITANIUM

Brooksbank, Leddicotte, and Dean (1958) have studied the precision of activation analysis for the determination of titanium in aluminium base alloys.

TUNGSTEN

Neutron activation methods of analysis have been developed by Brooksbank, Leddicotte, and Reynolds (1956) for the determination of trace amounts of tungsten in titanium, its alloys and compounds. Leliaert, Hoste, and Eeckhaut (1959) used decay curve analysis for the determination of tungsten in steel, resorting to a radiochemical separation when interfering elements were present. A radiochemical method was also used by James and Richards (1957) to determine tungsten in silicon, but Morrison and Cosgrove (1955) succeeded in analysing silicon by direct γ-ray spectrometry. This technique was used by Jervis and Mackintosh (1959) for the determination of tungsten in high-purity aluminium.

URANIUM

Methods for the determination of uranium are based on fission of uranium 235 or activation of uranium 238. These may be used for the determination of the isotope itself or, by reference to a standard of known isotopic composition, for the determination of the element. Bretscher and Martin (1943) determined uranium 235 via the fission counting rate on neutron irradiation. Cameron (1950) counted the gross beta activity of the fission products, while May and Leveque (1958) counted the gross gamma activity of fission products from uranium 235 in uranium oxide. Seyfang and Smales (1953) used a method based on the separation of barium 140 and this was later improved by Seyfang (1955) to give a precision of 0·44 per cent. Hudgens and Meyer (1956) gave the weight of sample needed as from a few mg for materials rich in uranium 235 up to 2 g for uranium materials with the normal isotopic ratio. γ-ray spectrometry, after activation with a Ra/Be neutron source, was used by Nelson and Aaron (1957) to determine uranium 235 in uranium. Uranium 238 was determined by Mahlman and Leddicotte (1955) using the separation of neptunium 239. This isotope was also used by Smales, Mapper, and Seyfang (1960) to determine uranium in beryllium, but direct γ-ray spectrometry was possible. Uranium 238 can also be determined via the short-lived uranium 239. Combinations of the two methods of analysis have been used by Leddicotte and Brooksbank (1957) for the determination of U^{235}/U^{238} ratios in various materials.

VANADIUM

Smales and Mapper (1957) used non-destructive decay curve analysis to determine vanadium in graphite. A non-destructive method was also used by Leliaert, Hoste, and Eeckhaut (1958 b) for vanadium in steel. The manganese activity from the steel was used to check on any flux irregularities. Brooksbank, Leddicotte, and Reynolds (1956) developed methods for the determination of vanadium in titanium and its alloys and compounds. Recently, Brownlee (1960) has used rapid radiochemical separation methods to determine vanadium in several types of samples.

YTTRIUM (cf. Rare Earths)

Süe (1951) determined yttrium in the presence of cerium by activation and resolution of the beta activities by absorption curve methods. Lindner and Peter (1946) also discussed the quantitative determination of yttrium by neutron activation.

ZINC

Direct γ-ray spectrometry was used by Jervis and Mackintosh (1959) to determine zinc in aluminium and by Morrison and Cosgrove (1955) to determine zinc in silicon. Kant, Cali, and Thompson (1956) also determined zinc in silicon but preferred a radiochemical separation method. The latter technique was also necessary for the determination of zinc in germanium (Jakovlev, 1956; Alimarin, Jakovlev, and Zhabin, 1955), and for zinc in silicon carbide (Lowe, Thompson, and Cali, 1959). Brooksbank, Leddicotte, and Dean (1958) have examined the precision of zinc determinations in aluminium alloys.

ZIRCONIUM

Aten (1943) used non-destructive fast neutron activation analysis to determine zirconium in hafnium. Hudgens and Dabagian (1952) used a radiochemical purification method, but separated the daughter product niobium 95 to avoid having to separate zirconium from hafnium. They obtained an accuracy of about 1 per cent.

13

RADIOCHEMICAL SEPARATIONS

Notes

THE nuclear reaction recommended, half-life or lives of daughter nuclides, and the cross-section and percentage natural abundance of parent are given first. From these the expected activity per gramme can be calculated.

The irradiation time is generally omitted, since in most cases it is best to activate for one half-life, except when this is too long to be practicable.

Only unusual apparatus is listed. It is assumed that the laboratory will be equipped with a centrifuge, hot plates, distillation and filtration apparatus, separating funnels, etc.

Reagent concentrations are quoted in percentages w/v for uniformity. Note that the commoner liquid reagents are supplied in the following strengths: H_2SO_4, 98%; HNO_3, 100% (fuming) and 70%; HCl, 36%; HBr, 48%; HF, 40%; $HClO_4$, 72%; NH_3, 60%.

Standards should be selected as described in Chapter 7. They should be irradiated in dilute solution where possible, and hence only soluble chemicals are suitable. Specpure reagents are preferable, but not essential. The amount required should be calculated to give a count rate of at least 1000 counts/minute (see Table 2.1).

Separations are selected from the literature and may not be suitable for all types of samples. They are divided into numbered steps for convenience. The primary step almost always involves getting the sample into solution, and the commonest methods of doing this are:

(a) Metals: dissolve in hot HCl, HNO_3, or a mixture of these acids.

(b) Biological material: dissolve in hot 1:1 $HNO_3 + HClO_4$.

(c) Minerals: fuse with solid Na_2O_2 in a nickel crucible at 500° C, and extract the residue with water or dilute acid.

Counting techniques are suggestions only, and may be modified to suit the equipment available.

Sensitivities are not generally given as they depend so much on the available neutron flux and counting equipment. They may be estimated from Table 2.1.

Interferences from other nuclear reactions, both established and putative, are mostly included, as are some common radiochemical contaminants.

List of abbreviations

°C	degrees Celsius	p	proton
cm	centimetres	pH	$-\log_{10}$ hydrogen ion concen-
c.p.m.	counts per minute		tration
d	deuteron	p.p.m.	parts per million by weight
g	gramme(s)	ppt	precipitate
keV	thousand electron volts	spt	supernatant liquid
mC	millicuries	t	triton
mg	milligrammes	$t_{\frac{1}{2}}$	half-life
min	minutes	w/v	weight per unit volume
ml	millilitres	α	alpha particle
mm	millimetres	γ	gamma ray
mμ	10^{-7} cm	μ	10^{-4} cm
M	molar	μamp	microampere
MeV	million electron volts	μC	microcurie
n	neutron		

Deuterium. Using the reaction $H^2(\gamma, n) H^1$.

Cross-section. 0·0016 barns.   *Natural abundance.* 0·015%.

Apparatus. 1 curie Na^{24} surrounded by annular 10–50 ml containers. Lead and paraffin wax shielding (cf. Fig. 4.3). Vacuum line.

Reagents. O_2 cylinder.

Standards. D_2O standards, made by serial dilution of 100% D_2O with H_2O, in 10–50 ml aliquots.

Preliminary separation. The sample is converted to water, if necessary by burning in dry oxygen, and the water distilled off.

Counting technique. Count prompt neutrons with an annular ionization chamber lined with B^{10} or a ring of $B^{10}F_3$ counters. Counting time is generally less than 10 min.

Sensitivity. 0·02% D_2O by volume in 50 ml sample, or 2 mg D.

Interferences. Li, B, Cd, and lanthanons could interfere by neutron absorption and Be by neutron production by $Be^9(\gamma, n) 2He^4$.

References. Haigh (1953), Odeblad (1956 b).

Helium. Using the reaction $He^3(n, p) H^3$; $t_{\frac{1}{2}}$ 12 years.

Cross-section. 5400 barns.   *Natural abundance.* 0·00013%.

Irradiation time. 10 days.

Apparatus. Vacuum line with Toepler pump.

Reagents. Pd thimble; W filament; H_2 cylinder.

Standard. He containing 10^{-6} g He^3.

Radiochemical separation

(1) Activate 3·5 ml gas at 70 cm pressure. After activation pump gas into vacuum line with 3 ml H_2 carrier.

(2) Pass through Pd thimble to remove H_2.

(3) Pass over W filament at 1000° C to break down water or hydrocarbons and recycle gas.

Counting technique. Count 18 keV betas from Pd thimble with 4π ionization chamber.

Interferences. Li interferes if solid samples are used, by $Li^6(n, \alpha) H^3$.

Reference. Fireman and Schwarzer (1957).

Lithium. Using the reaction $Li^6(n, \alpha) H^3$; $t_{\frac{1}{2}}$ 12 years.

Cross-section. 950 barns.   *Natural abundance.* 7·4%.

Irradiation time. 12 days.

Apparatus. Vacuum line for distillation of water.

Reagents. Ca powder; liquid N_2.

Standard. 10^{-3} g Li as Li_2CO_3 of known isotopic composition.

Radiochemical separation. Break irradiated silica ampoules in vacuum line, and pass gases not condensed by a liquid N_2 trap into an ion chamber. Add Ca to irradiated solution to liberate H_2 for transfer to counter.

Counting technique. Count 18 keV betas with 4π ionization chamber.

Sensitivity. 2×10^{-8} g Li^6 (corresponding to $2·7 \times 10^{-7}$ g natural Li).

Interferences. Self-shielding during irradiation may be measurable in solutions more than 0·01 M in Li^6. The silica ampoules may contain at least 5 p.p.m. Li which can give a high blank. Deuterium interferes by the $H^2(n, \gamma) H^3$ reaction.

Reference. Kaplan and Wilzbach (1954).

Beryllium. Using the $Be^9(\gamma, n) 2He^4$ reaction.

Cross-section. 0·001 barns.   *Natural abundance.* 100%.

Irradiation time. 10–100 min, or longer for samples of very low Be content.

Apparatus. 100–250 millicuries Sb^{124}. Annular Perspex or aluminium sample holders. Paraffin wax and lead shielding (cf. Fig. 4.3).

Standards. Weigh 1·0, 5·0, and 25·0 g ignited specpure BeO into aluminium cans and make up to 500 g with 100-mesh SiO_2. Mix thoroughly and load 50–500 g into annular sample holders for activation.

Counting technique. Count prompt neutrons with six BF_3 neutron counters arranged hexagonally round the sample.

Sensitivity. 8×10^{-4} g Be.

Interferences. Elements with high neutron cross-sections such as B, Cd, Sm, and Gd could interfere.

Remarks. Sb^{124} has a 60-day half-life and must be renewed every two to three months.

References. Gaudin and Pannell (1951), Milner and Edwards (1959), Iredale (1960).

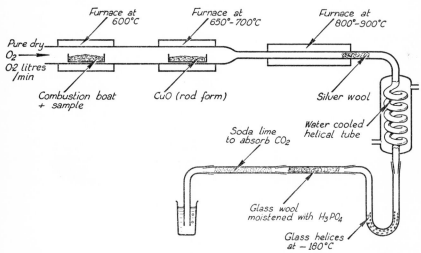

Fig. 13.1. Combustion train for separating C^{11} from proton activated boron in silicon matrix: after Gill, 1958.

Boron. Using the reaction $B^{11}(p, n) C^{11}$; $t_{\frac{1}{2}}$ 20 min.

Cross-section. 0·1 barns.   *Natural abundance.* 81·2%.

Irradiation time. 20 min in 1 μamp beam of 9 MeV protons.

Apparatus. Combustion train (Fig. 13.1), silica boats, furnaces, etc.

Reagents. Ag wool; CuO (rod form); SiC powder; Pb_3O_4; PbO_2; soda lime (10–14 mesh); H_2SO_4, 98%; HNO_3, 25%, 12% in HF; H_3PO_4, 90%; liquid N_2; O_2 free from CO_2.

Standards. 10^{-8}–10^{-6} g B dispersed in Si.

Sample preparation. Samples should be solid and < 3 mm thick. They should be etched with acid and wrapped in 50 μ Ta foil, which must be cooled during the irradiation.

Radiochemical separation

    (1) Etch surface of sample 1·5 min with HNO_3/HF.

    (2) Grind sample with 20 g Pb_3O_4, 2 g PbO_2, and 10 mg SiC.

(3) Ignite at 600° C in dry O_2 flowing at 200 ml/min and pass evolved gas over CuO (rod form) at 650° C.

(4) Pass gas through furnace tube at 850° C with exit plugged with Ag wool.

(5) Pass gas through water-cooled spiral and condense at −180° C for 3 minutes.

(6) Warm trap and sublime CO_2 through glass wool moistened with H_3PO_4 into a soda-lime tube.

Chemical yield. 100%; could be measured by replacing the soda-lime tube with $Ba(OH)_2$ solution and weighing $BaCO_3$ ppt.

Counting technique. Count 0·96 MeV positrons from soda-lime granules with scintillation or end-window Geiger counter.

Sensitivity. 10^{-9} g B.

Interferences. Nitrogen could interfere by $N^{14}(p, \alpha) C^{11}$, but has a lower cross-section than boron. $C^{12}(p, pn) C^{11}$ has a threshold energy of 19 MeV.

Reference. Gill (1958).

Carbon. Using $C^{12}(d, n) N^{13}$; $t_{\frac{1}{2}}$ 10 min.

Cross-section. 0·04 barns.   *Natural abundance.* 98·9%.

Irradiation time. 10 min using 4 MeV deuterons.

Reagents. HCl, 18% and 1·5%; NaOH, 40%; NH_4Cl, 5%.

Standard. 10^{-4} g C as benzoic acid.

Radiochemical separation

Dissolve sample in hot 18% HCl in flask and add 1 ml NH_4Cl. Run in excess NaOH and distil in current of air; collect distillate in 20 ml 1·5% HCl.

Chemical yield. 90–100%. Determine amount of NH_3 distilled by back titration of HCl.

Separation time. 10 min.

Counting technique. Count 1·2 MeV positrons in liquid beta counter.

Sensitivity. $2·5 \times 10^{-7}$ g C.

Interferences. N could interfere by the reaction $N^{14}(d, t) N^{13}$, which has a low cross-section. No other N isotope has a half-life > 7 seconds.

Reference. Albert, Chaudron, and Süe (1953).

Nitrogen. Using the reaction $N^{14}(d, n) O^{15}$; $t_{\frac{1}{2}}$ 2 min.

Cross-section. 0·03 barns.   *Natural abundance.* 99·6%.

Irradiation time. 2·1 min in a 3 μamp beam of 5 MeV deuterons.

Standard. 10^{-4} g N as NH_4Cl.

Counting technique. Count 2·7 MeV gammas with a scintillation counter and a single-channel analyser.

Sensitivity. $< 10^{-6}$ g N.

Interferences. O, Al, Ag, V, Nb, and Tl yield nuclides with half-lives between 1 and 5 min after deuteron activation, and may not easily be resolved. O could interfere by $O^{16}(\gamma, n) O^{15}$.

Reference. Süe (1955).

Oxygen. Using the reaction $O^{18}(p, n) F^{18}$; $t_{\frac{1}{2}}$ 1·9 hours.

Cross-section. 0·2 barns. *Natural abundance.* 0·20%.

Irradiation time. 4 min in a 10 μamp beam of 4·5 MeV protons.

Reagents. Ag_2SO_4; $Pb(NO_3)_2$; H_2SO_4, 50%; HCl, 36%; NaOH, 5%; $AgNO_3$, 4%; NaCl, 10%; NaF, 10%; Sodium acetate; glass wool.

Standard. 10^{-3} g O as K_2CO_3.

Radiochemical separation (suggested method)

(1) Place sample in round-bottomed flask containing 0·25 g glass wool, 0·5 g Ag_2SO_4, and 1 ml NaF. Add 50 ml of H_2SO_4 and steam distil at 140°–150° C for about 40 minutes.

(2) Add 2 drops NaCl to distillate and 0·5 ml $AgNO_3$, boil and spin down AgCl.

(3) Add 3 ml NaCl to spt, boil and spin down AgCl again.

(4) Make just alkaline with NaOH, add 3 ml NaCl, 1 ml HCl, and 5 g $Pb(NO_3)_2$. Heat to 70°C and add 5 g sodium acetate, cool and stand 20 minutes with occasional stirring. Spin down PbClF and wash twice with water and once with acetone.

Chemical yield. About 50%. Dry PbClF at 250° C and weigh.

Separation time. 1·5 hours for four samples.

Counting technique. Count 0·65 MeV positrons with end-window Geiger counter.

Sensitivity. 10^{-7} g O^{18} (corresponding to 5×10^{-5} g natural O).

Interferences. Large amounts of F could interfere by $F^{17}(\gamma, n) F^{18}$, and Ne could interfere by $Ne^{21}(p, \alpha) F^{18}$.

Remarks. For biological material, chemical separation is unnecessary if the sample is aged for 2 hours after activation and counting is carried out with a single or multi-channel γ-spectrometer focused on the 0·51 MeV peak of F^{18}. The main loss in chemical yield comes in step (4).

References. Fogelström-Fineman *et al.* (1957), Osmond and Smales (1954).

Fluorine. Using the reaction $F^{19}(n, \gamma) F^{20}$; $t_{\frac{1}{2}}$ 12 sec.

Cross-section. 0·009 barns.   *Natural abundance.* 100%.

Standard. 10^{-5} g F as LiF.

Radiochemical separation. None.

Counting technique. Count 1·6 MeV gammas with scintillation counter and gamma spectrometer.

Interferences. Sodium interferes because of the $Na^{23}(n, \alpha) F^{20}$ reaction. Neon could interfere by $Ne^{20}(n, p) F^{20}$.

References. Leveque and Goenvec (1955), Atchison and Beamer (1956).

Neon. Using the reaction $Ne^{22}(n, \gamma) Ne^{23}$; $t_{\frac{1}{2}}$ 40 sec.

Cross-section. 0·036 barns.   *Natural abundance.* 8·9%.

Apparatus. Vacuum line.

Reagents. Absorbent charcoal; soda lime; Cu turnings; Ca filings; argon gas.

Standard. 10^{-4} g Ne.

Radiochemical separation (suggested technique)

(1) If sample is not already gaseous, melt it with a suitable flux *in vacuo* and pump off evolved gases in a stream of argon.

(2) Pass gases successively through soda lime, red-hot copper, and calcium at 500° C.

(3) Condense gases on charcoal at −190° C and pass residual gas into counter.

Counting technique. Count 4·2 MeV betas in gas-flow counter.

Interferences. The main impurities are likely to be 1·8-hour A^{41}, 29-second O^{19}, and 7·4 second N^{16}. Gases from rocks rich in α-emitters may contain excessive amounts of Ne^{22} (Wetherill and Ingram, 1953).

Reference. E. J. Wilson (personal communication).

Sodium. Using the reaction $Na^{23}(n, \gamma) Na^{24}$; $t_{\frac{1}{2}}$ 15 hours.

Cross-section. 0·56 barns.   *Natural abundance.* 100%.

Reagents. HCl, 36% and 3·5%; NaCl, 2·5% Na; zinc uranyl acetate, 30%; ethanol; ethanol saturated with HCl; Zeo-Karb 225, < 50 μ.

Standard. 10^{-6} g Na as NaCl.

Radiochemical separation

(1) Dissolve the sample in HCl containing 2 ml NaCl and evaporate. Add 15 ml ethanol/HCl reagent and cool in ice. Spin and wash ppt with ethanol.

(2) Dissolve the NaCl in 0·5 ml water, add 25 ml zinc uranyl acetate reagent and digest at room temperature. Spin and wash ppt with ethanol. Add ethanol/HCl reagent to ppt, spin and wash with ethanol.

(3) Dissolve ppt in 0·5 ml water, transfer to $10 \times 0·5$ cm diameter Zeo-Karb 225 column and wash in with 1 ml water. Elute with 3·5% HCl at 0·25 ml/min, discard first ml, then collect 2 ml.

(4) Add 15 ml ethanol/HCl reagent to eluate, cool in ice, spin and wash ppt twice with ethanol.

Chemical yield. 80% with careful sampling of ion exchange column eluate; weigh as NaCl.

Separation time. 4 hours for six samples.

Counting technique. Count all betas above 2 MeV with end-window Geiger counter.

Interferences. The chemistry removes Li, K, and other monovalent ions. Polyvalent ions are removed by ion exchange. $Fe(OH)_3$ and sulphide scavenges could be included. Mg could interfere by $Mg^{24}(n, p)Na^{24}$ and Al by $Al^{27}(n, \alpha)Na^{24}$.

Reference. Smales and Loveridge (1955).

Magnesium. Using the reaction $Mg^{26}(n, \gamma)Mg^{27}$; $t_{\frac{1}{2}}$ 9·5 min.

Cross-section. 0·03 barns.   *Natural abundance.* 11·1%.

Reagents. HCl, 36%; NH_3, 6%; $CuCl_2$, 1% Cu; $FeCl_3$, 10%; $MgCl_2$, 1% Mg; ammonium acetate, 50%; H_2S generator; $(NH)_2HPO_4$, 10%.

Standard. 10^{-5} g Mg as $MgSO_4$.

Radiochemical separation (suggested method)

(1) Dissolve sample in HCl containing 2 ml $MgCl_2$, 2 drops $FeCl_3$, and 1 ml $CuCl_2$. Add 1 ml ammonium acetate and neutralize with NH_3. Spin down $Fe(OH)_3$ and reject it.

(2) Pass H_2S through spt, spin and reject CuS ppt.

(3) Add 2 ml $(NH_4)_2HPO_4$ and NH_3 to keep solution at pH 8–9. Stand 2 min in ice and spin down $MgNH_4PO_4$. Wash with NH_3.

Chemical yield. About 70%; weigh as $MgNH_4PO_4$, or ignite to $Mg_2P_2O_7$.

Separation time. 15 min per sample.

Counting technique. Count 1·02 MeV gammas with scintillation counter and gamma spectrometer.

Interferences. Aluminium and silicon could interfere by $Al^{27}(n, p)Mg^{27}$ and $Si^{30}(n, \alpha)Mg^{27}$. Cu^{66} has a 1·04 MeV γ-ray which could interfere.

Reference. Meinke (1949).

Aluminium. Using the reaction $Al^{27}(n, \gamma) Al^{28}$; $t_{\frac{1}{2}}$ 2·3 min.

Cross-section. 0·21 barns.   *Natural abundance.* 100%.

Radiochemical separation. None.

Counting technique. Count 1·8 MeV gammas with scintillation counter and gamma spectrometer.

Interferences. Silicon could interfere by $Si^{28}(n, p) Al^{28}$ and phosphorus by $P^{31}(n, \alpha) Al^{28}$. The most serious interference would probably be the 1·77 MeV γ-ray from Mn^{56}.

Reference. Caldwell and Mills (1959).

Silicon. Using the reaction $Si^{30}(n, \gamma) Si^{31}$; $t_{\frac{1}{2}}$ 2·6 hours.

Cross-section. 0·11 barns.   *Natural abundance.* 3·1%.

Reagents. Na_2CO_3; Na_2WO_4; HNO_3, 70% and 18%; HCl, 36% and 18%; $Hg_2(NO_3)_2$, 50%; $MnCl_2$, 1% Mn; Na_2SiO_3, 2·5% Si; Na_2WO_4, 1% W; ethanol; diethyl ether.

Standard. 10^{-5} g Si as Na_2SiO_3.

Radiochemical separation

   (1) Dissolve sample in 36% HCl and 70% HNO_3 in the presence of 1 ml Na_2SiO_3. Evaporate to dryness, treat residue with 18% HCl, spin and discard solution.

   (2) Wash residue with hot 18% HCl until white. Filter, wash with water and ignite. Fuse with 40 mg Na_2WO_4 and 300 mg Na_2CO_3 and dissolve the melt in hot water.

   (3) Add 1 ml $MnCl_2$ dropwise, stir, spin and discard ppt. Neutralize to methyl red with 18% HNO_3, add excess $Hg_2(NO_3)_2$, spin and discard ppt. Add 1 ml Na_2WO_4 dropwise, stir, spin and discard ppt.

   (4) Add 5 ml 36% HCl and evaporate to dryness. Treat residue with 18% HCl, spin and discard solution. Wash residue with warm 18% HCl, water, ethanol, and ether, and dry in air.

Chemical yield. Determine by ignition to SiO_2 at 700° C after counting.

Separation time. 1·5 hours.

Counting technique. Count 1·5 MeV betas with end-window Geiger counter.

Interferences. Radiochemical purity is sacrificed somewhat in favour of speed. It is necessary to plot decay and subtract long-lived impurities (e.g. W). P and S could interfere by $P^{31}(n, p) Si^{31}$ and $S^{34}(n, \alpha) Si^{31}$ reactions.

Reference. Short and Williams (1958).

Phosphorus. Using the reaction $P^{31}(n, \gamma) P^{32}$; $t_{\frac{1}{2}}$ 14 days.

Cross-section. 0·19 barns.   *Natural abundance.* 100%.

Reagents. NH_4NO_3; HNO_3, 70%; HCl, 36%; NH_3, 60% and 6%; KNO_3, 1%; $AsCl_3$, 1% As; $CuCl_2$, 1% Cu; $La(NO_3)_3$, 1% La; $(NH_4)_2HPO_4$, 1% P; $SbCl_3$, 1% Sb; ammonium molybdate (8% MoO_3 in 6% NH_4NO_3); Mg reagent (10% $MgCl_2$ in 20% NH_4Cl); oxalic acid, 10%; ethanol; diethyl ether; H_2S generator.

Standard. 2×10^{-5} g P as $NH_4H_2PO_4$.

Radiochemical separation

(1) Dissolve sample in HNO_3 in the presence of 1 ml $(NH_4)_2HPO_4$. Evaporate to small bulk and dilute with water. Add 3 ml Mg reagent, neutralize to methyl red with NH_3, stand 2 min and add excess NH_3. Spin and wash ppt with 6% NH_3.

(2) Dissolve ppt in HCl, add 1 ml each of $AsCl_3$, $SbCl_3$, and $CuCl_2$, dilute and saturate with H_2S. Spin and discard ppt. Boil to remove H_2S, add 1 ml $La(NO_3)_3$, 2 ml oxalic acid and NH_3 until $La(OH)_3$ ppts but solution remains acid to methyl red. Spin and discard ppt. Add more As, Sb, and Cu carriers and repeat H_2S scavenge; spin and discard ppt.

(3) Boil spt to expel H_2S, add 3 ml Mg reagent, neutralize to methyl red with NH_3, stand 2 min and add excess NH_3. Spin and wash ppt with 6% NH_3. Dissolve ppt in 1 ml HNO_3, dilute to 10 ml, spin and discard ppt if any. Dilute to 40 ml, add 3 g NH_4NO_3 and 20 ml ammonium molybdate. Shake well, spin and wash ppt with KNO_3.

(4) Dissolve ppt in minimum 60% NH_3, add 3 ml Mg reagent, spin and wash ppt with 6% NH_3. Dissolve in HCl, dilute to 12 ml, add 3 ml Mg reagent, neutralize to methyl red with 60% NH_3, and add 3 ml excess. Stand overnight, spin, wash with 6% NH_3, ethanol, and ether. Dry *in vacuo*.

Chemical yield. 60–80%; weigh as $MgNH_4PO_4$.

Separation time. 24 hours for six samples.

Counting technique. Count 1·7 MeV betas with end-window Geiger counter.

Interferences. S interferes by $S^{32}(n, p)P^{32}$ and Cl by $Cl^{35}(n, \alpha)P^{32}$.

Reference. Cali, Lowe, Reilly, and Thompson (1957).

Sulphur. Using the reaction $S^{32}(n, p)P^{32}$; $t_{\frac{1}{2}}$ 14 days.

Cross-section. 0·011 barns.   *Natural abundance.* 4·2%.

Reagents. As for phosphorus, also $BaCl_2$, 1% Ba; $(NH_4)_2SO_4$, 1% S.

Standard. 2×10^{-5} g S as $(NH_4)_2SO_4$.

Radiochemical separation. As for phosphorus, again using $(NH_4)_2HPO_4$

as phosphorus carrier, but with the following extra stage between (1) and (2). Dissolve in HCl, add 1 ml $(NH_4)_2SO_4$, and excess $BaCl_2$. Spin and discard ppt.

Chemical yield. 60–80%.

Separation time. 24 hours for six samples.

Counting technique. Count 1·7 MeV betas with end-window Geiger counter.

Interferences. Phosphorus interferes seriously by $P^{31}(n, \gamma) P^{32}$; chlorine could also interfere by $Cl^{35}(n, \alpha) P^{32}$.

References. Cali, Lowe, Reilly, and Thompson (1957), Gibbons and Simpson (1960 c).

Chlorine. Using the reaction $Cl^{37}(n, \gamma) Cl^{38}$; $t_{\frac{1}{2}}$ 35 min.

Cross-section. 0·56 barns.   *Natural abundance.* 24·5%.

Reagents. HNO_3, 70% and 18%; H_3PO_4, 90%; NaOH, 5%; $AgNO_3$, 4%; $Fe(NO_3)_3$, 10%; $KMnO_4$, 2%; $NaNO_2$, 1%; NH_4Cl, 2% Cl; NH_4Br, 5%; NH_4I, 5%; acetone; carbon tetrachloride.

Standard. 10^{-5} g Cl as NH_4Cl.

Radiochemical separation

(1) Dissolve sample in 5 ml 70% HNO_3 and 1 ml H_3PO_4 containing 0·5 ml NH_4Cl. Distil for 5 min at 150° C, collecting distillate in NaOH, using apparatus of Fig. 8.1.

(2) Add 2 drops NH_4I, 5 drops $NaNO_2$ and acidify with 18% HNO_3. Extract three times with CCl_4, discarding organic layers. Add 2 drops NH_4Br and oxidize with $KMnO_4$; extract three times with CCl_4, discarding organic layers.

(3) Add 5 drops $Fe(NO_3)_3$, neutralize with NaOH and spin down $Fe(OH)_3$.

(4) Acidify spt with 70% HNO_3, add 3 ml $AgNO_3$ and spin down AgCl. Wash with water and acetone.

Chemical yield. Over 70%.

Separation time. 20 min for one sample, 60 min for eight.

Counting technique. Count 4·8 MeV betas with end-window Geiger counter.

Interferences. Active bromine and iodine may remain if separation inadequate. Excess potassium could interfere by $K^{41}(n, \alpha) Cl^{38}$.

Reference. Bowen (1959 c).

Argon. Using the reaction $A^{40}(n, \gamma) A^{41}$; $t_{\frac{1}{2}}$ 1·8 hours.

Cross-section. 0·53 barns.   *Natural abundance.* 99·6%.

Apparatus. Vacuum line (Fig. 13.2).

Reagents. 5:1 CuO powder/asbestos fibre; activated charcoal; Ca powder; helium gas.

Standard. 10^{-6} g A.

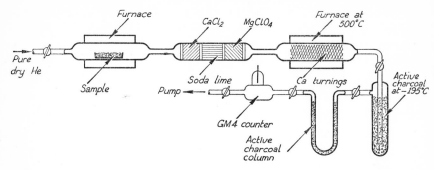

FIG. 13.2. Apparatus for separation of the inert gases after activation.

Radiochemical separation

(1) If sample is not already gaseous, dissolve or melt it and pump off evolved gases in a stream of carrier He.

(2) Pass gases over Ca at $500°$ C and activated charcoal at $-195°$ C.

(3) Raise charcoal to room temperature and elute with a stream of He through another charcoal column at $-45°$ C. A elutes between O_2 and Kr.

Counting technique. Count 1·2 MeV betas with gas-flow counter.

Interferences. K could interfere by $K^{41}(n, p) A^{41}$ and Ca by $Ca^{44}(n, \alpha) A^{41}$.

References. Stoenner and Zahringer (1958), Wänke and König (1959), E. J. Wilson (personal communication).

Potassium. Using the reaction $K^{41}(n, \gamma) K^{42}$; $t_{\frac{1}{2}}$ 12 hours.

Cross-section. 1·0 barns.   *Natural abundance.* 6·8%.

Reagents. H_2SO_4, 98%; HNO_3, 70% and 35%; $HClO_4$, 72%; HF, 40%; NaOH, 40%; $FeCl_3$, 1% Fe; H_2PtCl_6, 10%; KCl, 1% K; $Na_3Co(NO_2)_6$, 10%; acetic acid; ethanol.

Standard. 10^{-5} g as K_2CO_3.

Radiochemical separation

(1) Dissolve sample in H_2SO_4/HF in the presence of 5 ml KCl. Evaporate to fumes, add 10 ml HF and evaporate to fumes. Add 10 ml 70% HNO_3 and 5 ml $HClO_4$ and evaporate to fumes. Spin down $KClO_4$ and wash with ethanol.

(2) Dissolve ppt in 10 ml water. Add 1 ml $FeCl_3$ and excess NaOH and boil. Spin and reject ppt.

(3) Acidify spt with acetic acid, add excess $Na_3Co(NO_2)_6$, spin and wash ppt with water.

(4) Dissolve ppt by boiling with 2 ml 35% HNO_3, cool and add 2 further ml 35% HNO_3, 15 ml ethanol, and 1 ml 10% H_2PtCl_6. Spin and wash ppt three times with ethanol.

Chemical yield. 60–80%.

Separation time. About 2 hours for six samples.

Counting technique. Count betas with energies > 2 MeV with end-window Geiger counter.

Interferences. Active Rb and Cs would not be separated, but would show up in decay studies. Ca could interfere by $Ca^{42}(n,p)K^{42}$ and Sc by $Sc^{45}(n,\alpha)K^{42}$. 50 mg K gives 1·4 betas/second from its K^{40} content.

Reference. Salmon (1957 a).

Calcium. Using the reaction $Ca^{44}(n,\gamma)Ca^{45}$; $t_{\frac{1}{2}}$ 153 days.

Cross-section. 0·67 barns.   *Natural abundance.* 2·0%.

Reagents. $KClO_3$; HNO_3, 70% and 95%; HCl, 36% and 1·5%; NH_3, 60%; $BaCl_2$, 1% Ba; $CaCl_2$, 1% Ca; $CuCl_2$, 1% Cu; $Fe(NO_3)_3$, 1% Fe; $SrCl_2$, 1% Sr; oxalic acid, 10%; ammonium oxalate, 4%; H_2S generator.

Standard. 10^{-5} g Ca as $CaCO_3$.

Radiochemical separation

(1) Dissolve sample in 36% HCl+70% HNO_3 containing 5 ml $CuCl_2$ and 3 ml $CaCl_2$, evaporate to small bulk and dilute with 1·5% HCl. Heat to boiling, saturate with H_2S, spin and reject ppt.

(2) Boil spt to expel H_2S, dilute, neutralize with NH_3 and add 1 ml excess. Neutralize with oxalic acid, add slight excess, boil and add 5 ml ammonium oxalate. Spin and wash ppt with water.

(3) Dissolve calcium oxalate ppt in minimum of 70% HNO_3, add 1 ml each of $SrCl_2$ and $BaCl_2$, and 20 ml 95% HNO_3. Spin and reject ppt. Add 1 ml each of $SrCl_2$ and $BaCl_2$, and 20 ml 95% HNO_3. Spin and reject ppt.

(4) Evaporate spt to 5 ml, add 5 ml ammonium oxalate and excess NH_3. Spin and wash ppt with water.

(5) Dissolve ppt in 70% HNO_3 and destroy oxalate with 1 g $KClO_3$. Add 1 ml $Fe(NO_3)_3$ and excess NH_3, spin and reject ppt.

(6) Acidify with oxalic acid and boil with 5 ml ammonium oxalate. Spin, wash ppt with water and dry at 110° C.

Chemical yield. 20–50%; weigh as calcium oxalate.

Separation time. 2 hours.

Counting technique. Count 0·25 MeV betas with end-window Geiger counter, correcting for self-absorption.

Interferences. Sc could interfere by $Sc^{45}(n,p)$ Ca^{45} and Ti by $Ti^{48}(n,\alpha)Ca^{45}$. Active Sr may not be adequately separated.

References. Atchison and Beamer (1952), Meinke (1949).

Scandium. Using the reaction $Sc^{45}(n,\gamma)Sc^{46}$; $t_{\frac{1}{2}}$ 85 days.

Cross-section. 12 barns.   *Natural abundance.* 100%.

Reagents. HNO_3, 70%; HCl, 36%; $HClO_4$, 72%; NH_3, 60%; NH_4SCN, 50%; $ScCl_3$, 1% Sc; cupferron, 6%; sodium benzene sulphinate, 4%; chloroform; diethyl ether; Na_2O_2.

Standard. 10^{-6} g Sc as $ScCl_3$ (dissolve Sc_2O_3 in pure HCl).

Radiochemical separation

(1) Dissolve sample by fusion with 2 g Na_2O_2 in Ni crucible and extract with dilute HCl containing 0·5 ml $ScCl_3$. Add NH_3 till alkaline and spin down $Sc(OH)_3$.

(2) Dissolve ppt in 2 ml HCl, add excess NH_3 and spin down $Sc(OH)_3$ again.

(3) Dissolve ppt in 2 ml HCl, add 10 ml water and transfer to 100 ml separating funnel. Add 5 ml cupferron and extract three times with 20 ml chloroform, discarding the organic layer.

(4) Transfer aqueous phase to a 250 ml beaker, and evaporate with HNO_3 and $HClO_4$ to destroy organic matter. Dilute to 10 ml and filter off any silica ppt.

(5) Add excess NH_3 to filtrate and spin down $Sc(OH)_3$.

(6) Dissolve ppt in 4 ml HCl, dilute to 20 ml and transfer to 250 ml separating funnel. Add 50 ml NH_4SCN and extract twice with 50 ml ether.

(7) Combine ether extracts and evaporate off ether. Add 10 ml water and heat, adding HNO_3 dropwise until NH_4SCN is oxidized. Evaporate to fumes with 2 ml $HClO_4$.

(8) Add 10 ml water and excess NH_3; spin down $Sc(OH)_3$.

(9) Dissolve ppt in 2 ml HCl, dilute to 5 ml and neutralize with NH_3. Clear solution by adding 1 drop HCl and run in 4 ml sodium benzene sulphinate solution. Spin down ppt and wash three times with 5 ml water.

Chemical yield. 60–70%; weigh as scandium benzene sulphinate.

Separation time. 3–4 hours; samples should not be counted for 14 days in order to allow Sc^{48}, Sc^{49}, and Sc^{50} (and much of the 3·4-day Sc^{47}) to decay.

Counting technique. Count 0·89 or 1·12 MeV gammas with scintillation counter and gamma spectrometer.

Interferences. $Ti^{46}(n,p)Sc^{46}$ is much the most serious and amounts to 1·6 p.p.m. $Ti^{47}(n,p)Sc^{47}$, $V^{50}(n,\alpha)Sc^{47}$, and $Ca^{46}(n,\gamma)Ca^{47} \to Sc^{47}$ could be important.

Reference. Kemp and Smales (1960 *a*).

Titanium. Using the reaction $Ti^{50}(n,\gamma)Ti^{51}$; $t_{\frac{1}{2}}$ 5·8 min.

Cross-section. 0·14 barns.   *Natural abundance.* 5·35%.

Apparatus. Spectrophotometer.

Reagents. Na_2O_2; H_2SO_4, 10%; HCl, 36%; NH_3, 60%; NaOH, 5%; H_2O_2, 3%; $Fe(NO_3)_3$, 1% Fe; ammonium titanyl oxalate, 0·1% Ti; Cupferron, 6%; di-isopropyl ether.

Standard. 10^{-5} g Ti as ammonium titanyl oxalate.

Radiochemical separation

(1) Fuse sample in Ni crucible with 1 ml ammonium titanyl oxalate and 4 g Na_2O_2 and dissolve melt in 10 ml water; transfer to centrifuge tube and spin down residue.

(2) Add HCl to residue till acid, add 1 drop ferric nitrate and make alkaline with NH_3; spin down TiO_2.

(3) Transfer to 100 ml separating funnel with 20 ml H_2SO_4 and add 10 ml cupferron. Cool in ice and extract with 10 ml isopropyl ether. Wash ether layer once with 20 ml NaOH at $< 10°$ C, and once with 20 ml H_2SO_4.

Chemical yield. Convert sample to yellow pertitanic acid by evaporating off the ether over H_2SO_4 and adding H_2O_2. Measure absorption at 420 mμ with spectrophotometer.

Separation time. 13 min per sample.

Counting technique. Count 0·32 MeV gammas from ether fraction with a scintillation counter and gamma spectrometer.

Interferences. Vanadium and chromium could interfere by $V^{51}(n,p)Ti^{51}$ and $Cr^{54}(n,\alpha)Ti^{51}$. Mn^{56}, V^{52}, and I^{128} are the commonest radiochemical impurities.

Reference. Kim (1960).

Vanadium. Using the reaction $V^{51}(n,\gamma)V^{52}$; $t_{\frac{1}{2}}$ 3·8 min.

Cross-section. 4·5 barns.   *Natural abundance.* 99·7%.

Reagents. Na_2O_2; HCl, 36%; NH_3, 60%; H_2O_2, 3%; $AlCl_3$, 1% Al; NH_4VO_3, 1% V; cupferron, 6%; oxine (10% 8-hydroxy quinoline in

25% acetic acid); chloroform; EDTA, 5% ethylene diamine tetra-acetic acid.

Standard. 10^{-6} g V as NH_4VO_3.

Radiochemical separation

(1) Dissolve sample in 1 g fused Na_2O_2 in Ni crucible. Cool and dissolve melt in equal volumes of HCl and H_2O_2 containing 0·5 ml NH_4VO_3 and 1 ml $AlCl_3$.

(2) Add oxine and excess NH_3, and filter or spin off $Al(OH)_3$ ppt.

(3) Acidify spt with HCl, cool in ice, add 2 ml cupferron+2 ml EDTA and shake for 1 min with $CHCl_3$ in separating funnel. Run off lower layer through filter paper for counting.

Chemical yield. 50%; compare absorption of $CHCl_3$ solution at 360 mμ with standards.

Separation time. 10 min for two samples.

Counting technique. Count 2·6 MeV betas with liquid Geiger counter.

Interferences. 2·8-min Al^{28}, 5-min Cu^{66}, 35-min Cl^{38}, and 14·6-min Mo^{101} are common contaminants. Excess Cr and Mn in the sample could interfere by $Cr^{52}(n, p)V^{52}$ and $Mn^{55}(n, \alpha)V^{52}$.

Remarks. For biological material it may be useful to substitute a CuS scavenge (in the presence of tartrate) and/or an AgCl scavenge for step 2.

References. Brownlee and Kaiser (1959), Bowen and Cawse (1959), Kemp and Smales (1960*b*).

Chromium. Using the reaction $Cr^{50}(n, \gamma)Cr^{51}$; $t_{\frac{1}{2}}$ 27 days.

Cross-section. 13·5 barns.   *Natural abundance.* 4·4%.

Reagents. H_2SO_4, 10%; HNO_3, 70%; HCl, 18%; NH_3, 6%; NaOH, 5%; H_2O_2, 3%; $BaCl_2$, 5%; $CuCl_2$, 1% Cu; $FeCl_3$, 1% Fe; $K_2Cr_2O_7$, 1% Cr; $(NH_4)_2S_2O_8$, 10%; formic acid; acetic acid; ammonium acetate, 50%; diethyl ether; H_2S generator.

Standard. 10^{-7} g Cr (dissolve Cr in redistilled HCl).

Radiochemical separation

(1) Dissolve sample in HNO_3, add 1 ml $K_2Cr_2O_7$ and oxidize if necessary with $(NH_4)_2S_2O_8$.

(2) Add HCO_2H and HCl and boil to reduce to Cr^{3+}; add 1 ml $CuCl_2$, pass H_2S and spin down CuS.

(3) To spt, add NH_3 dropwise to avoid excess and boil. Spin down $Cr(OH)_3$ and reject spt.

(4) Dissolve ppt in NaOH+H_2O_2, add 1 drop $FeCl_3$ and spin down $Fe(OH)_3$.

(5) Cool spt to 0° C, acidify with H_2SO_4 and H_2O_2 and extract twice with cold ether in separating funnel without delay.

(6) Re-extract H_3CrO_8 into NH_3, and transfer aqueous layer to centrifuge tube.

(7) Add 2 ml $CH_3CO_2NH_4$, and CH_3CO_2H to bring to pH 5. Boil and add $BaCl_2$ till precipitation is complete. Spin down $BaCrO_4$ and wash three times with H_2O.

Chemical yield. Weigh as $BaCrO_4$.

Counting technique. Count 0·32 MeV gammas with scintillation counter and gamma spectrometer.

Interferences. Excess iron could interfere by $Fe^{54} (n, \alpha) Cr^{51}$.

Remarks. If step (5) is carried out at room temperature, the dichromate merely oxidizes the H_2O_2 and no blue peroxy complex is formed. Chromium can also be distilled as CrO_2Cl_2 (Pijck, 1960).

References. Meinke (1949), Kleinberg (1958).

Manganese. Using the reaction $Mn^{55} (n, \gamma) Mn^{56}$; $t_{\frac{1}{2}}$ 2·6 hours.

Cross-section. 13·3 barns.   *Natural abundance.* 100%.

Reagents. HNO_3, 100%; HCl, 6%; NH_3, 60%; Na_2CO_3, 10%; H_2O_2, 15%; $Cu(NO_3)_2$, 10%; $Fe(NO_3)_3$, 10%; $MnCl_2$, 5% Mn; $NaClO_3$, 50%; $NH_4H_2PO_4$, 10%; $Y(NO_3)_3$, 10%; ammonium acetate, 50%; ammonium sulphide, 50%.

Standard. 10^{-7} g Mn (dissolve MnO_2 in redistilled HCl).

Radiochemical separation

(1) Dissolve sample in 10 ml HNO_3 and add 0·2 ml $MnCl_2$ and 1 drop each of $Cu(NO_3)_2$, $Y(NO_3)_3$, and $NH_4H_2PO_4$. Add 1 ml $NaClO_3$ with care, boil, spin down MnO_2 and wash twice with 5 ml water.

(2) Dissolve ppt in 3 ml HCl+1 ml H_2O_2 and bring to pH 7 with NH_3 and ammonium acetate. Add 5 drops $Fe(NO_3)_3$ and 1 drop $NH_4H_2PO_4$ and spin down $Fe(OH)_3$.

(3) Acidify spt with HCl, add 3 drops $Cu(NO_3)_2$ and enough ammonium sulphide to ppt CuS. Spin down CuS and wash once with hot HCl.

(4) Make spt+washings alkaline with 3 ml ammonium sulphide, boil and spin down MnS; wash ppt twice with water.

(5) Dissolve ppt in 1 ml HNO_3, dilute, filter off sulphur and ppt Mn with excess Na_2CO_3.

(6) Dissolve ppt in 10 ml HNO_3. Add 1 ml $NaClO_3$, boil, spin down MnO_2 and wash three times with 10 ml water.

Chemical yield. About 70%; weigh as MnO_2.

Separation time. 2·5 hours for eight samples.

Counting technique. Count 2·8 MeV betas with end-window Geiger counter, or 0·85 MeV gammas with scintillation counter.

Interferences. Excess Fe and Co could interfere by $Fe^{56}(n, p)Mn^{56}$ and $Co^{59}(n, \alpha)Mn^{56}$ respectively. P^{32} may contaminate the MnO_2.

Remarks. The final MnO_2 ppt retains traces of $NaClO_3$, etc. Hence do not use acetone or organic liquids for slurrying. For a solvent extraction technique, see Matuszek and Sugihara (1961).

Reference. Bowen and Cawse (1959).

Iron. Using the reaction $Fe^{58}(n, \gamma)Fe^{59}$; $t_{\frac{1}{2}}$ 45 days.

Cross-section. 0·98 barns.   *Natural abundance.* 0·33%.

Reagents. HNO_3, 70%; HCl, 18%; $HClO_4$, 72%; NH_3, 60%; $AsCl_3$, 1% As; $FeCl_3$, 1% Fe; $CuCl_2$, 1% Cu; $KMnO_4$, 10%; $NH_4H_2PO_4$, 1% P; $Pd(NO_3)_2$, 1% Pd; $SbCl_3$, 1% Sb; acetic acid, 1%; ammonium acetate, 50%; oxine (2% 8-hydroxy quinoline in 6% acetic acid); diethyl ether equilibrated with 18% HCl.

Standard. 10^{-5} g Fe as $FeSO_4$.

Radiochemical separation

(1) Dissolve sample in $HNO_3/HClO_4$ containing 10 ml $FeCl_3$, evaporate to fumes, evaporate with HCl and take up in HCl. Add sufficient $KMnO_4$ to maintain pale straw colour and extract Fe three times with ether. Wash combined ether layers with $HCl/KMnO_4$. Back extract three times into water, evaporate to 20 ml and acidify with HCl.

(2) Add 1 ml each of $AsCl_3$, $CuCl_2$, $PdCl_2$, and $SbCl_3$, saturate with H_2S and filter.

(3) Add excess NH_3 to spt, spin down Fe_2S_3 and reject spt.

(4) Dissolve ppt in HNO_3+HCl, dilute and add excess NH_3, spin down $Fe(OH)_3$.

(5) Dissolve ppt in HCl, add 1 ml $NH_4H_2PO_4$ and 1 ml $KMnO_4$. Extract three times with ether and re-extract ether layers three times with water.

(6) Add excess NH_3 to aqueous phase and spin down $Fe(OH)_3$.

(7) Dissolve ppt in HCl, add 5 ml ammonium acetate and 5 ml oxine, warm, spin down ferric oxinate and wash with acetic acid and water.

Chemical yield. 60–70%; weigh as ferric oxinate.

Separation time. 3 hours for six samples.

Counting technique. Count 0·46 MeV betas with end-window Geiger counter, correcting for self-absorption. Co^{60} interferes with γ-ray counting.

Interferences. Cobalt interferes by Co^{59} (n, p) Fe^{59} and nickel could interfere by Ni^{62} (n, α) Fe^{59}.

Reference. Cali, Lowe, Reilly, and Thompson (1957).

Cobalt. Using the reaction Co^{59} (n, γ) Co^{60}; $t_{\frac{1}{2}}$ 5·2 years.

Cross-section. 20 barns.   *Natural abundance.* 100%.

Reagents. ZnO; H_2SO_4, 98%; HNO_3, 70% and 18%; HCl, 36% and 6%; KOH, 40%; KNO_2, 50%; $NaNO_2$, 10%; $Co(NO_3)_2$, 1% Co; $Cu(NO_3)_2$, 1% Cu; $Fe(NO_3)_3$, 10%; $Ni(NO_3)_2$, 1% Ni; acetic acid; ammonium citrate, 40%; dimethylglyoxime, 1% in methanol; 1-nitroso 2-naphthol, 10% in acetic acid; thionalide, 1% in methanol.

Standard. 10^{-6} g Co as $Co(NO_3)_2$.

Radiochemical separation

(1) Dissolve sample in 70% $HNO_3 + 36\%$ HCl containing 1 m $Co(NO_3)_2$, 2 ml $Cu(NO_3)_2$, and 1 ml $Ni(NO_3)_2$. Dilute with water, add 5 ml $Fe(NO_3)_3$, 10 ml $NaNO_2$, 5 ml ammonium citrate, and excess NH_3. Add 10 ml dimethylglyoxime slowly, spin and discard ppt.

(2) Acidify spt with 18% HNO_3, heat to 80° C, add 10 ml thionalide and filter.

(3) Add 20 ml 70% HNO_3 to spt and evaporate to dryness. Add 10 ml H_2SO_4 and evaporate to fumes. Dilute with water, add excess ZnO and filter.

(4) Heat spt, add 5 ml 1-nitroso 2-naphthol, boil and filter.

(5) Ignite ppt at 800° C, dissolve in 36% HCl, add 0·5 ml $Fe(NO_3)_3$ and excess NH_3 and filter.

(6) Add excess KOH to spt, boil to expel NH_3 and spin down $Co(OH)_2$.

(7) Dissolve ppt in 6% HCl, add acetic acid and 6 ml KNO_2. Spin and wash ppt with water and ethanol.

Chemical yield. 50–90%.

Separation time. 6–8 hours for six samples.

Counting technique. Count 1·17 and/or 1·33 MeV gammas with scintillation counter.

Interferences. Ni interferes by Ni^{58} (n, p) Co^{58} and Ni^{60} (n, p) Co^{60}. For equal weights of Ni and Co the error is 0·07%. This is overcome by measuring Co^{60} gammas only with a spectrometer. Cu could interfere by Cu^{63} (n, α) Co^{60}.

References. Smales, Mapper, and Wood (1957); cf. also Kaiser and Meinke (1960) who used 10-min Co^{60m}.

Nickel. Using the reaction $Ni^{64}(n, \gamma) Ni^{65}$; $t_{\frac{1}{2}}$ 2·6 hours.

Cross-section. 1·6 barns.   *Natural abundance.* 1·0%.

Reagents. HNO_3, 70%; HCl, 36%; NH_3, 60%; $Bi(NO_3)_2$, 1%; $BaCl_2$, 1% Ba; $CaCl_2$, 3%; $CuCl_2$, 1% Cu; $Fe(NO_3)_3$, 10%; KSCN, 20%; $MnCl_2$, 1% Mn; $NaNO_2$, 10%; $NaNO_3$, 10%; Na_2SO_3, 15%; $(NH_4)_2CO_3$, 20%; $Ni(NO_3)_2$, 1% Ni; $SrCl_2$, 1% Sr; bromine water; ammonium citrate, 40%; dimethylglyoxime, 1% in methanol; thionalide, 1% in methanol.

Standard. 10 μg Ni.

Radiochemical separation

(1) Dissolve sample in HNO_3+HCl containing 1 ml $Ni(NO_3)_2$. Dilute with water, add 5 ml $Fe(NO_3)_3$, 10 ml $NaNO_2$, 5 ml ammonium citrate and excess NH_3. Add 10 ml dimethylglyoxime slowly and filter.

(2) Dissolve ppt in HCl, add 0·1 ml $CuCl_2$ and 1 ml HNO_3 and heat gently. Cool, neutralize with NH_3, re-acidify with HCl and add 2 ml $NaNO_3$. Add 2 ml thionalide, filter and discard Cu ppt.

(3) Add 5 ml $Bi(NO_3)_2$ and slight excess NH_3, filter and discard ppt.

(4) Add 5 ml dimethylglyoxime, filter, wash and dissolve ppt in HCl. Add 1 ml HNO_3 and boil. Add NH_3 until only just acid, then add 1 ml $CuCl_2$, 2 ml Na_2SO_3, and 2 ml KSCN. Filter and discard CuSCN ppt.

(5) Add excess NH_3 and 5 ml dimethylglyoxime and filter.

(6) Dissolve ppt in HCl, add 1 ml $MnCl_2$ and 0·2 ml each of $CaCl_2$, $SrCl_2$, $BaCl_2$, and $Fe(NO_3)_3$, 2 ml HNO_3, 5 ml Br_2 water and boil to remove excess Br_2. Add slight excess NH_3 and 5 ml $(NH_4)_2CO_3$ and filter; discard ppt.

(7) Add 5 ml dimethylglyoxime, spin and wash ppt with hot water and ethanol.

Chemical yield. 50–90%; weigh as nickel dimethylglyoxime complex.

Separation time. 2–4 hours.

Counting technique. Count 2·1 MeV betas with end-window Geiger counter.

Interferences. Excess Cu or Zn could interfere by $Cu^{65}(n, p) Ni^{65}$ and $Zn^{68}(n, \alpha) Ni^{65}$.

Reference. Smales, Mapper, and Wood (1957).

Copper. Using the reaction $Cu^{63}(n, \gamma) Cu^{64}$; $t_{\frac{1}{2}}$ 12·8 hours.

Cross-section. 4·3 barns.   *Natural abundance.* 69%.

Reagents. HNO_3, 70%; NH_3, 60% and 6%; $Co(NO_3)_2$, 10%; $CuCl_2$, 1%

Cu; $Fe(NO_3)_3$, 10%; KSCN, 20%; $Mn(NO_3)_2$, 10%; Na_2SO_3, 15%; $NH_4H_2PO_4$, 10%; acetic acid; salicylaldoxime, 2% in ethanol; washing reagent (1% in both Na_2SO_3 and KSCN).

Standard. 10^{-6} g Cu (dissolve CuO in redistilled HNO_3).

Radiochemical separation

(1) Dissolve sample in HNO_3, add 1 ml $CuCl_2$ and 1 drop each of $Co(NO_3)_2$, $Mn(NO_3)_2$, and $NH_4H_2PO_4$. Dilute to 5% in HNO_3, add 1 ml Na_2SO_3 and 1 ml KSCN. Boil and spin down CuSCN; wash twice with hot washing reagent.

(2) Dissolve ppt in 0·5 ml hot HNO_3, add 5 drops $Fe(NO_3)_3$ and 1 drop each of $Mn(NO_3)_2$ and $NH_4H_2PO_4$, then 60% NH_3, till solution is dark brown. Boil and spin down $Fe(OH)_3$ ppt.

(3) Acidify spt with acetic acid till pale blue. Then add 0·5 ml HNO_3, 1 ml Na_2SO_3, and 1 ml KSCN. Boil and spin down CuSCN; wash with hot washing reagent.

(4) Dissolve ppt in 0·5 ml HNO_3, add 6% NH_3 till dark blue and CH_3CO_2H till pale. Add 3 ml salicylaldoxime and boil for 3 min. Spin and wash ppt twice with water and once with acetone.

Chemical yield. About 70%. The copper salicylaldoxime complex is readily washed and dried, whereas CuSCN is slightly soluble if washed with water.

Separation time. 2 hours for eight samples.

Counting technique. Count 0·6 MeV betas with end-window Geiger counter.

Interferences. Excess zinc interferes by $Zn^{64}(n,p)Cu^{64}$; 1 g Zn yields Cu^{64} equivalent to 7×10^{-4} g Cu.

Reference. Bowen (1959 a).

Zinc. Using the reaction $Zn^{68}(n,\gamma)Zn^{69} \rightarrow Zn^{69m}$; $t_{\frac{1}{2}}$ 14 hours (Zn^{69m} 1 hour).

Cross-section. 0·1 barns.   *Natural abundance.* 18·6%.

Reagents. HNO_3, 70%; NaOH, 40%; H_2O_2, 15%; $Co(NO_3)_2$, 10%; $Cu(NO_3)_2$, 10%; KSCN, 20%; $Mn(NO_3)_2$, 10%; Na_2SO_3, 15%; acetic acid; oxalic acid, 10%; zinc acetate, 1% Zn; KHgSCN: dissolve 39 g KSCN in 100 ml water; stir in 27 g $HgCl_2$ while diluting to 1000 ml; sodium quinaldate: dissolve 5 g quinaldic acid in the minimum of warm NaOH and make up to 250 ml.

Standard. 2×10^{-5} g Zn: dissolve ZnO in redistilled HNO_3.

Radiochemical separation

(1) Dissolve sample in HNO_3, add 2 ml zinc acetate and 1 drop each

of $Cu(NO_3)_2$ and $Mn(NO_3)_2$ and dilute to 5% in HNO_3. Add 1 ml Na_2SO_3 and 1 ml KSCN, boil and spin down CuSCN; add another drop of $Cu(NO_3)_2$ and repeat this step.

(2) Cool spt in ice and add 1 ml oxalic acid, 0.5 ml HNO_3, 1 drop $Co(NO_3)_2$, and 5 ml KHgSCN. After standing for 10 min, spin down $Zn(HgSCN)_2$.

(3) Dissolve ppt in 0.5 ml hot HNO_3, add 4 ml water and 5 ml KHgSCN. Stand in ice for 10 min and spin.

(4) Dissolve ppt in 0.5 ml hot HNO_3, add 5 drops $Co(NO_3)_2$, 1 drop H_2O_2 and NaOH till solution is dark brown. Boil and spin down $Co(OH)_2$.

(5) Bring spt to pH 5 with acetic acid and NH_3, and add 3 ml sodium quinaldate. Boil and spin down zinc quinaldate.

(6) Dissolve ppt in 0.5 ml HNO_3 and repeat step (5). Wash ppt twice with water and once with acetone.

Chemical yield. About 70%; weigh as zinc quinaldate.

Separation time. About 2.5 hours for eight samples.

Counting technique. Count 0.92 MeV betas with end-window Geiger counter. Counting should not be started until about 6 hours after activation to allow the Zn^{69m} daughter to equilibrate.

Interferences. Excess Ga or Ge could interfere by $Ga^{69}(n,p)Zn^{69}$ and $Ge^{72}(n,\alpha)Zn^{69}$; 2-day Zn^{72} is a rare fission product from activated uranium.

Reference. Bowen (1959 a).

Gallium. Using the reaction $Ga^{71}(n,\gamma)Ga^{72}$; $t_{\frac{1}{2}}$ 14 hours.

Cross-section. 4.0 barns.   *Natural abundance.* 39.9%.

Reagents. HCl, 36% and 18%; NaOH, 40%; $Cu(NO_3)_2$, 10%; $Fe(NO_3)_3$, 10%; $Ga(NO_3)_3$, 1% Ga; $Mn(NO_3)_2$, 10%; $NH_4H_2PO_4$, 10%; $Y(NO_3)_3$, 10%; acetic acid; ammonium acetate, 50%; ammonium molybdate, 10%; ammonium sulphide, 50%; diethyl ether; formic acid; oxine (2% 8-hydroxy quinoline in ethanol).

Standard. 10^{-6} Ga as $Ga(NO_3)_3$.

Radiochemical separation

(1) Dissolve sample in 36% HCl, add 1 ml $Ga(NO_3)_3$ and 1 drop each of $Ca(NO_3)_2$, $Mn(NO_3)_2$, $Y(NO_3)_3$, and $NH_4H_2PO_4$. Cool, dilute to 18% in HCl and wash into a 50 ml separating funnel with excess of 18% HCl.

(2) Shake with 10 ml of ether, run aqueous layer to waste and wash ether layer twice with 5 ml 18% HCl.

(3) Extract ether layer with two 5 ml portions of water.

(4) Boil aqueous extracts till free of ether, acidify with HCl and add 5 drops ammonium sulphide, 1 drop $Cu(NO_3)_2$, 1 drop ammonium molybdate, and 1 drop formic acid. Spin down CuS.

(5) Add 5 drops $Fe(NO_3)_3$ and 1 drop $NH_4H_2PO_4$ to spt; make alkaline with NaOH. Spin, add 2 drops $Fe(NO_3)_3$ and spin down $(FeOH)_3$.

(6) Acidify spt with HCl, add 5 drops $Fe(NO_3)_3$ and NaOH till solution is dark brown. Spin down $Fe(OH)_3$ again.

(7) Bring spt to pH 6 with acetic acid and ammonium acetate and add 3 ml oxine. Boil and spin down Ga oxinate; wash three times with water.

Chemical yield. About 60%; weigh as gallium oxinate.

Separation time. 2·5 hours for eight samples.

Counting technique. Count 0·64 MeV betas with end-window Geiger counter.

Interferences. Excess Ge, As, or U could interfere by $Ge^{72}(n,p)Ga^{72}$, $As^{75}(n,\alpha)Ga^{72}$, and $U^{235}(n,f)Ga^{72}$, etc.

Remarks. Gallium oxinate is soluble in acetone, which should therefore not be used for slurrying.

References. Brown and Goldberg (1949), Morris and Brewer (1954), Bowen and Cawse (1959).

Germanium. Using the reaction $Ge^{76}(n,\gamma)Ge^{77}$; $t_{\frac{1}{2}}$ 12·3 hours.

Cross-section. 0·08 barns.   *Natural abundance.* 7·8%.

Reagents. HNO_3, 70%; HCl, 36%; $HClO_4$, 72%; HF, 40%; NH_3, 60%; H_2O_2, 15%; $AsCl_3$, 1% As; $CoCl_2$, 1% Co; $CuCl_2$, 1% Cu; $FeCl_3$, 1% Fe; $GeCl_4$, 1% Ge; $SbCl_3$, 1% Sb; oxalic acid; tannic acid, 5%; thio-acetamide, 2%; H_2S generator.

Standard. 5×10^{-4} g Ge as ammonium germanium oxalate.

Radiochemical separation

(1) Dissolve in $HCl/HNO_3/HF/HClO_4$ in the presence of 2 ml $GeCl_4$. Evaporate to fumes of $HClO_4$ (HF prevents loss of Ge). Dilute with HCl, add 1 ml each of $CuCl_2$, $AsCl_3$, and $SbCl_3$ and 5 g oxalic acid. Add excess thioacetamide, filter and discard ppt.

(2) Add 25 ml tannic acid and neutralize with NH_3. Spin down ppt and dissolve it in $HCl+H_2O_2$.

(3) Transfer solution to distillation apparatus and steam distil in presence of 1 ml each $AsCl_3$, $CoCl_2$, $CuCl_2$, and $FeCl_3$.

(4) Acidify distillate, saturate with H_2S, spin and wash GeS_2 ppt with H_2S solution and finally with water.

Chemical yield. 90%; weigh as GeS_2.

Separation time. 2–3 hours for several samples.

Counting technique. Count 2·2 MeV betas with end-window Geiger counter.

Notes. $Ge^{74}(n, \gamma) Ge^{75}$ and $Ge^{70}(n, \gamma) Ge^{71}$ have also been used for greater sensitivity.

Interferences. Selenium could interfere in all cases by $Se^{74}(n, \alpha) Ge^{71}$, $Se^{78}(n, \alpha) Ge^{75}$, and $Se^{80}(n, \alpha) Ge^{77}$. Arsenic could interfere in Ge^{75} method by $As^{75}(n, p) Ge^{75}$ and uranium could interfere by $U^{235}(n, f) Ge^{77}$ and Ge^{78}.

Reference. Smales, Mapper, Morgan, Webster, and Wood (1959).

Arsenic. Using the reaction $As^{75}(n, \gamma) As^{76}$; $t_{\frac{1}{2}}$ 1·1 days.

Cross-section. 5·4 barns.   *Natural abundance.* 100%.

Apparatus. Distillation assembly with tap funnel, splash-head, and swan-neck delivery tube.

Reagents. H_2SO_4, 98%; HNO_3, 70%; HCl, 36%; $HClO_4$, 72%; HBr, 48%; H_2O_2, 15%; $AsCl_3$, 1% As; $NH_4H_2PO_2$, 50%.

Standard. 10^{-7} g As as $AsCl_3$ (dissolve As_2O_3 in redistilled HCl).

Radiochemical separation

(1) Dissolve sample in $H_2O_2/HNO_3/H_2SO_4/HClO_4$ containing 5 ml $AsCl_3$. Evaporate to fumes, dilute to 20 ml with water and add 20 ml HCl. Add excess $NH_4H_2PO_2$ at 90° C, spin down As ppt and wash with water.

(2) Dissolve As in 10 ml HCl+5 drops H_2O_2 and distil, rejecting distillate. Repeat distillation.

(3) Add 10 ml HBr and distil, collecting distillate under 10 ml water. Repeat twice more.

(4) Add 4 ml $NH_4H_2PO_2$ to combined distillates from (3) and keep at 90°C for 30 min. Spin and wash ppt three times with water.

Chemical yield. About 90%. Final washing must be thorough to remove all $NH_4H_2PO_2$; weigh as As.

Separation time. 2–4 hours for four to six samples.

Counting technique. Count betas with energy > 2 MeV with end-window Geiger counter.

Interferences. Se, Br, and Ge could interfere by $Se^{76}(n, p) As^{76}$, $Se^{77}(n, p) As^{77}$, $Br^{79}(n, \alpha) As^{76}$, and $Ge^{76}(n, \gamma) Ge^{77} \rightarrow As^{77}$. Radiochemical contamination may appear if splash-heads are inefficient. As^{77} is a rare fission product of uranium.

Reference. Smales and Pate (1952 a).

Selenium. Using the reaction $Se^{74}(n, \gamma) Se^{75}$; $t_{\frac{1}{2}}$ 120 days.

Cross-section. 26 barns.   *Natural abundance.* $0 \cdot 93\%$.

Reagents. HNO_3, 70%; HCl, 36%; $HClO_4$, 72%; HBr, 48%; NH_2OH; HCl, 20%; Se, 1% in HNO_3; SO_2 generator; ethanol.

Standard. 10^{-4} g Se as H_2SeO_3.

Radiochemical separation

(1) Dissolve sample under reflux in $HNO_3/HClO_4$ containing 5 ml Se/HNO_3 and evaporate to fumes of $HClO_4$. Add 10 ml HCl and evaporate to small bulk.

(2) Distil with 10 ml HBr, three times, collecting distillate in hydroxylamine hydrochloride. Heat to 90° C until ppt coagulates and spin it down.

(3) Dissolve ppt in minimum of HNO_3. Add HCl and reduce with SO_2. Spin down Se and wash with water and ethanol.

Chemical yield. About 70%; weigh as the element.

Separation time. About 4 hours for six samples.

Counting technique. Count $0 \cdot 27$ MeV gammas with scintillation counter and gamma spectrometer.

Interferences. Kr could interfere by $Kr^{78}(n, \alpha) Se^{75}$. Other interferences are eliminated by delaying counting for a few days.

References. Leddicotte *et al.* (1959), Fineman, Ljunggren, Forsberg, and Erwall (1959), Schindewolf (1960).

Bromine. Using the reaction $Br^{79}(n, \gamma) Br^{80m} \rightarrow Br^{80}$; $t_{\frac{1}{2}}$ 4·4 hours (18 min for Br^{80}).

Cross-section. 2·9 barns.   *Natural abundance.* $50 \cdot 6\%$.

Reagents. HNO_3, 70% and 18%; H_3PO_4, 90%; NaOH, 5% and 0·5%; $AgNO_3$, 4%; $Fe(NO_3)_3$, 10%; $KMnO_4$, 2%; NH_4Br, 4% Br; carbon tetrachloride.

Standard. 2×10^{-7} g Br as NH_4Br.

Radiochemical separation

(1) Place sample in round bottomed flask with 0·5 ml NH_4Br, 1 ml H_3PO_4, and sufficient 70% HNO_3 to dissolve it. Fit distillation head (Fig. 8.1), using a PTFE sleeve, and distil in a slow current of air for 5 min at 150–180° C. Collect distillate in 10 ml 5% NaOH, which must not be neutralized by the acids distilled over.

(2) Add 1 drop $Fe(NO_3)_3$ to distillate and spin down $Fe(OH)_3$: reject ppt.

(3) Transfer spt to separating funnel containing 5 ml CCl_4. Acidify

with 18% HNO_3 and add $KMnO_4$ drop by drop till a pink colour just persists. Shake and extract three times with CCl_4.

(4) Re-extract Br_2 from combined CCl_4 extracts by shaking with 10 ml 0·5% NaOH.

(5) Transfer aqueous layer to centrifuge tube, acidify with 18% HNO_3 and add 3 ml $AgNO_3$. Spin down AgBr and wash ppt twice with water and once with acetone.

Chemical yield. 70% is normal; weigh as AgBr.

Separation time. 1·5 hours for eight samples.

Counting technique. Count 2·0 MeV betas with end-window Geiger counter.

Interferences. Kr and U could interfere by the reactions $Kr^{80}(n,p)Br^{80}$ and $U^{235}(n,f)$ 1·5-day Br^{82}, 2·3-hour Br^{83}, etc. I^{128} is not removed by the procedure given above, but should have decayed before counting starts.

Remarks. Steps (3) and (4) can be left out if counting is delayed for 6 to 8 hours to allow Cl^{38} to decay. Counting should in any case be delayed 3 hours to allow 18 min Br^{80m} to equilibrate. Substitution of ammonium carbonate for nitric acid in step (5) might improve decontamination from Cl^{38}.

Reference. Bowen (1959 c).

Krypton. Using the reaction $Kr^{84}(n,\gamma)Kr^{85}$; $t_{\frac{1}{2}}$ 4·4 hours.

Cross-section. 0·1 barns.   *Natural abundance.* 57% (but see below).

Apparatus. Vacuum line (Fig. 13.2).

Reagents. 5:1 CuO powder/asbestos fibre; Mg powder; activated charcoal; helium gas.

Standard. 10^{-5} g Kr.

Radiochemical separation (suggested method)

(1) If sample is not already gaseous, dissolve or melt it and pump off evolved gases in a stream of carrier helium.

(2) Pass gases over Mg at 500° C and activated charcoal at −195° C.

(3) Raise charcoal to room temperature and elute with a stream of helium through a charcoal column at −45° C. H_2, N_2, O_2, and A elute before Kr, which in turn elutes before Xe.

Counting technique. Count 0·83 MeV betas with gas-flow counter.

Interferences. 1·8-hour A^{41} may contaminate the product. If the sample contained uranium, Kr^{85} and other nuclides may be produced by fission.

Remarks. The isotopic composition of atmospheric Kr differs greatly from that of Kr retained by radioactive minerals.

References. Wilson, Evans, Chadwick, Eakins, and Taylor (1955), Wilson and Taylor (1958).

Rubidium. Using the reaction $Rb^{85}(n, \gamma) Rb^{86}$; $t_{\frac{1}{2}}$ 19 days.

Cross-section. 0·7 barns.   *Natural abundance.* 72·2%.

Reagents. Na_2O_2; HNO_3, 35%; HCl, 36%, 1·7% and 0·35%; NaOH, 40%; CsCl, 4% Cs; $FeCl_3$, 10%; H_2PtCl_6, 10%; $Na_3Co(NO_2)_6$, 10%, freshly prepared; RbCl, 4% Rb; acetic acid; ethanol; Zeo-Karb 315,† 85–120 mesh.

Standard. 10^{-5} g Rb as RbCl.

Radiochemical separation

(1) Fuse sample with Na_2O_2, 1 ml RbCl, and 1 ml CsCl. Dissolve in water, add 2 ml $FeCl_3$ and acidify with 36% HCl. Neutralize with NaOH and filter.

(2) Acidify spt with acetic acid, add 1 ml $FeCl_3$, neutralize with NaOH and filter.

(3) Acidify spt with acetic acid, add 10 ml $Na_3Co(NO_2)_6$ and cool in ice for 5 min. Spin and wash ppt with water.

(4) Dissolve ppt in HNO_3, evaporate to dryness and dissolve in 5 ml water. Transfer to Zeo-Karb 315† column (25 cm long × 1 cm diameter), elute K with 600 ml 0·35% HCl at 0·5 ml/min and reject eluate. Elute Rb with 100 ml 1·7% HCl according to predetermined elution curves.

(5) Evaporate second eluate to dryness, dissolve in water and neutralize with NaOH. Centrifuge and filter.

(6) Acidify spt with acetic acid, add 10 ml $Na_3Co(NO_2)_6$, stand in ice for 5 min, spin and wash ppt with water.

(7) Dissolve ppt in HNO_3, add ethanol and H_2PtCl_6, cool in ice, spin and wash ppt three times with ethanol.

Chemical yield. 50–70%; weigh as Rb_2PtCl_6.

Separation time. 8 hours, including ion exchange.

Counting technique. Count 1·8 MeV betas with end-window Geiger counter.

Interferences. Sr gives 0·7 p.p.m. apparent Rb due to $Sr^{86}(n, p) Rb^{86}$, Y gives 0·1 p.p.m. apparent Rb due to $Y^{89}(n, \alpha) Rb^{86}$ and U gives 0·2 p.p.m. apparent Rb due to $U^{235}(n, f) Rb^{86}$. 40 mg Rb gives 80 c.p.m. on end-window counter from its Rb^{87} content.

References. Smales and Salmon (1955), Cabell and Smales (1957).

† This resin is now obsolete, but Zeo-Karb 215 is similar in properties.

Strontium. Using the reaction $Sr^{86}(n, \gamma) Sr^{87}$; $t_{\frac{1}{2}}$ 2·8 hours.

Cross-section. 1·3 barns.   *Natural abundance.* 10%.

Reagents. HNO_3, 100% and 80%; HCl, 6%; NH_3, 60%; $Cu(NO_3)_2$, 10%; $Fe(NO_3)_3$, 10%; K_2CrO_4, 10%; $Mn(NO_3)_2$, 10%; Na_2CO_3, 10%; $NH_4H_2PO_4$, 10%; $Y(NO_3)_3$, 10%; acetic acid; ammonium acetate, 50%; ammonium oxalate, 4%; barium acetate, 10%; strontium acetate, 10% Sr; acetone.

Standard. 10^{-5} g Sr as $SrCl_2$ (dissolve $SrCO_3$ in redistilled HCl).

Radiochemical separation

    (1) Dissolve sample in 10 ml 100% HNO_3 and add 0·2 ml strontium acetate and 1 drop each of $Cu(NO_3)_2$, $Mn(NO_3)_2$, $Y(NO_3)_3$, and $NH_4H_2PO_4$. Cool in ice for 10 min and spin down $Sr(NO_3)_2$.

    (2) Dissolve ppt in 2 ml H_2O and repeat step (1), using 80% HNO_3. Wash ppt with 80% HNO_3.

    (3) Dissolve ppt in 2 ml NH_3 and make up to 10 ml with water. Boil with 2 drops $Fe(NO_3)_3$ and 1 drop $Mn(NO_3)_2$. Spin down the $Fe(OH)_3$.

    (4) Add 4 ml Na_2CO_3 to spt and spin down $SrCO_3$.

    (5) Dissolve ppt in warm acetic acid. Add ammonium acetate till pH is 5·0, then 2 drops barium acetate and boil. Add K_2CrO_4 and spin down $BaCrO_4$. Add 2 more drops barium acetate and spin again.

    (6) Bring spt to pH 4 after adding 4 ml ammonium oxalate and 1 drop $NH_4H_2PO_4$. Spin down SrC_2O_4 and wash twice with water and once with acetone.

Chemical yield. 90% is obtainable; weigh as SrC_2O_4.

Separation time. 2·5 hours for eight samples.

Counting technique. Count 0·39 MeV gammas with scintillation counter, preferably with a gamma spectrometer.

Interferences. Inactive Ca may not be completely separated and then gives rise to an impossibly high chemical yield. Zr and U interfere by $Zr^{90}(n, \alpha) Sr^{87}$ and $U^{235}(n, f) Sr^{87}$, Sr^{89}, etc. The latter can be serious.

Remarks. For mineral samples it may be necessary to scavenge with CuS and CoS.

References. Harrison and Raymond (1955), Bowen and Cawse (1959).

Yttrium. Using the reaction $Y^{89}(n, \gamma) Y^{90}$; $t_{\frac{1}{2}}$ 2·7 days.

Cross-section. 1·2 barns.   *Natural abundance.* 100%.

Reagents. HNO_3, 70%; HCl, 18%; HF, 40% and 10%; H_3BO_3, 3%; NH_3, 6%; $Y(NO_3)_3$, 1% Y; $ZrO(NO_3)_2$, 10%; ammonium oxalate, 4%; methanol; TBP reagent (60% tributyl phosphate, 40% gulf solvent BT, freshly equilibrated with 70% HNO_3).

Standard. 10^{-7} g Y (dissolve Y_2O_3 in distilled HNO_3).

Radiochemical separation

(1) Dissolve sample in HNO_3 containing 1 ml $Y(NO_3)_3$, transfer to polythene tube and dilute to 10% in HNO_3. Add 2 ml $ZrO(NO_3)_2$ and make solution 8% in HF. Spin down YF_3 and wash ppt with 10 ml 10% HF.

(2) Dissolve ppt in 2 ml $H_3BO_3 + 2$ ml HNO_3, dilute and make alkaline with NH_3. Spin down $Y(OH)_3$.

(3) Dissolve ppt in 50 ml HNO_3, transfer to 100 ml separating funnel and shake 5 min with 10 ml TBP reagent. Discard aqueous layer and wash TBP twice with 50 ml HNO_3.

(4) Re-extract Y from TBP by shaking three times with 10 ml portions of water.

(5) Combine aqueous fractions and add NH_3; spin down $Y(OH)_3$.

(6) Dissolve ppt in HCl, add 20 ml ammonium oxalate and boil 10 min, then cool in ice and spin down $Y_2(C_2O_4)_3$ and wash twice with water and once with methanol.

Chemical yield. 50%; weigh as Y_2O_3 after ignition at 80° C for 30 min.

Separation time. 2 hours.

Counting technique. Count 2·3 MeV betas with end-window Geiger counter.

Interferences. Zr, Nb, and U could interfere by $Zr^{90}(n,p)Y^{90}$, $Nb^{93}(n,\alpha)Y^{90}$ and $U^{235}(n,f)Y^{90}$, Y^{91}, Y^{92}, Y^{93}, etc. Fission is the most important interference.

Remarks. Steps (1) to (5) can be repeated to improve decontamination. Lanthanides are separated by the solvent extraction.

Reference. Kleinberg (1958).

Zirconium. Using the reaction $Zr^{96}(n,\gamma)Zr^{97} \rightarrow Nb^{97}$; $t_{\frac{1}{2}}$ 17 hours (1·2 hours for Nb^{97}).

Cross-section. 0·1 barns.   *Natural abundance.* 2·8%.

Reagents. H_2SO_4, 98% and 2·4%; HNO_3, 70%; HCl, 36% and 6%; HF, 40%; H_3BO_3, 3%; NH_3, 6%; $Ba(NO_3)_2$, 5% Ba; $La(NO_3)_3$, 1% La; $ZrO(NO_3)_2$, 1% Zr; mandelic acid, 16%; Zeo-Karb 225, 200–400 mesh.

Standard. 10^{-4} g Zr as $ZrO(NO_3)_2$.

Radiochemical separation

(1) Dissolve sample in HNO_3 in polythene tube and dilute to 15% in HNO_3. Add 4 ml $ZrO(NO_3)_2$ and make solution 10% in HF. Add 0·5 ml $La(NO_3)_2$ and spin down LaF_3. Repeat LaF_3 scavenge five times.

(2) Add 1 ml $Ba(NO_3)_2$ to spt and spin down $BaZrF_6$.

(3) Dissolve ppt in 4 ml $H_3BO_3 + 1$ ml HNO_3. Add 2 ml $Ba(NO_3)_2$ and 2 ml HF and spin down $BaZrF_6$ again.

(4) Dissolve ppt in 4 ml $H_3BO_3 + 4$ ml 36% HCl. Dilute with 15 ml water and add 3 drops 98% H_2SO_4. Stand 15 min and spin down $BaSO_4$.

(5) Make spt alkaline with NH_3 and spin down $Zr(OH)_4$.

(6) Dissolve ppt in 2·4% H_2SO_4 and elute on 80 cm $\times$ 0·05 cm^2 Zeo-Karb 225 column at 0·15 ml/min for about 11 hours. Zr is eluted in the 60–100 ml fraction of eluate and Hf is left on the column.

(7) Add 10 ml mandelic acid to eluate fraction, spin down zirconium mandelate and wash three times with water.

Chemical yield. 75%; ignite final ppt at 800° C for 1 hour and weigh as ZrO_2.

Separation time. About 18 hours for eight samples.

Counting technique. Count 1·9 MeV betas with end-window Geiger counter: delay count for 12 hours to allow Nb^{97} to equilibrate.

Interferences. Mo and U could interfere by $Mo^{100}(n, \alpha) Zr^{97}$ and $U^{235}(n, f) Zr^{97}$ respectively.

Remarks. Steps (3) and (5) may be repeated if necessary. Step (1) removes lanthanides, and step (3) niobium.

References. Kleinberg (1958), Herr, Merz, Eberhardt, and Signer (1958).

Niobium. Using the reaction $Nb^{93}(n, \gamma) Nb^{94m}$; $t_{\frac{1}{2}}$ 6·6 min.

Cross-section. 1·0 barns.   *Natural abundance.* 100%.

Reagents. $K_2S_2O_7$; HCl, 27%; NH_3, 60%; $Ca(NO_3)_2$, 2% Ca; oxalic acid, 10%, 0·4%, and 0·1%; 4-methyl 2-pentanone equilibrated with 27% HCl; 1 μC Nb^{95}; Niobium carrier: dissolve 2·60 g potassium niobate in 20 ml water, heat and add 1·5 ml 70% HNO_3. Spin down the niobic acid and wash it three times with hot 2% NH_4NO_3. Dissolve ppt in 20 ml hot 10% oxalic acid, cool and make up to 100 ml.

Standard. 10^{-5} g Nb aliquot of niobium carrier.

Radiochemical separation

(1) Fuse sample with 4 g $K_2S_2O_7$ in Ni crucible for 5 min. Digest melt in 35 ml water containing 5 ml 10% oxalic acid, 0·1 ml Nb carrier, and 0·01 μC Nb^{95}; filter and wash residue with 15 ml 0·1% oxalic acid.

(2) Transfer to 250 ml separating funnel, add 150 ml HCl and extract three times with 15 ml portions of 4-methyl 2-pentanone.

(3) Combine organic extracts and shake three times with 15 ml portions of 0·4% oxalic acid.

(4) Boil aqueous layer free from solvent; add 5 ml $Ca(NO_3)_2$ and make alkaline with NH_3. Spin down ppt and wash with dilute $Ca(NO_3)_2$.

Chemical yield. 30%, determined by counting 0·76 MeV gamma rays from Nb^{95} after a few hours' decay.

Separation time. 12 min.

Counting technique. Count 0·017 MeV gammas from Nb^{94m} with scintillation counter and gamma spectrometer.

Interferences. Mo and U could interfere by $Mo^{94}(n,p)Nb^{94}$ and $U^{235}(n,f)Nb^{94}$, Nb^{97}, Nb^{98}, and Nb^{99}. Zirconium could interfere by $Zr^{96}(n,\gamma)Zr^{97} \rightarrow Nb^{97}$.

Reference. Brownlee (1960).

Molybdenum. Using the reaction $Mo^{98}(n,\gamma)Mo^{99} \rightarrow Tc^{99m}$; $t_{\frac{1}{2}}$ 2·8 days (6 hours for Tc^{99m}).

Cross-section. 0·45 barns. *Natural abundance.* 23·8%.

Reagents. HNO_3, 70%; HCl, 36% and 18%; NaOH, 40%; $Cu(NO_3)_2$, 10%; $Fe(NO_3)_3$, 10%; $NH_4H_2PO_4$, 10%; $Y(NO_3)_3$, 10%; ammonium molybdate, 1% Mo; ammonium sulphide, 50%; acetone; α-benzoin oxime, 2% in ethanol; diethyl ether; formic acid.

Standard. 2×10^{-5} g Mo as ammonium molybdate.

Radiochemical separation

(1) Dissolve sample in HCl containing 1 ml ammonium molybdate and 1 drop each of $Cu(NO_3)_2$, $Y(NO_3)_3$, and $NH_4H_2PO_4$. Make 18% in HCl and transfer to separating funnel containing 10 ml ether. Shake and wash ether layer twice with 5 ml portions of 18% HCl.

(2) Re-extract Mo from ether with two 5 ml portions of water.

(3) Combine aqueous extracts and boil out the ether. Acidify with HCl, add 1 drop formic acid and 5 drops ammonium sulphide. Spin down MoS_3, add 2 drops $Cu(NO_3)_2$ and spin again.

(4) Dissolve ppt in 0·5 ml hot HNO_3, add 5 drops $Fe(NO_3)_3$ and 1 drop $NH_4H_2PO_4$ and make alkaline with NaOH. Spin down $Fe(OH)_3$.

(5) Make spt 10% in HNO_3, add 3 ml α-benzoin oxime and 3 ml acetone. Spin down Mo oximate.

(6) Dissolve ppt in hot NaOH and repeat steps (4) and (5), preferably twice.

(7) Wash final Mo α-benzoin oxime ppt twice with water and once with acetone.

Chemical yield. About 60%; the molybdenum can be weighed as the oxime complex, or ignited to MoO_3.

Separation time. 4 hours for eight samples.

Counting technique. Count 1·2 MeV betas with end-window Geiger counter. It is best to allow 2 days' decay to avoid counting Mo^{93} and to ensure equilibration of Mo^{99} with its daughter product Tc^{99m}.

Interferences. Ru and U could interfere by $Ru^{102}(n, \alpha) Mo^{99}$ and $U^{235}(n, f) Mo^{99}$ respectively.

Reference. Bowen (1959 b).

Molybdenum. Using the reaction $Mo^{100}(n, \gamma) Mo^{101} \rightarrow Tc^{101}$; $t_{\frac{1}{2}}$ 15 min.

Cross-section. 0·2 barns.   *Natural abundance.* 9·5%.

Reagents. HCl, 18% and 6%; $NaHCO_3$; $NaReO_4$, 1% Re; bromine water; chloroform; tetraphenyl·arsonium chloride, 1%.

Standard. 2×10^{-5} g Mo as ammonium molybdate.

Radiochemical separation

(1) Dissolve sample in 10 ml 18% HCl, add 5 ml bromine water and 0·5 ml $NaReO_4$. Stand for 15 min to allow Tc^{101} to build up.

(2) Boil off Br_2 and add about 7 g $NaHCO_3$ with care. Transfer to 100 ml separating funnel, dilute to 30 ml and adjust to pH 8. Add 2 ml tetraphenyl arsonium chloride and 20 ml chloroform and shake for 2 min.

(3) Run lower layer into beaker containing 10 ml 6% HCl and boil off $CHCl_3$. Add 2 ml bromine water and boil off excess Br_2.

(4) Add 2 ml tetraphenyl arsonium chloride, cool with liquid N_2 and spin or filter off ppt; wash twice with 3 ml ice-cold water.

Chemical yield. 60% by weighing tetraphenyl arsonium perrhenate; could also be measured using Tc^{99} tracer.

Separation time. 15 min (+15 min wait in step (1)).

Counting technique. Count 0·3 MeV gammas with a scintillation counter and gamma spectrometer. Radiochemical purity is inadequate for beta counting.

Interferences. Ru and U could interfere by $Ru^{101}(n, p) Tc^{101}$ and $U^{235}(n, f) Tc^{99}$, Tc^{101}, Tc^{104}, Tc^{105}, etc.

Reference. Meinke (1959).

Ruthenium. Using the reaction $Ru^{104}(n, \gamma) Ru^{105}$; $t_{\frac{1}{2}}$ 4·5 hours.

Cross-section. 6·7 barns.   *Natural abundance.* 18·5%.

Reagents. Mg dust; $NaBiO_3$; HNO_3, 70%; $HClO_4$, 72%; H_3PO_4, 90%; HBr, 48%; NaOH, 40%; $RuCl_3$, 1% Ru; NH_4Br, 1% Br; ethanol.

Standard. 10^{-4} g Ru as ammonium aquochlororuthenite.

Radiochemical separation

(1) Place sample in round-bottomed flask and add 1 ml $RuCl_3$. Dissolve in 1 ml NH_4Br, 1 ml H_3PO_4 and 10 ml HNO_3, adding 10 ml $HClO_4$ and 1 g $NaBiO_3$ to oxidize organic matter. Distil in a stream of air until oily drops of RuO_4 no longer come over.

(2) Wash distillate into a fresh round-bottomed flask with HNO_3 and redistil into NaOH.

(3) Add 4 ml ethanol to distillate and boil. Spin down black RuO_2.

(4) Dissolve ppt in 1 ml hot HBr, make alkaline with NaOH, boil and spin down RuO_2. Repeat this once more.

(5) Dissolve ppt in hot HBr, cool and add Mg dust slowly until black Ru appears. Destroy excess Mg by boiling with HBr and spin down Ru. Wash three times with water.

Chemical yield. 50%; weigh as Ru metal.

Separation time. 3 hours for two samples.

Counting technique. Count 1·15 MeV betas with end-window Geiger counter.

Interferences. Pd and U could interfere by $Pd^{108}(n, \alpha) Ru^{105}$ and $U^{235}(n, f) Ru^{105}$. Radionuclides of Os and Br may be incompletely separated.

Reference. Kleinberg (1958).

Rhodium. Using the reaction $Rh^{103}(n, \gamma) Rh^{104}$; $t_{\frac{1}{2}}$ 4·4 min.

Cross-section. 12 barns.   *Natural abundance.* 100%.

Apparatus. Spectrophotometer.

Reagents. Na_2O_2; HCl, 36% and 18%; NaOH, 40%; $RhCl_3$ (0·1% Rh in 3% HCl); pyridine; tartaric acid, 50%.

Standard. 10^{-6} g Rh as ammonium chlororhodite.

Radiochemical separation

(1) Dissolve sample in 5 g molten Na_2O_2 in Ni crucible and take up cooled melt in 20 ml 36% HCl containing 5 ml $RhCl_3$, 5 drops tartaric acid, and 8 ml pyridine. Filter off SiO_2 and wash with 5 ml 18% HCl.

(2) Transfer filtrate to 100 ml separating funnel and shake with 15 ml NaOH. Reject lower aqueous layer.

Chemical yield. Measure absorption of rhodium-pyridine complex at 420 mμ with spectrophotometer.

Separation time. 7 min.

Counting technique. Count 0·56 MeV gammas with scintillation counter and gamma spectrometer.

Interferences. Pd, Ag, and U could interfere by $Pd^{104}(n,p)Rh^{104}$; $Ag^{107}(n,\alpha)Rh^{104}$, $U^{235}(n,f)Rh^{104}$, etc. Iridium would not be separated, and excess Ru would interfere by $Ru^{104}(n,\gamma)Ru^{105} \to$ 36-hour Rh^{105}.

Reference. Steele (1960).

Palladium. Using the reaction $Pd^{108}(n,\gamma)Pd^{109}$; $t_{\frac{1}{2}}$ 14 hours.

Cross-section. 12 barns.　　*Natural abundance.* 26·8%.

Reagents. Au foil; Mg powder; Na_2O_2; Pd foil; HNO_3, 70%; HCl, 36% and 6%; NH_3, 60%; $AgNO_3$, 1% Ag; $Co(NO_3)_2$, 1% Co; $CuCl_2$, 1% Cu; $Fe(NO_3)_3$, 1% Fe; KCl, 1% K; KI, 10%; $Mn(NO_3)_2$, 1% Mn; $NaNO_3$, 1% Na; $Zn(NO_3)_2$, 1% Zn; bromine water; dimethylglyoxime, 1% in methanol; ethanol, 50%; ethyl acetate.

Standard. 10^{-6} g Pd as ammonium chloropalladite.

Radiochemical separation

(1) Fuse sample with Na_2O_2 and dissolve mixture in 36% HCl/HNO_3 in presence of 10 mg Pd and 30 mg Au foils. Evaporate to dryness, dissolve in 36% HCl/HNO_3 and evaporate again. Dissolve in 1 ml 36% HCl, add 20 ml water, spin and reject any ppt.

(2) Add 1 ml each of $Co(NO_3)_2$, $CuCl_2$, KCl, $Mn(NO_3)_2$, $NaNO_3$, and $Zn(NO_3)_2$, and excess Mg powder; warm to expel H_2, cool and spin; wash ppt with hot water.

(3) Dissolve Au+Pd in 36% HCl/HNO_3, and evaporate nearly to dryness. Dissolve residue in 6% HCl, transfer to separating funnel and extract Au with ethyl acetate.

(4) Add 1 ml each of $Co(NO_3)_2$, $CuCl_2$, KCl, $Mn(NO_3)_2$, $NaNO_3$, and $Zn(NO_3)_2$ to the aqueous layer, heat nearly to boiling and add 5 ml 1% dimethylglyoxime. Spin and wash ppt with water.

(5) Dissolve ppt in 36% HCl/HNO_3, dilute, add 1 ml each of $Fe(NO_3)_3$ and $Mn(NO_3)_2$ and 2 ml bromine water. Warm, add excess NH_3, boil, filter and reject ppt.

(6) Acidify spt with 6% HCl and repeat steps (4) and (5).

(7) Add 1 ml $AgNO_3$ to spt and 1 ml KI, boil, filter and reject ppt.

(8) Acidify spt with 6% HCl and repeat step (4).

(9) Dissolve ppt in 36% HCl/HNO_3. Dilute and add 5 ml dimethylglyoxime. Spin and wash ppt with water and 50% ethanol.

Chemical yield. 50–60%; weigh as palladium dimethylglyoxime complex.

Separation time. 3 hours.

Counting technique. Count 1·0 MeV betas with end-window Geiger counter.

Interferences. Ag could interfere by $Ag^{109}(n,p)Pd^{109}$ and Cd by $Cd^{112}(n,\alpha)Pd^{109}$. U could interfere by $U^{235}(n,f)Pd^{109}$, Pd^{111}, and Pd^{112}. Decontamination from activities other than palladium is excellent.

Reference. Vincent and Smales (1956).

Silver. Using the reaction $Ag^{109}(n,\gamma)Ag^{110m}$; $t_{\frac{1}{2}}$ 253 days.

Cross-section. 3·2 barns.   *Natural abundance.* 100%.

Apparatus. Micro-electrolysis cell (Fig. 8.4).

Reagents. H_2SO_4, 98%; HNO_3, 70%; HCl, 18%; $HClO_4$, 72%; HF, 40%; NH_3, 60%; NaOH, 40%; $AgNO_3$, 1% Ag; $FeCl_3$, 10%; KIO_3, 1·5%; ammonium sulphide, 50%; plating solution (70 ml 15% NaCN +10 ml 20% NaOH).

Standard. 10^{-6} g Ag as $AgNO_3$.

Radiochemical separation

(1) Dissolve sample in $HNO_3/HClO_4$ containing 2 ml $AgNO_3$, adding HF if necessary. Evaporate to fumes and then to small bulk. Dissolve in water, acidify with HNO_3 and ppt AgCl with minimum HCl. Spin and wash ppt with hot water.

(2) Dissolve ppt in NH_3, dilute with water and add 0·5 ml $FeCl_3$. Filter and discard ppt.

(3) Add 1 ml ammonium sulphide and spin down Ag_2S.

(4) Dissolve ppt in HNO_3 and dilute with water. Ppt AgCl with minimum HCl, spin and wash with water.

(5) Dissolve ppt in 8 ml plating solution. Electrolyse at 4 volts for 15 min and wash Pt cathode with water. Dissolve Ag in HNO_3 and repeat steps (4) and (5).

(6) Dissolve Ag in HNO_3, add excess 20% NaOH and spin down Ag_2O.

(7) Dissolve ppt in minimum H_2SO_4, dilute, boil and add 1 ml KIO_3. Spin, dissolve ppt in NH_3 discarding any residue. Acidify with H_2SO_4, spin down $AgIO_3$ and wash with water and ethanol. Dry at 110° C.

Chemical yield. 60%; weigh as $AgIO_3$.

Separation time. About 4 hours for six samples.

Counting technique. Count 0·54 MeV betas with end-window Geiger counter.

Interferences. Cd and In interfere by $Cd^{110} (n,p) Ag^{110}$ and $In^{113} (n,\alpha) Ag^{110}$ respectively, giving several p.p.m. apparent Ag. U gives 7·5-day Ag^{111} in low yield as a fission product.

References. Morris and Killick (1960 a); cf. also Kusaka (1960) for rapid technique using 2·3-min Ag^{108}.

Cadmium. Using the reaction $Cd^{114} (n, \gamma) Cd^{115}$; $t_{\frac{1}{2}}$ 2·2 days.

Cross-section. 1·1 barns. *Natural abundance.* 28·8%.

Reagents. $KHSO_3$; H_2SO_4, 10%; HCl, 18%; NH_3, 60%; NaOH, 40%; Ag_2SO_4, 1% Ag; $CdSO_4$, 1% Cd; $CuCl_2$, 1% Cu; $FeCl_3$, 1% Fe; KHgSCN (dissolve 39 g KSCN in 100 ml water and stir in 27 g $HgCl_2$ while diluting to 1 litre); KSCN, 20%; NH_4Cl, 20%; $(NH_4)_2HPO_4$, 1% P; $Pd(NO_3)_2$, 1% Pd; $ZnSO_4$, 1% Zn; ammonium acetate, 50%; pyridine; H_2S, saturated solution; H_2S generator.

Standard. 10^{-5} g Cd as $CdSO_4$.

Radiochemical separation

(1) Dissolve sample in the presence of 2 ml $CdSO_4$, add excess NaOH and spin down $Cd(OH)_2$.

(2) Dissolve ppt in HCl. Almost neutralize with NH_3, add 1 ml $ZnSO_4$ and excess KHgSCN, cool in ice, spin and discard ppt.

(3) Add KSCN and pyridine to spt, coagulate by shaking and spin.

(4) Dissolve ppt in HCl, dilute to 0·6% HCl, add 1 ml $ZnSO_4$ and 1 ml $(NH_4)_2HPO_4$ and saturate with H_2S. Spin down CdS and wash with H_2S solution.

(5) Dissolve ppt in HCl. Boil to expel H_2S, add 1 ml $CuCl_2$ and dilute to 0·06% HCl. Add 0·5 g $KHSO_3$ and 1 ml KSCN, spin and discard ppt.

(6) Saturate spt with H_2S, spin and wash ppt with H_2S solution.

(7) Dissolve ppt in H_2SO_4, boil to expel H_2S, add 1 ml Ag_2SO_4 and ppt AgCl with 5 drops HCl. Spin down and discard ppt.

(8) Add 1 ml $Pd(NO_3)_2$ and excess HCl to spt, and saturate with H_2S. Spin down and discard ppt.

(9) Add NH_3 to spt till CdS begins to ppt, then saturate with H_2S. Spin down CdS.

(10) Dissolve ppt in HCl, add 1 ml $FeCl_3$, dilute and add NH_3 till $Fe(OH)_3$ begins to ppt. Clear solution with HCl, add 5 drops of ammonium acetate, warm, spin down and discard ppt.

(11) Just acidify with HCl, saturate with H_2S, spin and wash ppt with H_2S water.

(12) Dissolve ppt in HCl, boil to expel H_2S, dilute and neutralize

with NH_3. Add 1·5 ml NH_4Cl and 1·5 ml $(NH_4)_2HPO_4$, spin and wash ppt with water and ethanol. Dry at 110° C.

Chemical yield. 60–70%; weigh as $CdNH_4PO_4.H_2O$.

Separation time. 4–6 hours for six samples.

Counting technique. Count 1·1 MeV betas with end-window Geiger counter.

Interferences. In and Sn interfere by $In^{115}(n,p)Cd^{115}$ and $Sn^{118}(n,\alpha)Cd^{115}$. Cd^{115} is a fission product of U^{235}.

Reference. Gibbons (1960 a).

Indium. Using the reaction $In^{113}(n,\gamma)In^{114m}$; $t_{\frac{1}{2}}$ 50 days.

Cross-section. 56 barns.   *Natural abundance.* 4·3%.

Reagents. Na_2O_2; HCl, 36%, 18%, and 15%; $HClO_4$, 72%; HBr, 48% and 24%; NH_3, 60%; NaOH, 40%; $BaCl_2$, 1% Ba; $CuCl_2$, 1% Cu; $FeCl_3$, 1% Fe; $InCl_3$, 0·3% In in 3% HCl; Na_2SO_3, 15%; $NiCl_2$, 1% Ni; ammonium acetate, 50%; acetate buffer (27% sodium acetate in 6% acetic acid); diethyl ether; ethanol, 5%; oxine (5% 8-hydroxy quinoline in ethanol).

Standard. 10^{-6} g In as $InCl_3$.

Radiochemical separation

(1) Fuse sample with sodium peroxide, dissolve in water, add excess 36% HCl containing 15 ml $InCl_3$ and 1 ml $NiCl_2$ and boil. Make alkaline with NH_3 and spin down $In(OH)_3$.

(2) Dissolve ppt in 10 ml $HClO_4$ and evaporate to fumes. Dilute with hot water, filter and wash ppt with hot water. Reject ppt.

(3) Combine spt and washings, add excess NaOH and spin.

(4) Dissolve ppt in 6% HCl, add 2 ml Na_2SO_3 and excess NH_3 and spin.

(5) Dissolve ppt in 11 ml 48% HBr, dilute with 9 ml water to 36% HBr, transfer to separating funnel and extract twice with ether. Wash combined ether layers with 24% HBr, and back extract with 18% HCl three times. Wash acid layers with ether.

(6) Add 1 ml $FeCl_3$ to aqueous solution and extract with ether twice. Add a further ml $FeCl_3$ and extract with ether three times, rejecting ether layers.

(7) Add 1 ml $CuCl_2$ and NH_3 till blue, then 36% HCl till colour fades. Add 1 ml excess HCl and dilute to 2% in HCl. Saturate with H_2S at 60° C and discard ppt. Boil to expel H_2S, add 1 ml $CuCl_2$ and saturate with H_2S at 60° C. Reject ppt.

(8) Add 4 ml ammonium acetate to spt, saturate with H_2S at 70–

$80°$ C, spin and dissolve InS_3 in $1·5\%$ HCl. Add 4 ml ammonium acetate, saturate with H_2S and spin again.

(9) Dissolve ppt in $1·5\%$ HCl, boil to expel H_2S and add 1 ml $BaCl_2$. Add excess NH_3 and spin.

(10) Dissolve $In(OH)_3$ ppt in 4 drops 36% HCl. Dilute with water and add 2 ml oxine. Heat to $55°$ C and add 5 ml acetate buffer slowly. Spin and wash with hot 5% ethanol.

Chemical yield. 50%; weigh as indium oxinate.

Separation time. 2–3 hours.

Counting technique. Count $0·19$ MeV gammas with scintillation counter.

Interferences. Sn gives 100 p.p.m. apparent In due to $Sn^{114}(n, p)In^{114}$ and U gives 2 p.p.m. apparent In due to $U^{235}(n, f)In^{114}$. Cd might interfere by $Cd^{114}(n, \gamma)Cd^{115m} \to 4·5$-hour In^{115}.

Reference. Smales, Smit, and Irving (1957).

Tin. Using the reaction $Sn^{120}(n, \gamma)Sn^{121}$; $t_\frac{1}{2}$ $1·1$ days.

Cross-section. $0·14$ barns.   *Natural abundance.* $32·5\%$.

Reagents. Na_2O_2; H_2SO_4, 98%; HCl, 36% and 6%; HF, 40%; H_3BO_3, 3%; NaOH, 40%; $AsCl_3$, 1% As; $FeCl_3$, 1% Fe; $La(NO_3)_3$, 1% La; $SbCl_3$, 1% Sb; $SnCl_4$, 1% Sn; ammonium molybdate, 1% Mo; bromine water; cupferron, 6%; ethanol; H_2S generator.

Standard. 10^{-4} g Sn as ammonium chlorostannate.

Radiochemical separation

(1) Fuse sample with Na_2O_2, dissolve in water and acidify with 36% HCl. Add 2 ml $SnCl_4$ and dilute to 6% HCl. Add slight excess bromine water, saturate with H_2S, spin and wash ppt with 6% HCl.

(2) Dissolve ppt in 1 ml 36% HCl and dilute to 6% HCl. Add slight excess bromine water, saturate with H_2S, spin and wash ppt with 6% HCl.

(3) Dissolve ppt in 1 ml 36% HCl, add bromine water, 1 ml each of $AsCl_3$, $SbCl_3$, and ammonium molybdate, $0·5$ ml H_2SO_4, $0·5$ ml HF, and dilute to 15 ml. Saturate with H_2S, warm, add 1 ml $La(NO_3)_3$, spin down and discard ppt.

(4) Add 10 ml H_3BO_3 to spt, warm and saturate with H_2S. Spin down SnS_2 and reject spt.

(5) Repeat steps (3) and (4). Dissolve SnS_2 in 36% HCl, add bromine water, 1 ml $FeCl_3$ and excess NaOH, spin, add 1 ml $FeCl_3$, spin down and discard ppts.

(6) Add 5 ml cupferron to spt, cool in ice and add 36% HCl until permanent ppt forms. Filter and wash thoroughly with water.

(7) Char cautiously and finally ignite at 700° C for 1 hour. Slurry and wash residue with water and finally with ethanol.

Chemical yield. 60–70%; weigh as SnO_2.

Separation time. About 4 hours.

Counting technique. Count 0·38 MeV betas with end-window Geiger counter, correcting for self-absorption.

Interferences. Sb, Te, and U could interfere by $Sb^{121}(n,p)Sn^{121}$, $Te^{124}(n,\alpha)Sn^{121}$, and $U^{235}(n,f)Sn^{121}$.

Reference. Cali, Lowe, Reilly, and Thompson (1957).

Antimony. Using the reaction $Sb^{121}(n,\gamma)Sb^{122}$; $t_{\frac{1}{2}}$ 2·8 days.

Cross-section. 6·8 barns.   *Natural abundance.* 57%.

Reagents. As powder; KNO_3; NaOH; $Na_2S_2O_4$; P, red; Sb powder; HCl, 36%; NaOH, 5%; H_2O_2, 3%; $Co(NO_3)_2$, 1% Co; $Cr_2(SO_4)_3$, 1% Cr; $CuCl_2$, 1% Cu; $FeSO_4$, 1% Fe; I_2, 1·2% in 1·6% KI; $KClO_3$, 50%; KOH, 10%, saturated with H_2S; $La(NO_3)_3$, 1% La; NH_4SCN, 50%; $Sr(NO_3)_2$, 1% Sr; $Zn(NO_3)_2$, 1% Zn; H_2S generator.

Standard. 10^{-7} g Sb as $SbCl_3$.

Radiochemical separation

(1) Fuse sample with NaOH in presence of 40 mg Sb, 50 mg As, and 1 g KNO_3. Dissolve melt in water, add 2 ml $CuCl_2$ and 20 ml H_2O_2 and dilute to 100 ml. Boil, cool, add 5 g $Na_2S_2O_4$ and boil 10 min. Add 2 g $Na_2S_2O_4$, boil and spin.

(2) Dissolve ppt in 5 ml HCl and 5 ml H_2O_2, dilute to 100 ml and saturate with H_2S. Centrifuge, digest ppt with KOH/H_2S, spin and discard ppt.

(3) Acidify spt with HCl and spin down Sb_2S_3.

(4) Dissolve ppt in 5 ml HCl+1 ml $KClO_3$. Add 1 ml each of $Co(NO_3)_3$, $Cr_2(SO_4)_3$, $CuCl_2$, $FeSO_4$, $La(NO_3)_3$, $Sr(NO_3)_2$, and $Zn(NO_3)_2$, dilute to 100 ml, boil and saturate with H_2S. Spin, digest ppt with KOH/H_2S, spin down and discard ppt.

(5) Acidify spt with HCl and spin down Sb_2S_3.

(6) Dissolve ppt in 5 ml HCl+1 ml $KClO_3$. Add 5 ml KI_3, 0·5 g red P, and 10 ml HCl. Heat, filter and dilute filtrate to 100 ml with water. Almost neutralize with NaOH, boil, add 25 ml NH_4SCN and heat for 15 min. Spin down red ppt and wash thoroughly with water.

Chemical yield. 70–80%; weigh as Sb_2S_3.

Separation time. 2 hours for six samples.

Counting technique. Count 1·4 and 2·0 MeV betas with end-window Geiger counter.

Interferences. Te and U could interfere by $Te^{122}(n,p)Sb^{122}$ and $U^{235}(n,f)Sb^{126}$ and Sb^{127}; care must be taken to decontaminate from traces of Au^{198}.

Reference. Smales, Mapper, Wood, and Salmon (1957).

Tellurium. Using the reaction $Te^{126}(n,\gamma)Te^{127}$; $t_{\frac{1}{2}}$ 9·4 hours.

Cross-section. 0·8 barns.   *Natural abundance.* 18·7%.

Reagents. Te; Na_2O_2; HNO_3, 70%; HCl, 36%, 18%, 12%, and 1·7%; NH_3, 60%; $FeCl_3$, 1% Fe; SO_2 generator; De-Acidite FF, 100–200 mesh.

Standard. 10^{-5} g Te (dissolved in redistilled HNO_3).

Radiochemical separation

(1) Fuse sample with Na_2O_2 and 20 mg Te. Cool, dissolve in 18% HCl, pass SO_2 and spin down Te.

(2) Dissolve ppt in 1:3 HNO_3/36% HCl; add slight excess NH_3 and 5 drops $FeCl_3$. Stir well, filter and discard ppt.

(3) Absorb solution on De-Acidite FF column, 4 cm long × 0·8 cm diameter and wash with 10 ml 12% HCl. Elute with 17% HCl and collect 10 ml eluate.

(4) Pass SO_2 through eluate, spin and wash ppt with SO_2 solution and with water.

Chemical yield. 50–80%.

Separation time. 1–2 hours for six samples.

Counting technique. Count 0·70 MeV betas with end-window Geiger counter.

Interferences. Separation gives 10^4 decontamination factor from Ag, Ce, Co, Cs, Hg, Ir, Nb, Ru, Sb, Se, Si, Ta, Zn, and Zr. I interferes by $I^{127}(n,p)Te^{127}$ and Xe could interfere by $Xe^{130}(n,\alpha)Te^{127}$, but is unlikely to be present. U interferes by $U^{235}(n,f)$ 1·2-day Te^{131} and 3·2-day Te^{132} which show up in decay studies.

Reference. Schindewolf (1960).

Iodine. Using the reaction $I^{127}(n,\gamma)I^{128}$; $t_{\frac{1}{2}}$ 25 min.

Cross-section. 5·6 barns.   *Natural abundance.* 100%.

Reagents. HNO_3, 70% and 18%; H_3PO_4, 90%; NH_3, 60%; NaOH, 5% and 0·5%; $AgNO_3$, 4%; $NaNO_2$, 1%; NH_4Br, 5%; NH_4Cl, 5%; NH_4I, 1% I; carbon tetrachloride.

Standard. 10^{-6} g I as NH_4I.

Radiochemical separation

(1) Add sample to round-bottomed flask containing 1 ml H_3PO_4, 5 ml 70% HNO_3, and 2 ml NH_4I. Fit distillation head (Fig. 8.1) and

distil in a slow current of air from a sand bath at 150°–180° C. Collect distillate in 10 ml 5% NaOH in a separating funnel; chase iodine over with a hot-air blower if necessary.

(2) Acidify distillate with 18% HNO_3; add 5 drops $NaNO_2$, 1 drop NH_4Cl, and 1 drop NH_4Br. Shake three times with 5 ml portions of CCl_4.

(3) Re-extract I_2 from combined CCl_4 layers by shaking with 10 ml 0·5% NaOH.

(4) Repeat steps (2) and (3) once or twice more.

(5) Transfer aqueous layer to centrifuge tube, add 2 ml NH_3, 5 drops NH_4Cl, and 3 ml $AgNO_3$. Boil and spin down AgI. Wash ppt once with 18% HNO_3 and twice with water.

Chemical yield. About 70%; weigh as AgI.

Separation time. 1 hour for six samples.

Counting technique. Count 1·6 and 2·1 MeV betas with end-window Geiger counter if Cl^{38} has been completely removed. If it has not, count 0·45 and 0·53 MeV gammas with scintillation counter and gamma spectrometer.

Interferences. Uranium in the sample will interfere by producing fission product iodine, e.g. $U^{235}(n,f)I^{132}$, I^{134}, etc. Xe could interfere by $Xe^{128}(n,p)I^{128}$, and excess Te by $Te^{130}(n,\gamma)Te^{131} \to$ 8-day I^{131}.

Reference. Bowen (1959 c).

Xenon. Using the reaction $Xe^{132}(n,\gamma)Xe^{133}$; $t_{\frac{1}{2}}$ 5·6 days.

Cross-section. 0·2 barns.   *Natural abundance.* 26·9% (but see remarks below).

Apparatus. Vacuum line (Fig. 13.2).

Reagents. Mg powder; activated charcoal; helium gas.

Standard. 10^{-6} g Xe.

Radiochemical separation (suggested method)

(1) If sample is not already gaseous, dissolve or melt it and pump off evolved gases in a stream of carrier He.

(2) Pass gases successively over Mg at 500° C and activated charcoal at −195° C.

(3) Warm charcoal to room temperature, and elute with He through a second charcoal column at −45° C. When Kr has been eluted, warm column to 50° C and elute Xe.

Counting technique. Count 0·35 MeV betas with gas-flow counter.

Interferences. Kr^{85} could contaminate the product, together with Xe isotopes (including Xe^{133}) produced by fission of uranium in the sample. Cs could interfere by $Cs^{133}(n,p)Xe^{133}$.

Remarks. The isotopic composition of atmospheric Xe differs greatly from that of Xe retained by radioactive minerals.

References. Wilson and Taylor (1958), Wilson, Dibbs, Richards, and Eakins (1958).

Caesium. Using the reaction $Cs^{133}(n, \gamma) Cs^{134}$; $t_{\frac{1}{2}}$ 2·1 years.

Cross-section. 30 barns.   *Natural abundance.* 100%.

Reagents. Na_2O_2; HNO_3, 35%; HCl, 36%, 3·5%, 1·7%, and 0·35%; NaOH, 40%; CsCl, 4% Cs; $FeCl_3$, 10%; H_2PtCl_6, 10%; $Na_3Co(NO_2)_6$, 10%; RbCl, 4% Rb; acetic acid; ethanol; Zeo-Karb 315,† 85–120 mesh.

Standard. 10^{-6} g Cs as CsCl.

Radiochemical separation

(1) Fuse sample with Na_2O_2, 1 ml CsCl, and 1 ml RbCl. Dissolve in water, add 1 ml $FeCl_3$ and acidify with HCl. Neutralize with NaOH, filter and reject ppt.

(2) Acidify spt with acetic acid, add 0·5 ml $FeCl_3$ and neutralize with NaOH. Filter and reject ppt.

(3) Acidify spt with acetic acid, add $Na_3Co(NO_2)_6$ and cool in ice. Spin and wash ppt with water.

(4) Dissolve ppt in nitric acid, evaporate to dryness and dissolve residue in water. Transfer to Zeo-Karb 315† column (25 cm long × 1 cm diameter), elute K with 600 ml 0·35% HCl at 0·5 ml/min and reject. Elute Rb with 200 ml 1·7% HCl and reject. Elute Cs with 200 ml 3·5% HCl according to predetermined elution curves.

(5) Evaporate Cs eluate to dryness, dissolve in water, add excess NaOH, filter and reject ppt.

(6) Acidify spt with acetic acid, add $Na_3Co(NO_2)_6$, spin and wash ppt with water.

(7) Dissolve ppt in HNO_3; add ethanol and H_2PtCl_6. Cool in ice, spin and wash ppt with ethanol.

Chemical yield. 50–70%; weigh as Cs_2PtCl_6.

Separation time. 12 hours including ion exchange.

Counting technique. Count 0·65 MeV betas with end-window Geiger counter. Allow 30 hours for Cs^{134m} to decay.

Interferences. Ba gives 10 p.p.m. apparent Cs by $Ba^{134}(n, p) Cs^{134}$, La gives 1 p.p.m. apparent Cs by $La^{137}(n, \alpha) Cs^{134}$, and U gives 220 p.p.m. apparent Cs by $U^{235}(n, f) Cs^{134}$ and Cs^{137}.

References. Smales and Salmon (1955), Cabell and Smales (1957).

Barium. Using the reaction $Ba^{138}(n, \gamma) Ba^{139}$; $t_{\frac{1}{2}}$ 1·4 hours.

Cross-section. 0·5 barns.   *Natural abundance.* 70·4%.

† This resin is now obsolete, but Zeo-Karb 215 is similar in properties.

Reagents. HNO_3, 100% and 70%; HCl, 6%; NH_3, 60%; $Cu(NO_3)_2$, 10%; $Fe(NO_3)_3$, 10%; K_2CrO_4, 50%; $Mn(NO_3)_2$, 10%; Na_2CO_3, 10%; $NH_4H_2PO_4$, 10%; $Y(NO_3)_3$, 10%; acetic acid; ammonium acetate, 50%; barium acetate, 10% Ba.

Standard. 10^{-5} g Ba as $Ba(NO_3)_2$.

Radiochemical separation

(1) Dissolve sample in 10 ml 100% HNO_3; add 0·2 ml barium acetate and 1 drop each of $Cu(NO_3)_2$, $Mn(NO_3)_2$, $Y(NO_3)_3$, and $NH_4H_2PO_4$. Cool in ice for 10 min and spin down $Ba(NO_3)_2$.

(2) Dissolve ppt in 2 ml water; add 8 ml 100% HNO_3 and 4 ml 70% HNO_3. Spin down $Ba(NO_3)_2$ and wash with 70% HNO_3.

(3) Dissolve ppt in 1 ml NH_3 and make up to 10 ml with water. Add 1 drop $Mn(NO_3)_2$ and 1 drop $Fe(NO_3)_2$, and spin down $Fe(OH)_3$.

(4) Add 4 ml Na_2CO_3 to spt and spin down $BaCO_3$.

(5) Dissolve ppt in hot acetic acid, boil and add 4 ml ammonium acetate, 1 drop $NH_4H_2PO_4$, 1 drop strontium acetate, and a few drops of K_2CrO_4 till no more ppt forms. Spin down $BaCrO_4$.

(6) Dissolve ppt in hot HCl and repeat step (5) twice. Wash $BaCrO_4$ three times with water.

Chemical yield. 80–90%; weigh as $BaCrO_4$.

Separation time. 2 hours for eight samples.

Counting technique. Count 2·2 MeV betas with end-window Geiger counter.

Interferences. La, Ce, and U could interfere by $La^{139}(n,p)Ba^{139}$, $Ce^{142}(n,\alpha)Ba^{139}$, and $U^{235}(n,f)Ba^{139}$.

References. Harrison and Raymond (1955), Bowen and Cawse (1959). Uranium determination (p. 268).

Lanthanum–Lutecium (excluding Promethium) using the reactions given on p. 256.

Apparatus. Fraction collector; resin column with controlled temperature jacket.

Reagents. H_2SO_4, 98%; HNO_3, 70%; HCl, 6% and 1·5%; HF, 40%; H_3BO_3, 3%; NH_3, 60%; H_2O_2, 3%; specpure $CaCl_2$, 0·2% Ca; oxalic acid, 10%; Zeo-Karb 225 in NH_4 form (300–330 mesh).

Eluant A: 5% citric acid brought to pH 3·20 with NH_3 and degassed.

,,	B	,,	,,	3·25	,,	,,
,,	C	,,	,,	3·34	,,	,,
,,	D	,,	,,	3·48	,,	,,
,,	E	,,	,,	4·00	,,	,,

Lanthanide carrier: La, Ce, Pr, Nd, Sm, and Y, 0·0075%.

Eu, Gd, and Dy, 0·0025%.

Tb, Ho, Er, Tm, Yb, and Lu, 0·0005%.

TABLE 13.1. *Activation data for lanthanides*

Reaction	$t_{\frac{1}{2}}$	Beta energy (MeV)	σ (barns)	% Natural abundance
$La^{139}(n, \gamma) La^{140}$	1·67 days	1·34	8·5	99·9
$Ce^{142}(n, \gamma) Ce^{143}$	1·37 days	1·13	1·0	11·1
$Pr^{141}(n, \gamma) Pr^{142}$	19 hours	2·16	10	100
$Nd^{146}(n, \gamma) Nd^{147}$	12 days	0·81	1·8	17·1
$Sm^{152}(n, \gamma) Sm^{153}$	1·9 days	0·65	140	26·8
$Eu^{151}(n, \gamma) Eu^{152}$	13 years	1·46	7400	47·8
$Gd^{158}(n, \gamma) Gd^{159}$	18 hours	0·95	4	24·5
$Tb^{159}(n, \gamma) Tb^{160}$	72 days	0·57	22	100
$Dy^{164}(2n, \gamma) Dy^{166}$	3·4 days	0·30	2100+5000	28·1
$Ho^{165}(n, \gamma) Ho^{166}$	1·12 days	1·85	60	100
$Er^{168}(n, \gamma) Er^{169}$	9·0 days	0·34	2	27·1
$Tm^{169}(n, \gamma) Tm^{170}$	129 days	0·95	130	100
$Yb^{174}(n, \gamma) Yb^{175}$	4·2 days	0·47	60	31·6
$Lu^{176}(n, \gamma) Lu^{177}$	6·8 days	0·50	4000	2·6

Standards. 10^{-8} g Ho, Lu, Sm, Yb; 5×10^{-8} g Eu, La, Pr, Tb, Tm; 2×10^{-6} g Ce, Dy, Er, Gd, Nd. Dissolve dry oxides in distilled HNO_3 and dilute before taking aliquots.

Radiochemical separation

(1) Dissolve sample in HNO_3, add 20 ml lanthanide carrier and boil with 2 drops H_2O_2. Add excess NH_3, spin down $M(OH)_3$ and wash with water.

(2) Dissolve ppt in 6% HCl, add excess oxalic acid and spin down $M_2(C_2O_4)_3$.

(3) Dissolve ppt in 3 ml H_2SO_4, cool, dilute, add NH_3 and spin down $M(OH)_3$.

(4) Dissolve ppt in 6% HCl, transfer to polythene centrifuge tube and add HF. Spin down MF_3 and wash twice with water.

(5) Dissolve ppt in 1:1 HNO_3/H_3BO_3, add NH_3 and spin down $M(OH)_3$.

(6) Repeat steps (2)–(5) once more.

(7) Dissolve ppt in 3 ml 1·5% HCl, pour through a 10 cm long $\times$ 0·4 cm diameter column of Zeo-Karb 225. Wash column with water.

(8) Slurry resin onto main ion exchange column, 115 cm long $\times$ 0·5 cm diameter, and slurry a further 0·5 g clean resin above this to prevent back diffusion. Siphon off excess water and elute with eluant A at 45° C. After 3 hours increase the column temperature to 80° C and connect up fraction collector.

(9) Replace eluants as follows:

After 20 hours change to eluant B
    40   ,,   ,,   C
    70   ,,   ,,   D
    90   ,,   ,,   E

(10) Treat each fraction containing peak activity with 5 ml $CaCl_2$ and excess oxalic acid. Spin and wash ppt twice with water.

Chemical yields. Reactivate CaC_2O_4 ppts from standard, sample, and blank for half-life of lanthanide and count them. From the counts the relative amounts of carrier separated can be calculated.

Separation time. About 4 days.

Counting technique. The fraction collector can be fitted with an automatic ratemeter and recorder, or all fractions can be liquid counted. The CaC_2O_4 precipitates are readily counted with an end-window beta counter.

Remarks. (1) The weights of lanthanides used in the carrier are not critical, and those quoted involve the minimum of expense. (2) Spec-pure lanthanide oxides are suitable for standards with the possible exception of Ho_2O_3. (3) The lanthanides are eluted in the reverse order of their atomic weights, and are invariably accompanied by yttrium, which elutes between Ho and Dy.

Interferences. There are many nuclear transmutations which could interfere with lanthanide determinations.

In addition to (n, p), (n, α), and $(2n, \gamma)$ reactions within the lanthanide group (including reactions yielding Pm^{147}, Pm^{148}, Pm^{149}, and Pm^{151}, which elute between Sm and Nd), the following could be important:

$Ba^{138} (2n, \gamma) Ba^{140} \rightarrow La^{140}$, $Hf^{178} (n, \alpha) Yb^{175}$, $Hf^{177} (n, p) Lu^{177}$, and $Ta^{180} (n, \alpha) Lu^{177}$. U yields many lanthanide nuclides in good yield including La^{140}, Ce^{143}, Nd^{147}, Pm^{149}, Sm^{153}, and Gd^{159}, by fission, but none heavier than Tb.

Reference. Cornish (1953).

Hafnium. Using the reaction $Hf^{180} (n, \gamma) Hf^{181}$; $t_{\frac{1}{2}}$ 45 days.

Cross-section. 10 barns.   *Natural abundance.* 35·2%.

Reagents. H_2SO_4, 2·4%; HNO_3, 70%; HF, 40%; H_3BO_3, 3%; NH_3, 60%; $Ba(NO_3)_2$, 10%; $HfO(NO_3)_2$, 1% Hf; $La(NO_3)_3$, 1% La; Zeo-Karb 225, 200–400 mesh, NH_4 form.

Standard. 10^{-7} g Hf (dissolve HfO_2 in $H_2SO_4 + HF$).

Radiochemical separation

(1) Dissolve sample in $HNO_3 + HF$ in polythene tube. Add 1 ml each of $HfO(NO_3)_2$ and $La(NO_3)_3$, boil and spin down LaF_3. Add more La and spin down LaF_3 again.

(2) Cool and dilute spt to 15% in HNO_3, add 1 ml $Ba(NO_3)_2$ and spin down $BaHfF_6$. Wash with water.

(3) Dissolve ppt in 1:1 HNO_3/H_3BO_3, add excess NH_3 and spin down $Hf(OH)_4$.

(4) Dissolve ppt in 2·4% H_2SO_4 and transfer to 80 cm × 0·05 cm² Zeo-Karb 225 column. Zr is eluted first and, if elution is carried out at 0·15 ml/min, the Hf appears in the 110–150 ml fraction of eluate.

(5) Add excess NH_3 to Hf eluate fraction, spin down $Hf(OH)_4$ and wash three times with water.

Chemical yield. 70%; ignite at 800° C and weigh as HfO_2.

Separation time. 17 hours for eight samples.

Counting technique. Count 0·41 MeV betas with end-window Geiger counter, correcting for self-absorption.

Interferences. Excess Ta or W could interfere by $Ta^{181}(n, p) Hf^{181}$ and $W^{184}(n, \alpha) Hf^{181}$.

References. Meinke (1949), Herr, Merz, Eberhardt, and Signer (1958).

Tantalum. Using the reaction $Ta^{181}(n, \gamma) Ta^{182}$; $t_{\frac{1}{2}}$ 115 days.

Cross-section. 19 barns.   *Natural abundance.* 100%.

Reagents. Na_2O_2; H_2SO_4, 16%; H_2SO_4, 32% containing 0·5% HF; HNO_3, 100%; HF, 40%; NH_3, 60%; H_2O_2, 3%; $Fe(NO_3)_3$, 10%; Na_3TaO_4, 3% Ta, stabilized with tartaric acid; NH_4NO_3, 10%; ethanol; di-isopropyl ketone equilibrated with H_2SO_4/HF reagent; tri-2,2'dipyridyl ferrous sulphate, 6%.

Standard. 10^{-7} g Ta as oxalate.

Radiochemical separation

(1) Fuse sample with Na_2O_2 and obtain a solution in H_2SO_4 containing 1 ml Na_3TaO_4. Add 5 ml NH_4NO_3, 1 drop $Fe(NO_3)_3$, and make alkaline with NH_3. Spin down $Fe(OH)_3$ and wash with $NH_4NO_3 + NH_3$.

(2) Stir ppt with boiling 10% HNO_3 and spin down $Ta(OH)_5$.

(3) Dissolve ppt in H_2SO_4/HF reagent and transfer to separating funnel containing 10 ml di-isopropyl ketone. Shake up and wash the organic layer twice with H_2SO_4/HF reagent; reject aqueous layer.

(4) Re-extract Ta into aqueous layer by shaking with 10 ml H_2O_2 (spin to break emulsion if necessary).

(5) Make alkaline with NH_3, boil to destroy H_2O_2 and spin down $Ta(OH)_5$.

(6) Repeat steps (3), (4), and (5).

(7) Dissolve ppt in 1–2 drops HF, dilute to 5 ml and add 10 drops tri-2,2′dipyridyl $FeSO_4$. Spin down $Fe(Dipy)_3(TaF_6)_2$, wash twice with water and once with ethanol.

Chemical yield. 50%; weigh as $Fe(Dipy)_3(TaF_6)_2$.

Separation time. 5 hours for eight samples.

Counting technique. Count 0·51 MeV betas with end-window Geiger counter, correcting for self-absorption.

Interferences. W gives 0·23 p.p.m. Ta by $W^{182}(n,p)Ta^{182}$ and Re gives 4·4 p.p.m. Ta by $Re^{185}(n,\alpha)Ta^{182}$.

Remarks. Hexone may be used instead of di-isopropyl ketone.

Reference. Atkins and Smales (1960).

Tungsten. Using the reaction $W^{186}(n,\gamma)W^{187}$; $t_{\frac{1}{2}}$ 24 hours.

Cross-section. 34 barns.   *Natural abundance.* 28·7%.

Reagents. Na_2O_2; H_2SO_4, 10%; HNO_3, 100% and 70%; NH_3, 60%; $Cu(NO_3)_2$, 10%; $Fe(NO_3)_3$, 10%; $MgCl_2$, 10%; Na_2WO_4, 1% W; $NH_4H_2PO_4$, 10%; ammonium acetate, 50%; α-benzoin oxime, 2% in ethanol; chloroform; cupferron, 6%; tartaric acid, 5%.

Standard. 10^{-7} g W (dissolve WO_3 in redistilled NH_3).

Radiochemical separation

(1) Fuse sample with Na_2O_2 and 2 ml Na_2WO_4 in Ni crucible, cool, make 50% in HNO_3 and boil. Spin down WO_3.

(2) Dissolve ppt in NH_3, add 1 drop $Fe(NO_3)_3$ and spin down $Fe(OH)_3$.

(3) Make spt about 50% in HNO_3, boil and spin down WO_3.

(4) Repeat steps (2) and (3) at least once.

(5) Dissolve ppt in NH_3 and transfer to separating funnel containing 10 ml $CHCl_3$ and 1 drop $Cu(NO_3)_2$. Acidify with tartaric acid and shake for 0·5 min. Run $CHCl_3$ layer to waste, add fresh $CHCl_3$ and repeat.

(6) Transfer aqueous layer to centrifuge tube and add 100% HNO_3 with care until the tartaric acid is destroyed and WO_3 precipitates. Spin down the WO_3.

(7) Dissolve ppt in NH_3; add 2 ml ammonium acetate, 2 drops $NH_4H_2PO_4$, and 4 drops $MgCl_2$. Spin down $MgNH_4PO_4$.

(8) To spt add 2 ml α-benzoin oxime and acidify with H_2SO_4. Spin down W-oximate.

(9) If sample contained much P, repeat steps (7) and (8) twice. Wash the final ppt three times with water.

Chemical yield. About 50%; ignite dried ppt at 540° C for 30 min to convert to WO_3 and weigh.

Separation time. 3 hours for eight samples.

Counting technique. Count 0·63 MeV betas with end-window Geiger counter.

Interferences. Re gives 3·5 p.p.m. apparent W by $Re^{187} (n, p) W^{187}$, and Os gives 1·3 p.p.m. apparent W by $Os^{190} (n, \alpha) W^{187}$. P^{32} is a common radiochemical contaminant.

References. Bowen (1960), Atkins and Smales (1960).

Rhenium. Using the reaction $Re^{187} (n, \gamma) Re^{188}$; $t_{\frac{1}{2}}$ 17 hours.

Cross-section. 75 barns.   *Natural abundance.* 62·9%.

Reagents. H_2SO_4, 98%; HNO_3, 70%; HCl, 36% and 6%; NaOH, 5%; H_2O_2, 30%; $Fe(NO_3)_3$, 10%; $NaReO_4$, 1% Re; ammonium acetate, 50%; bromine water; chloroform; tetraphenylarsonium chloride, 1%; H_2S generator.

Standard. 10^{-7} g Re as NH_4ReO_4.

Radiochemical separation

(1) Dissolve sample in 36% HCl ($+HNO_3$ if necessary) and add 0·5 ml $NaReO_4$. Boil, pass H_2S and spin down black Re_2S_7.

(2) Dissolve ppt in 3 ml NaOH + 1 drop H_2O_2. Add 1 drop $Fe(NO_3)_3$ and spin down $Fe(OH)_3$.

(3) Add 10 ml 36% HCl to spt, boil, pass H_2S and spin down Re_2S_7.

(4) Dissolve ppt in $H_2SO_4 + H_2O_2$ and distil in a current of air. Collect distillate in NaOH.

(5) Buffer distillate to pH 8 with HNO_3 and $CH_3CO_2NH_4$ and transfer to separating funnel. Add 2 ml tetraphenylarsonium chloride and 10 ml $CHCl_3$ and shake for 2 min.

(6) Boil organic layer with 10 ml 6% HCl till $CHCl_3$ has evaporated; add 2 ml bromine water and continue boiling till Br_2 is expelled. Add 2 ml tetraphenylarsonium chloride and stand in ice for 15 min. Spin down $(C_6H_5)_4AsReO_4$ and wash twice with ice-cold water.

Chemical yield. 30%; weigh as $(C_6H_5)_4AsReO_4$.

Separation time. 2 hours.

Counting technique. Count 2·1 MeV betas with end-window Geiger counter.

Interferences. Tc, produced by uranium fission or by decay of activated molybdenum, could contaminate the Re. Os and Ir could interfere by $Os^{188}(n, p) Re^{188}$ and $Ir^{191}(n, \alpha) Re^{188}$.

References. Meinke (1949), Fukai (1959).

Osmium. Using the reaction $Os^{192}(n, \gamma) Os^{193}$; $t_{\frac{1}{2}}$ 1·3 days.

Cross-section. 1·6 barns.　　*Natural abundance.* 41%.

Reagents. HNO_3, 70%; HCl, 36%; H_3PO_4, 90%; NaOH, 40%; NH_4Br, 1% Br; $(NH_4)_2OsCl_6$, 1% Os; H_2S generator; $NaBiO_3$.

Standard. 10^{-6} g Os as ammonium chlorosmate.

Radiochemical separation (suggested method)

(1) Dissolve sample in HNO_3 in distilling flask containing 1 ml H_3PO_4, 2 ml $(NH_4)_2$ $OsCl_6$, 1 ml NH_4Br, and 1 g $NaBiO_3$. Distil in stream of air and trap distillate in NaOH.

(2) Pass H_2S into distillate, acidify with HCl and spin down OsS_2.

(3) Repeat step (1), without adding more osmium.

(4) Acidify with HCl and add Mg powder till Os is precipitated. Boil with excess HCl, spin and wash ppt with water.

Chemical yield. Weigh as the metal.

Separation time. About 30 min per sample.

Counting technique. Count 1·13 MeV betas with end-window Geiger counter.

Interferences. Iridium and platinum could interfere by $Ir^{193}(n, p) Os^{193}$ and $Pt^{196}(n, \alpha) Os^{193}$. The separation may not remove the halogens, especially Br^{82}, nor traces of Ru, Mo, Tc, and Re.

Reference. Meinke (1949).

Iridium. Using the reaction $Ir^{193}(n, \gamma) Ir^{194}$; $t_{\frac{1}{2}}$ 19 hours.

Cross-section. 130 barns.　　*Natural abundance.* 61·5%.

Reagents. Mg dust; H_2SO_4, 98%; HNO_3, 70%; HCl, 36% and 6%; $HClO_4$, 72%; NaOH, 40% and 5%; $(NH_4)_2IrCl_6$, 1% Ir; $(NH_4)_2OsCl_6$, 1% Os; $PdCl_2$, 1% Pd; $(NH_4)_2PtCl_6$, 1% Pt; $NaBrO_3$, 10%; $NaHCO_3$, 10%; $Rh(NO_3)_3$, 1% Rh; $RuCl_3$, 1% Ru; $TiCl_3$, 10%; cupferron, 6%; dimethylglyoxime, 1% in methanol; pyridine; H_2S generator.

Standard. 10^{-7} g Ir as ammonium chloroiridate.

Radiochemical separation (suggested method)

(1) Dissolve sample in HNO_3; add 2 ml $(NH_4)_2IrCl_6$, 0·5 ml each of $(NH_4)_2OsCl_6$ and $RuCl_3$, and 10 ml $HClO_4$. Heat to fuming for 5 min,

cool and add twice remaining volume of water and 20 ml pyridine. Boil for 5 min.

(2) Transfer to 100 ml separating funnel and make alkaline with 40% NaOH. Reject aqueous layer. Wash blue pyridine layer three times with 20 ml 36% HCl, separating the layers each time by adding sufficient NaOH.

(3) Add 2 ml 10% NaOH to upper layer and evaporate off pyridine. Pass H_2S while adding 6% HCl dropwise to the boiling solution, cool and spin down Ir_2S_3.

(4) Dissolve ppt in $1:3$ $HNO_3/36\%$ HCl, add 1 ml $Rh(NO_3)_3$ and evaporate to fumes with 1 ml H_2SO_4. Cool, add 20 ml water, boil and ppt Rh with $TiCl_3$.

(5) Add excess cupferron to spt and cool in ice. Filter off Ti cupferrate.

(6) Add 0·5 ml each of $PdCl_2$ and $(NH_4)_2PtCl_6$, boil and add 5 ml dimethylglyoxime. Spin down and reject ppt.

(7) Bring to pH 7 with $NaHCO_3$, add 2 ml $NaBrO_3$ and boil. Spin down IrO_2.

(8) Dissolve ppt in hot 36% HCl and add Mg dust till Ir is completely precipitated. Boil with excess HCl, spin down Ir and wash three times with water.

Chemical yield. 50%; weigh as the metal.

Separation time. 2–3 hours.

Counting technique. Count 2·2 MeV betas with end-window Geiger counter.

Interferences. Au and Pt could interfere by $Pt^{194}(n,p)Ir^{194}$ and $Au^{197}(n,\alpha)Ir^{194}$. Pd, Ru, Rh, Os, Pt, and Au may not be separated completely.

Reference. Meinke (1949).

Platinum. Using the reaction $Pt^{196}(n,\gamma)Pt^{197}$; $t_{\frac{1}{2}}$ 18 hours.

Cross-section. 0·8 barns.   *Natural abundance.* 25·2%.

Reagents. Mg dust; HNO_3, 70%; HCl, 36% and 18%; $HClO_4$, 72%; NaOH, 10%; $FeCl_3$, 10%; $HAuCl_4$, 1% Au; $(NH_4)_2IrCl_6$, 1% Ir; $(NH_4)_2OsCl_6$, 1% Os; $(NH_4)_2PtCl_6$, 1% Pt; $PdCl_2$, 1% Pd; $Rh(NO_3)_3$, 1% Rh; $RuCl_3$, 1% Ru; $SnCl_2$, 10%; butyl acetate; dimethylglyoxime, 1% in methanol; H_2S generator.

Standard. 10^{-6} g Pt as ammonium chloroplatinate.

Radiochemical separation (suggested method)

(1) Dissolve sample in HNO_3; add 2 ml $(NH_4)_2PtCl_6$ and 0·5 ml

each of $RuCl_3$, $Rh(NO_3)_3$, $HAuCl_4$, $(NH_4)_2IrCl_6$, and $(NH_4)_2OsCl_6$. Fume with 10 ml $HClO_4$ till Os and Ru are volatilized.

(2) Take up residue in 18% HCl and transfer to separating funnel. Extract Au twice with butyl acetate and reject organic fractions.

(3) Add $SnCl_2$ to aqueous layer till it turns cherry red. Extract three times with butyl acetate and reject aqueous layer.

(4) Extract organic layer with NaOH and reject butyl acetate layer.

(5) Neutralize aqueous layer with 36% HCl and add an equal volume of this acid. Extract three times with butyl acetate and reject aqueous layer.

(6) Repeat step (4).

(7) Pass H_2S into aqueous layer while acidifying slowly with 36% HCl. Spin down PtS.

(8) Dissolve ppt in $1:3$ $HNO_3/36\%$ HCl, dilute 20-fold with water, and add 1 ml $PdCl_2$ and 5 ml dimethylglyoxime. Spin down and reject ppt.

(9) Add 2 drops $FeCl_3$ to spt and make alkaline with NaOH. Filter and reject ppt.

(10) Acidify spt with 36% HCl and add Mg dust to ppt Pt. Finally boil with excess HCl, spin down Pt and wash three times with water.

Chemical yield. 50%; weigh as the metal.

Separation time. 2–3 hours.

Counting technique. Count 0·67 MeV betas with end-window Geiger counter.

Interferences. Au and Hg could interfere by $Au^{197}(n,p)Pt^{197}$ and $Hg^{200}(n,\alpha)Pt^{197}$. Ru, Rh, Pd, Os, Ir, and Au may not be separated completely.

Reference. Meinke (1949).

Gold. Using the reaction $Au^{197}(n,\gamma)Au^{198}$; $t_{\frac{1}{2}}$ 2·7 days.

Cross-section. 96 barns.   *Natural abundance.* 100%.

Reagents. Mg powder; HNO_3, 70%; HCl 36%, 12%, and 1·5%; $HClO_4$, 72%; $HAuCl_4$, 1% Au; NaCl, 1% Na; $NH_4H_2PO_4$, 1% P; ethyl acetate; hydroquinone, 50%.

Standard. 10^{-6} g Au as NH_4AuCl_4.

Radiochemical separation

(1) Dissolve sample in 5 ml $HNO_3 + 2$ ml $HClO_4$ containing 3 ml $HAuCl_3$ and evaporate to fumes. Evaporate with $1:3$ $HNO_3/36\%$ HCl and take up residue in 1·5% HCl.

(2) Add 1 ml each of NaCl and $NH_4H_2PO_4$ and 0·1 g Mg; spin down Au ppt and wash twice with water.

(3) Dissolve ppt in 1:3 HNO_3/36% HCl, evaporate to small bulk and dissolve in 12% HCl. Transfer to separating funnel, extract with 30 ml ethyl acetate and wash organic layer twice with 20 ml 12% HCl.

(4) Evaporate organic layer to dryness, dissolve residue in 1:3 HNO_3/36% HCl and evaporate. Dissolve residue in 12% HCl and add 1 ml hydroquinone. Dissolve ppt in 1:3 HNO_3/36% HCl and repeat the precipitation. Spin down Au; wash with water and ethanol.

Chemical yield. 80%; weighing as the metal.

Separation time. About 4 hours for six samples.

Counting technique. Count 0·96 MeV betas with end-window Geiger counter.

Interferences. Mercury could interfere by $Hg^{198}(n,p)Au^{198}$, and platinum by $Pt^{198}(n,\gamma)Pt^{199} \to$ 3·1-day Au^{199}.

References. Vincent and Smales (1956), Gibbons (1958).

Mercury. Using the reaction $Hg^{196}(n,\gamma)Hg^{197m}$; $t_{\frac{1}{2}}$ 25 hours.

Cross-section. 3100 barns.   *Natural abundance.* 0·15%.

Reagents. H_2SO_4, 98% and 10%; H_2SO_4, 10%, saturated with SO_2; HNO_3, 70% and 25%; HCl, 36%, 27%, and 1·7%; HF, 40%; NaOH, 40%; $Hg(NO_3)_2$, 1% Hg; $IrCl_3$, 1% Ir; $SnCl_2$, 50%, freshly made up; De-Acidite FF, 100–200 mesh.

Standard. 10^{-5} g Hg as $Hg(NO_3)_2$.

Radiochemical separation

(1) Dissolve sample in 98% H_2SO_4 containing 1 ml $Hg(NO_3)_2$, adding HF if necessary. Evaporate to a paste and dissolve in 5 ml 70% HNO_3+1 ml 36% HCl. Dilute to 50 ml with 27% HCl and transfer to De-Acidite FF column, 12·5 cm long and 1·25 cm diameter.

(2) Elute unwanted impurities with, successively, 75 ml 27% HCl, 75 ml 1·7% HCl, 25 ml water, 75 ml 10% H_2SO_4, and 75 ml 10% H_2SO_4 saturated with SO_2. Then elute Hg with 75 ml 25% HNO_3 and bring eluate to pH 6·5 with NaOH.

(3) Saturate with H_2S, spin and wash HgS with water.

(4) Dissolve ppt in 70% HNO_3+36% HCl, add 1 ml $IrCl_3$ and evaporate almost to dryness. Add 5 ml 36% HCl and evaporate again. Dilute with water and add 5 drops $SnCl_2$. Spin and wash Hg ppt with water.

(5) Repeat step (4).

(6) Dissolve Hg in 70% HNO_3+36% HCl and bring to pH 7 with

NaOH. Saturate with H_2S, spin, wash ppt with water and ethanol and dry at 110° C.

Chemical yield. 50–80%; weigh as HgS.

Separation time. 2–3 hours for six samples.

Counting technique. Count 0·13 MeV gammas with scintillation counter and gamma spectrometer.

Reference. Ehmann and Huizenga (1959).

Thallium. Using reaction $Tl^{203}(n, \gamma) Tl^{204}$; $t_{\frac{1}{2}}$ 3·6 years.

Cross-section. 8 barns.   *Natural abundance.* 29·5%.

Reagents. HNO_3, 70%; HCl, 36%, 18%, and 1·5%; $HClO_4$, 72%; NH_3, 60%; $FeCl_3$, 1% Fe; $KClO_3$, 10%; K_2CrO_4, 10% and 1%; KI, 10%; Na_2SO_3, 15%; $TlNO_3$, 1% Tl; ethanol, 50%; di-isopropyl ether equilibrated with 18% HCl; SO_2 generator.

Standard. 10^{-5} g Tl as $TlNO_3$.

Radiochemical separation

(1) Dissolve in $HNO_3/HClO_4$ containing 2 ml $TlNO_3$. Evaporate to small bulk, add 36% HCl and evaporate. Add 10 ml water, acidify with 18% HCl and add 8 ml Na_2SO_3. Warm, add 2 ml KI and cool, spin and reject spt.

(2) Dissolve TlI ppt in HNO_3 and evaporate to dryness. Dissolve residue in 18% HCl, add $KClO_3$ and warm. Add appropriate holdback carriers, transfer to separating funnel and extract $TlCl_3$ three times with isopropyl ether. Wash ether layers with 18% HCl.

(3) Evaporate ether over 10 ml water, acidify with 18% HCl, reduce with Na_2SO_3, warm, add 2 ml KI, cool, spin and reject spt.

(4) Dissolve TlI ppt in HNO_3, and evaporate to dryness. Dissolve residue in 1·5% HCl, add 0·5 ml $FeCl_3$, reduce with SO_2 and add excess NH_3. Filter and discard ppt.

(5) Acidify spt with 18% HCl, reduce with Na_2SO_3 and add KI. Spin and wash TlI with HCl/KI.

(6) Dissolve ppt in HNO_3 and evaporate to dryness. Dissolve residue in 1·5% HCl, reduce with Na_2SO_3 and neutralize with NH_3. Heat to 80° C, add 10 ml 10% K_2CrO_4 and stand 1 hour. Spin, wash ppt with 1% K_2CrO_4 and 50% ethanol.

Chemical yield. 60%; weigh as Tl_2CrO_4.

Counting technique. Count 0·76 MeV betas with end-window Geiger counter.

Interferences. Pb gives 0·06 p.p.m. apparent Tl by $Pb^{204}(n, p) Tl^{204}$.

References. Cali, Lowe, Reilly, and Thompson (1957), Morris and

Killick (1960 a); see also Ehmann and Huizenga (1959) for ion exchange method, and Brownlee (1960) for rapid procedure using 4·2-min. Tl^{206}.

Lead. Using the reaction Pb^{208} (n, γ) Pb^{209}; $t_{\frac{1}{2}}$ 3·3 hours.

Cross-section. 0·0006 barns.　　*Natural abundance.* 52·4% (but see below).

Reagents. HNO$_3$, 70%; HCl, 6%; NH$_3$, 6%; AgNO$_3$, 4%; Hg$_2$(NO$_3$)$_2$, 10%; K$_2$CrO$_4$, 10%; Pb(NO$_3$)$_2$, 1% Pb; ammonium acetate, 50%; H$_2$S generator.

Standard. 10^{-4} g Pb as Pb(NO$_3$)$_2$.

Radiochemical separation (suggested method)

　　(1) Dissolve sample in HNO$_3$, add 2 ml Pb(NO$_3$)$_2$ and 1 drop each of AgNO$_3$ and Hg$_2$(NO$_3$)$_2$, and excess HCl. Spin and wash twice with cold water.

　　(2) Extract ppt twice with 10 ml boiling water. Pass H$_2$S through combined extracts and spin.

　　(3) Dissolve ppt in the minimum of HNO$_3$, then add ammonia and ammonium acetate till the pH is 5–6. Add 2 ml K$_2$CrO$_4$ and spin down ppt, wash twice with water. Repeat cycle till decontamination is achieved.

Chemical yield. 70%; weigh as PbCrO$_4$.

Separation time. $\frac{1}{2}$ hour per cycle.

Counting technique. Count 0·62 MeV betas with end-window Geiger counter.

Interferences. Bi could interfere by Bi^{209} (n, p) Pb^{209}. Radiogenic lead may have abnormal isotopic ratios.

Reference. Meinke (1949).

Bismuth. Using the reaction Bi^{209} (n, γ) Bi^{210} $\rightarrow$ Po^{210}; $t_{\frac{1}{2}}$ 138 days (Bi^{210} 5 days).

Cross-section. 0·019 barns.　　*Natural abundance.* 100%.

Reagents. 1 cm Ag disk; H$_2$SO$_4$, 98% and 10%; HNO$_3$, 70%; HCl, 36%, 27%, and 1·7%; HF, 40%; acetone; benzene; SO$_2$ generator; 1 μC Po^{208}; De-Acidite FF, 100–200 mesh.

Standard. 10^{-5} g Bi as Bi(NO$_3$)$_3$.

Radiochemical separation (allow 5 days after activation for Po^{210} to build up)

　　(1) Dissolve sample in 98% H$_2$SO$_4$ containing 0·01 μC Po^{208}, adding HF as necessary. Evaporate to a paste and dissolve in 5 ml

$HNO_3 + 1$ ml 36% HCl. Dilute to 50 ml with 27% HCl and transfer to De-Acidite FF column, 12·5 cm long and 1·25 cm diameter.

(2) Elute unwanted impurities successively with 75 ml 27% HCl, 75 ml $1·7\%$ HCl, and 25 ml water. Elute Po with 75 ml 10% H_2SO_4, boil, reduce with SO_2 and immerse a clean silver disk in the solution for 3 hours. Wash disk with benzene and acetone.

Chemical yield. Up to 90% (via Po[208] tracer activity).

Separation time. 4 hours including plating.

Counting technique. Count 5·30 MeV alphas from Po[210] and 5·11 MeV alphas from Po[208] with a 2π counter and alpha spectrometer.

Interferences. Few, as pulse-height analysis can be used to identify the Po[210] activity.

Reference. Ehmann and Huizenga (1959).

Thorium. Using the reaction $Th^{232}(n, \gamma) Th^{233}$; $t_{\frac{1}{2}}$ 22 min.

Cross-section. 7·5 barns.   *Natural abundance.* 100%.

Reagents. Al_2O_3, chromatographic; Na_2O_2; H_2SO_4, 10%; HNO_3, 18%; NH_3, 60%; H_2O_2, 15%; $KMnO_4$, 2%; $Th(NO_3)_4$, 10% Th in 1% HNO_3; diethyl ether; ethanol; oxalic acid; cellulose, chromatographic; uranyl nitrate: dissolve 52·7 mg $UO_2(NO_3)_2 6H_2O$ in 2 ml water, and elute through 10 g Zeo-Karb 225 with 50 ml 18% HNO_3 to remove Th^{234}: use within 2 days; holdback carrier: $0·5\%$ Ca, Ce, La, Rb, Y, and Zr as nitrates; HNO_3/ether eluant: stir 62 ml 70% HNO_3 with cold ether and make up to 500 ml.

Standard. 10^{-5} g as $Th(NO_3)_4$.

Radiochemical separation

(1) Fuse sample with Na_2O_2 for 15 min, then leach with 18% HNO_3 containing 2 ml $Th(NO_3)_4$ and 1 ml each of $UO_2(NO_3)_2$ and holdback carrier. Boil till solution clears and add 5% oxalic acid. Boil and spin down Th oxalate.

(2) Dissolve ppt in $H_2SO_4 + KMnO_4$, and add excess NH_3. Spin down $Th(OH)_4$.

(3) Dissolve ppt in $HNO_3 + H_2O_2$, add holdback carrier and $UO_2(NO_3)_2$ and repeat both precipitations. Wash ppt with water.

(4) Dissolve ppt in $HNO_3 + H_2O_2$, mix with Al_2O_3 and HNO_3/ether eluant and transfer to 2·5-cm diameter column containing 30 g Al_2O_3 above 10 g cellulose. Elute with 200 ml HNO_3/ether.

(5) Neutralize eluate with ammonia in current of air, separate layers and boil ammoniacal layer. Add oxalic acid, filter, wash ppt with water, ethanol, and ether and dry *in vacuo*.

Chemical yield. 35%; weigh as $Th(C_2O_4)_2 6 \cdot 8H_2O$.

Separation time. 1·5 hours.

Counting technique. Count 1·2 MeV betas with end-window Geiger counter.

Interferences. Uranium interferes due to $U^{238}(n, \gamma) U^{239}$ and $U^{235}(n, \gamma)$ $U^{236} \rightarrow$ 25-hour Th^{231}, but the Np^{239} activity may be filtered out with an Al absorber (100 $\mu g/cm^2$).

Reference. Jenkins (1955).

Uranium. Using the reaction $U^{238}(n, \gamma) U^{239}$; $t_{\frac{1}{2}}$ 24 min.

Cross-section. 3 barns.   *Natural abundance.* 99·3%.

Apparatus. 5 ml Pt crucible.

Reagents. HNO_3, 70% and 18%; HCl, 6%; HF, 40%; NH_3, 60%; $UO_2(NO_3)_2$, 1% U; acetic acid; ammonium acetate, 50%; chloroform; cupferron, 6%; EDTA (3% ethylene diamine tetra-acetic acid); $(NH_4)_2$EDTA (0·6% diammonium ethylene diamine tetra-acetate); oxine (1% 8-hydroxy quinoline in chloroform).

Standard. 10^{-7} g U as $UO_2(NO_3)_2$.

Radiochemical separation

(1) Add 2 ml $UO_2(NO_3)_2$ to sample and evaporate in platinum crucible after adding 1 ml 70% HNO and 0·5 ml HF. Repeat twice, the second time omitting the HF. Dissolve residue in 10 ml 18% HNO, make alkaline with NH_3 and spin down ppt.

(2) Dissolve ppt in 10 ml HCl, cool in ice and transfer to 50 ml separating funnel containing 10 ml cupferron. Extract twice by shaking with 10 ml portions of chloroform and reject organic layer.

(3) Add 5 ml EDTA to aqueous phase and neutralize with NH_3. Extract twice by shaking with 10 ml portions of oxine in chloroform and transfer organic layers to a fresh separating funnel.

(4) Wash chloroform phase with 5 ml $(NH_4)_2$EDTA, then shake with 20 ml HCl and reject organic layer.

(5) Boil aqueous phase and neutralize with NH_3 and acetic acid. Dilute to 50 ml and add 2 ml ammonium acetate. Filter off uranium oxinate and wash with water.

Chemical yield. 60–80%; ignite oxinate and weigh as U_3O_8.

Separation time. 30 min.

Counting technique. Count 1·2 MeV betas with end-window Geiger counter.

Interferences. Unimportant. 2·4-day Np^{239} builds up in the final ppt.

Reference. Das (1960).

Uranium. Using the reaction $U^{235}(n,f)Ba^{140}$; $t_{\frac{1}{2}}$ 13 days.

Cross-section. 580 barns.   *Natural abundance.* 0·72%.

Reagents. Zn powder; H_2SO_4, 10%; HCl, 36%; HCl, 30% in diethyl ether; NH_3, 60%; $BaCl_2$, 1% Ba; $FeCl_3$, 10%; KI, 5%; $La(NO_3)_3$, 1% La; NaOCl, 20%; $Na_2H_4TeO_6$, 1% Te; $SrCl_2$, 1% Sr; hydroxylamine hydrochloride.

Standard. 10^{-6} g U as $UO_2(NO_3)_2$.

Radiochemical separation

(1) Dissolve sample in the presence of 5 ml $BaCl_2$. Add 2 drops $La(NO_3)_3$ and excess NH_3. Spin, dissolve ppt in HCl and add 2 drops $SrCl_2$ and excess HCl/ether. Spin and wash ppt with HCl/ether. Dissolve $BaCl_2$ in water and ppt again with excess HCl/ether. Spin and wash ppt with HCl/ether.

(2) Dissolve ppt in water, add 5 drops $La(NO_3)_3$ and $Na_2H_4TeO_6$ and 3 mg Zn. Neutralize with NH_3 and spin, rejecting ppt.

(3) Add 1 drop KI and 2 drops NaOCl to spt and warm for 2 min. Acidify with HCl, add 0·1 g hydroxylamine hydrochloride and boil to remove I_2.

(4) Add 2 drops each of $SrCl_2$ and $La(NO_3)_3$ and 1 drop $FeCl_3$, neutralize with ammonia and filter. Wash with water and reject ppt.

(5) Dilute spt to 20 ml, acidify with HCl, boil and add 2 ml H_2SO_4. Spin down $BaSO_4$ and wash thoroughly with water. Dry at 500° C.

Chemical yield. About 80%; weigh as $BaSO_4$.

Separation time. 2–3 hours for two samples.

Counting technique. Count 1·0 MeV betas with end-window Geiger counter.

Interferences. Thorium and other heavy elements can lead to production of fission products. Barium interferes by production of Ba^{131} and Ba^{133} by (n,γ) processes, and large amounts will affect the chemical yield. The La^{140} daughter may be separated after equilibrium is reached and counted instead.

Reference. Seyfang and Smales (1953).

REFERENCES

ABELSON, P. H. *Researches in geochemistry.* Wiley, New York (1959).

AHRENS, L. H. *Quantitative spectrochemical analysis of silicates.* Pergamon, London (1954).

—— *Physics and chemistry of the earth.* Edit. Ahrens, L. H., Rankama, K., and Runcorn, S. Pergamon, London (1955).

AIDARKIN, B. S., GORSHKOV, G. V., GRAMMAKOV, A. G., ZHADIN, V. S., and KOLCHINA, A. G. *Trudy Radievogo Inst. V. G. Khlopina, Akad. Nauk S.S.S.R.* **5** (1957) 88.

AIROLDI, G., and GERMAGNOLI, E. *Energia Nucleare,* **4** (1957) 301.

AJZENBERG, F., and LAURITSEN, T. *Rev. Mod. Phys.* **27** (1955) 77.

ALBERT, P., CARON, M., and CHAUDRON, G. *C.R. Acad. Sci. Paris,* **233** (1951) 1108.

—— *Proc. Isotope Conf., Oxford,* **2,** 171. H.M. Stationery Office, London (1952).

—— *C.R. Acad. Sci. Paris,* **236** (1953) 1030.

ALBERT, P., CHAUDRON, G., and SÜE, P. *Bull. Soc. Chim. France* **C** (1953) 97.

ALBERT, R. D. *Rev. Sci. Instrum.* **24** (1953) 1096.

ALIMARIN, I. P., JAKOVLEV, J. V., and ZHABIN, A. I. *Primen. Mech. Atomov. Anal. Khim. Akad. Nauk S.S.S.R. Inst. Geokhim. i Anal. Khim.* (1955) 58.

ALLEN, A. O., DAVIS, T. W., ELMORE, G. V., HORMLEY, J. A., HAINES, B. M., and HOCHNADEL, C. J. U.S. Atomic Energy Commission Report ORNL 130 (1949).

ANDERS, E. *Geochim. Cosmochim. Acta,* **19** (1960 c) 53.

ANDERS, E., SEN SARMA, R. N., and KATO, P. H. *J. Chem. Phys.* **24** (1956) 622.

ANDERS, O. U. *Nucleonics,* **18,** no. 2 (1960 a) 179.

—— *Anal. Chem.* **32** (1960 b) 1368.

ANDERS, O. U., and GARDNER, D. G. Univ. Michigan Progress Report 6 (1957).

ANON. *Nucleonics,* **14,** no. 6 (1956) 105.

AOKI, F., and OKADA, M. *Rep. Govt. Chem. Ind. Res. Inst. Tokyo,* **54** (1959) 121.

ARDENNE, M. VON, and BERNHARD, F. *Z. Phys.* **122** (1944) 740.

ASADA, T., FURUTA, J., MASUDA, M., OKUMURA, M., and OKUMA, J. *Dai-I-Kai Gensh. Sympos. Holonshu,* (1957) 549.

ASHLEY, S. E. Q. *Anal. Chem.* **22** (1950) 1379.

ATCHISON, G. J., and BEAMER, W. H. *Ibid.* **24** (1952) 1812.

—— *Ibid.* **28** (1956) 237.

ATEN, A. H. W. *Ned. Tijdschr. Natuurk.* **10** (1943) 257.

ATKINS, D. H. F., and SMALES, A. A. *Advances Inorg. Chem. Radiochem.* **1** (1959) 315.

—— *Anal. Chim. Acta,* **22** (1960) 462.

BALDWIN, G. C., and CLARK, L. B. *Science,* **117** (1953) 9

BANCIE-GRILLOT, M. *C.R. Acad. Sci. Paris,* **242** (1956) 1159.

BANCIE-GRILLOT, M., and GRILLOT, E. *Ibid.* **237** (1953) 171.

BANKS, T. E., TUPPER, R., WHITE, E. M. A., and WORMALL, A. *Int. J. Appl. Rad. Isot.* **4** (1959) 221.

BARANOV, V. I., KRISTIANOV, V. K., and KARASEV, B. V. *Dokl. Akad. Nauk S.S.S.R.* **129** (1959) 1035.

BARKER, R. S. *Trans. Soc. Glass Technol.* **42** (1958) 101.

BARNES, R. K. Atomic Energy Research Establishment, Harwell, *Radioisotope Review Sheet* **B 10** (1960).

BASILE, R., HURE, S., LEVEQUE, P., and SCHUHL, C. *C.R. Acad. Sci. Paris,* **239** (1954) 422.

BATE, G. L., POTRATZ, H. A., and HUIZENGA, J. R. *Geochim. Cosmochim. Acta,* **18** (1960) 101.

BATE, L. C., and LEDDICOTTE, G. W. *Amer. Chem. Soc. Conf. Anal. Chem.,* paper 40, Pittsburgh (1958).

BAUER, C. A. *Phys. Rev.* **72** (1947) 354.

BAULCH, D. L., and DUNCAN, J. F. *Quart. Rev.* **12** (1958) 133.

BEARD, D. B., JOHNSON, R. G., and BRADSHAW, W. G. *Nucleonics,* **17,** no. 7 (1959) 90.

BEHARRELL, J. *Nature,* **149** (1942) 306.

BELL, A. R. *Science,* **120** (1954) 625.

BENSON, A. A. *Proc. 2nd U.N. Conf. on peaceful uses of atomic energy,* Geneva, 1958, **24** (1959) 289.

BERGSTRÖM, J. *Nature,* **184** (1959) 1504.

BERLMAN, I. B. *Nucleonics,* **11,** no. 2 (1953) 70.

BERTRAND, D. *C.R. Acad. Sci. Paris,* **215** (1942) 590.

—— *Bull. Amer. Mus. Nat. Hist.* **94** (1950) 409.

BEYDON, J., and FISHER, C. *Anal. Chim. Acta,* **8** (1953) 538.

BLACK, W. A. P., and MITCHELL, R. L. *J. Marine Biol. Ass. U.K.* **30** (1952) 575.

BLANCHARD, R. L., LEDDICOTTE, G. W., and MOELLER, D. W. *Proc. 2nd U.N. Conf. on Peaceful uses of atomic energy,* Geneva, 1958, **28** (1959 a) 511.

—— *J. Amer. Water Works Ass.* **51** (1959 b) 967.

BLASIUS, E., and GOTTLING, W. *Z. Anal. Chem.* **162** (1958) 423.

BLOCK, R. J., DURRUM, E. L., and ZWEIG, G. *A manual of paper chromatography and electrophoresis.* Academic Press, New York (1955).

BOCK, R., and HOCKSTEIN, K. G. *Z. Anal. Chem.* **138** (1953) 339.

BORCHERT, H. *Geochim. Cosmochim. Acta,* **2** (1952) 62.

BORG, D. C. *Proc. 2nd U.N. Conf. on peaceful uses of atomic energy,* Geneva, 1958, **24** (1959) 283.

BORN, G. I., VAISS, K. F., and KOBALADZE, M. G. *Trudy Kom. Anal. Khim. Akad. Nauk S.S.S.R. Inst. Geokhim. i Anal. Khim.* **7** (1956) 104.

BORN, H. J., and RIEHL, N. *Angew. Chem.* **72** (1960) 559.

BORN, H. J., and STARK, H. *Atomkern. Energie,* **4** (1959) 286.

BOWEN, H. J. M. *J. Marine Biol. Ass. U.K.* **35** (1956 a) 451.

—— *J. Nuclear Energy,* **3** (1956 b) 18.

—— *Int. J. Appl. Rad. Isot.* **4** (1959 a) 214.

—— Ibid. **5** (1959 b) 227.

—— *Biochem. J.* **73** (1959 c) 381.

—— Ibid. **77** (1960) 79.

BOWEN, H. J. M., ARTER, E., and CAWSE, P. A. *Nature,* **186** (1960) 383.

BOWEN, H. J. M., and CAWSE, P. A. Atomic Energy Research Establishment, Harwell, Report AERE R 2925 (1959).

—— unpublished work (1961).

BOWEN, H. J. M., and DYMOND, J. A. *Proc. Roy. Soc. B,* **144** (1955) 355.

—— *J. Exp. Bot.* **7** (1956) 264.

BOWEN, V. T., and SUTTON, D. *J. Marine Res.* **10** (1951) 153.

BOWIE, S. H. U., BISBY, H., BURKE, K. C., and HALE, F. H. *Bull. Inst. Min. Met. Trans.* **69** (1960) 329.

BOYD, G. A. *Autoradiography in biology and medicine.* Academic Press, New York (1960).

BOYD, G. E., and LARSON, Q. V. *J. Phys. Chem.* **60** (1956) 707.

BRADLEY, J. E. S., and BRADLEY, O. *Min. Mag.* **31** (1956) 165.

BREGER, E. K., ORMONT, B. F., KUTSEV, V. S., VITING, B. I., and CHAPHYZNIKOV, B. A. *Zhur. Neorg. Khim.* **2** (1957) 1696.

BRETSCHER, E., and MARTIN, E. B. U.K. Ministry of Supply Report BR 425 (1943).

BRODA, E., and ROHRINGER, G. *Naturwiss.* **40** (1953) 337.

BROOKS, R. R. *Analyst,* **85** (1960) 745.

BROOKSBANK, W. A., HANDLEY, T. H., LEDDICOTTE, G. W., LEE, N. D., and KEENAN, C. W. U.S. Atomic Energy Commission Report ORNL 867 (1957).

BROOKSBANK, W. A., and LEDDICOTTE, G. W. *J. Phys. Chem.* **57** (1953) 819.

BROOKSBANK, W. A., LEDDICOTTE, G. W., and DEAN, J. A. *Anal. Chem.* **30** (1958) 1785.

BROOKSBANK, W. A., LEDDICOTTE, G. W., and MAHLMAN, H. A. *J. Phys. Chem.* **57** (1953) 815.

BROOKSBANK, W. A., LEDDICOTTE, G. W., and REYNOLDS, S. A. *Anal. Chem.* **28** (1956) 1033.

BROOKSBANK, W. A., LEDDICOTTE, G. W., and STRAIN, J. E. *Nucl. Sci. Congress,* paper 308, Cleveland (1955).

BROWN, H., and GOLDBERG, E. D. *Science,* **109** (1949) 347.

BROWNELL, G. M. *Econ. Geol.* **54** (1959) 1103.

BROWNELL, G. M., BRAMADAT, K., KNUTSON, R. A., and TURNOCK, A. C. *Trans. Roy. Soc. Canad.* (iv), **51** (1957) 19.

BROWNLEE, J. L. Univ. Michigan Progress Report 9 (1960 *a*).

—— U.S. Atomic Energy Commission Report TID 6311 (1960 *b*).

—— Thesis, Univ. Michigan, June (1960 *c*).

BROWNLEE, J. L., and KAISER, D. G. Univ. Michigan Progress Report 8 (1959).

BRUES, A. M., and ROBERTSON, O. H. U.S. Atomic Energy Commission Report AECD 2009 (1947).

—— *J. Lab. Clin. Med.* **36** (1950) 804.

BURBIDGE, E. M., BURBIDGE, G. R., FOWLER, W. A., and HOYLE, F. *Rev. Mod. Phys.* **29** (1957) 547.

BURRILL, E. A., and GALE, A. J. *Activation Analysis.* High Voltage Engng. Co., Cambridge, Mass. (1954).

BURRILL, E. A., and MACGREGOR, M. H. *Nucleonics,* **18**, no. 12 (1960) 64.

BUTLER, E. B., and JOHNSTON, W. H. *Science,* **120** (1954) 543.

BUTLER, E. J., and FIELD, A. C. *Analyst,* **81** (1956) 615.

CABELL, M. J., and SMALES, A. A. Ibid. **82** (1957) 390.

CABELL, M. J., and THOMAS, A. Atomic Energy Research Establishment, Harwell, Report AERE C/R 1725 (1955).

CALDWELL, R. L., and MILLS, W. R. *Nucl. Instr. Methods,* **5** (1959) 312.

CALI, J. P., LOWE, L. F., REILLY, E. M., and THOMPSON, H. D. Air Force Research Centre, Bedford, Mass., Report ERD–CRRC–TM–57–103 (1957).

CALVET, E., BOIVENET, P., NOEL, M., THIBOU, H., MAILLARD, A., and TERTIAN, R. *Bull. Soc. Chim. France* (1953) 99.

CAMERON, A. E. U.S. Atomic Energy Commission Report TID 5213 (1950).

CAMERON, A. E., HERR, W., HERZOG, W., and LUNDEN, A. *Z. Naturforsch.* **11a** (1956) 203.

CAMPBELL, E. C., and NELSON, F., in FINSTON, H. L., and MISKEL, J. *Ann. Rev. Nucl. Sci.* **5** (1955) 269.

—— *J. Inorg. Nucl. Chem.* **3** (1956) 233.

CANTWELL, T., HAWKS, H. E., and RASMUSSEN, N. C. *A.I.M.E. meeting,* report 5820A8 (1958).

CHADWICK, J., and GOLDHABER, M. *Nature,* **134** (1934) 237.

CHAMBERS, L. A., FOTER, M. J., and CHOLAK, J. *Proc. Nat. Air Pollution Sympos.* **3**, 24, Los Angeles (1955).

CHAUVIN, R., and LEVEQUE, P. *Int. J. Appl. Rad. Isot.* **1** (1956) 115.

CHERDYNTSEV, V. V., and SUVAROVA, O. Y. *Trudy Inst. Yadern. Fiz. Akad. Nauk Kazakh.* **1** (1958) 166.

Chilean Iodine Educational Bureau, *Iodine content of foods.* London (1952).

CHOLAK, J., and HUBBARD, D. B. *Anal. Chem.* **20** (1948) 73 and 970.

CHOLAK, J., SCHAFER, L. J., and HOFFER, R. F. *Arch. Indust. Hyg. Occup. Med.* **2** (1950) 443.

COLEMAN, R. F. *Analyst,* **85** (1960) 285.

COLEMAN, R. F., and PERKIN, J. L. Ibid. **84** (1959) 233.

—— Ibid. **85** (1960) 154.

CONNALLY, R. E., and LEBOEUF, M. B. *Anal. Chem.* **25** (1953) 1095.

CONWAY, E. J. *Micro-diffusion and volumetric error.* Van Nostrand Princeton (1940).

COOK, G. B., and DUNCAN, J. F. *Modern radiochemical practice.* Clarendon Press, Oxford (1952).

COOK, G. B. et al., *Radioactivation analysis symposium.* Butterworth, London (1960).

COON, J. H. *Phys. Rev.* **75** (1949) 1355.

CORNAND, P., and GILLIS, J. *Ind. Chim. Belge,* **20,** Special no. (1955) 269.

CORNISH, F. W. Atomic Energy Research Establishment, Harwell, Report AERE C/R 1224 (1953).

COSGROVE, J. F., BASTIAN, R. P., and MORRISON, G. H. *Anal. Chem.* **30** (1958) 1872.

COVELL, D. F. Ibid. **31** (1959) 1785.

COWAN, G. A. U.S. Atomic Energy Commission Report UCRL 5679 (1960).

CRAIG, L. C., in YOE, J. H., and KOCH, H. J. *Trace analysis.* Chapman and Hall, London (1957).

CROUCH, E. A. C. Personal communication (1959).

CUER, P., and LONGCHAMP, J. P. *C.R. Acad. Sci. Paris,* **232** (1951) 1824.

CURIE, I. *J. Phys. Radium,* **13** (1952) 497.

—— *Bull. Soc. Chim. France,* **C** (1953) 94.

CURIE, I., and FARAGGI, H. *C.R. Acad. Sci. Paris,* **239** (1951) 959.

CURRAN, S. C. *Atomics,* **3** (1952) 5.

—— *Quart. Rev.* **7** (1953) 1.

CURRY, A. S. *Nature,* **171** (1953) 1026.

CURTIS, H. J., and TERESI, J. D. U.S. Atomic Energy Commission Report AECD 2872 (1946).

DALE, B. M. *Diss. Abstr.* **20** (1959) 472.

DALY, R. A. *Bull. Geol. Soc. Amer.* **54** (1943) 401.

DAS, S. Univ. Michigan Progress Report 9 (1960).

DAUDEL, P. *C.R. Acad. Sci. Paris,* **218** (1944) 234.

DAVENPORT, P. H. Personal communication (1959).

DAVIS, R., and SCHAEFFER, O. A. U.S. Atomic Energy Commission Report BNL 340 (1955).

DE, A. K., and MEINKE, W. W. *Anal. Chem.* **30** (1958) 1474.

DEBIESSE, C. J., CHALLANSONNET, J., and NEYRET, G. *C.R. Acad. Sci. Paris,* **232** (1951) 602.

DELBECQ, C. J., GLENDENIN, L. E., and YUSTER, P. H. *Anal. Chem.* **25** (1953) 350.

DENNES, E., TUPPER, R., and WORMALL, A. *Nature,* **187** (1960) 302.

DENT, J. N., and SHEPPARD, C. W. *J. Exp. Zool.* **135** (1957) 587.

DEUEL, H., and HUTSCHNEKER, K. *Chimia (Switz.),* **9** (1955) 49.

DeVoe, J. R. Univ. Michigan Progress Report 8 (1959).

DeVoe, J. R., Kim, C. K., and Meinke, W. W. *Talanta*, 3 (1960) 298.

Dewar, W. A., and Lenihan, J. M. A. *Scot. Med. J.* 1 (1956) 236.

Diamond, R. M., and Tuck, D. G. *Progr. Inorg. Chem.* 2 (1960) 109.

Dick, J. L. *Diss. Abstr.* 20 (1960) 2580.

Druyan, R., Mitchell, T. G., and King, E. R. *J. Lab. Clin. Med.* 52 (1958) 304.

Duckworth, H. E. *Mass spectroscopy*. Cambridge Univ. Press (1958).

Duval, C. *Inorganic thermogravimetric analysis*. Elsevier (1953).

Dyrrsen, D., and Nyman, P. O. *Acta Radiol.* 43 (1955) 421.

Ebert, K. H., Hernegger, F., König, H., and Wänke, H. *Geochim. Cosmochim. Acta*, 17 (1959) 349.

Edwards, L. C. *Int. J. Appl. Rad. Isot.* 1 (1956) 184.

Ehmann, W. D. *Geochim. Cosmochim. Acta*, 19 (1960) 149.

Ehmann, W. D., and Huizenga, J. R. Ibid. 17 (1959) 125.

Ehmann, W. D., and Kohmann, T. P. Ibid. 14 (1958) 364.

Eicholz, G. J. *Nucleonics*, 10, no. 12 (1952) 58.

Ellett, W. H., and Brownell, G. L. *Nucl. Instr. Methods*, 1 (1960) 56.

Emeleus, H. J., and Anderson, J. S. *Modern aspects of inorganic chemistry*. Routledge, London, 2nd ed. (1952).

Endt, P. M., and Braams, C. M. *Rev. Mod. Phys.* 29 (1957) 683.

Endt, P. M., and Kluyver, J. C. Ibid. 26 (1954) 95.

Engelhardt, W. von. *Chemie der Erde*, 10 (1936) 187.

Erion, W. E., Mott, W. E., and Shedlovsky, J. P. *Trans. Amer. Nucl. Soc.* 3 (1960) 253.

Facchini, J., and Orsini, L. *Nuovo Cimento*, 6 (1949) 241.

Fairbairn, H. W. *U.S. Geol. Survey Bull.* 980 (1950).

Faircloth, R. L. *Talanta*, 2 (1959) 135.

Faires, R. A., and Parkes, B. H. *Radioisotope laboratory techniques*. Newnes, London (1958).

Faraggi, H., Kohn, A., and Doumerc, J. *C.R. Acad. Sci. Paris*, 235 (1952) 714

Faul, H. *Nuclear Geology*. Wiley, New York (1954).

Feather, N. *Proc. Roy. Soc.* A 136 (1932) 709.

—— *Proc. Camb. Phil. Soc.* 34 (1938) 599.

Feigl, F. *Spot tests in inorganic analysis*. Elsevier (1958).

Feldman, C. *Anal. Chem.* 21 (1949) 1211.

Ficq, A. *C.R. Acad. Sci. Paris*, 233 (1951) 1684.

—— *J. Embryol. Exp. Morphol.* 2 (1954) 204.

Fineman, I., Ljunggren, K., Erwall, L. G., and Westermark, T. *Svensk. Papperstidnung.* 60 (1957) 132.

Fink, R. W. U.S. Atomic Energy Commission Report ORO 165 (1957).

Finston, H. L., and Miskel, J. *Ann. Rev. Nucl. Sci.* 5 (1955) 269.

Fireman, E. L. *Nature*, 181 (1958) 1725.

—— *Planet. Space Sci.* 1 (1959) 66.

Fireman, E. L., and Schwarzer, D. *Geochim. Cosmochim. Acta*, 11 (1957) 252.

Fischer, E. O., and Fritz, H. P. *Advances Inorg. Chem. Radiochem.* 1 (1959) 55.

Fisher, C. Commissariat à l'energie atomique. Paris, Report CEA 523 (1956).

Fisher, C., and Beydon, J. *Bull. Soc. Chim. France*, C (1953) 102.

Fogelström-Fineman, I., Holm-Hansen, O., Tolbert, B. M., and Calvin, M. *Int. J. Appl. Rad. Isot.* 2 (1957) 280.

Fore, H., and Morton, R. A. *Biochem. J.* 51 (1952) 598 and 600.

Foster, L. M., and Gaitanis, C. D. *Anal. Chem.* 27 (1955) 1342.

Fowler, I. L. Atomic Energy of Canada, Ltd., Report AECL 223 (1954).

FREEDMAN, M. S. *J. Chem. Phys.* **20** (1952) 1040.

FUKAI, R. Univ. Michigan Progress Report 8 (1959).

FUKAI, R., and MEINKE, W. W. *Nature*, **184** (1959) 815.

GADDIS, S. *J. Chem. Educ.* **19** (1942) 327.

GAITTET, J. *Ann. Chim.* **5** (1960) 1219.

GAITTET, J., and ALBERT, P. *C.R. Acad. Sci. Paris*, **247** (1958) 1861.

GALUZO, Y. G. *Izv. Vyssh. Ucheb. Zaved. Neft. Gaz.* (1958) 41.

GARNER, R. J. *Nature*, **184** (1959) 733.

GARRISON, W. M., and HAMILTON, J. G. *Chem. Rev.* **49** (1951) 237.

GAUDIN, A. M., DASHER, J., PANNELL, J. H., and FREYBERGER, W. C. *Mining Eng.* **187** (1950) 495.

GAUDIN, A. M., and PANNELL, J. H. *Anal. Chem.* **23** (1951) 1261.

GAUDIN, A. M., SENFTLE, A. P., and FREYBERGER, W. C. *Eng. Min. J.* **153**, no. 11 (1952) 95.

GAUTHIER, P. *Ind. Chim. Belge*, **20,** special no. 281 (1955).

GEILMANN, W. *Z. Anal. Chem.* **160** (1958) 410.

GENERAL ELECTRIC Co., U.S.A. *Chart of the nuclides* (1956).

GETOFF, V. N. *Atompraxis*, **5** (1959) 472.

GIBBONS, D. *Int. J. Appl. Rad. Isot.* **4** (1958) 45.

—— *Proc. Int. Sympos. Microchem.*, Birmingham, U.K., 1958, 332. Pergamon, London (1960).

GIBBONS, D., and HEWLETT, J. unpublished work (1958).

GIBBONS, D., LOVERIDGE, B. A., and MILLETT, R. J. Atomic Energy Research Establishment, Harwell, Report AERE I/R 2208 (1957).

GIBBONS, D., MAPPER, D., MILLET, R. J., and SIMPSON, H. Atomic Energy Research Establishment, Harwell, Report AERE I/R 2208, Supplement 1 (1960).

GIBBONS, D., and SIMPSON, H. *Pure and Appl. Chem.* **1** (1960 a) 135.

—— *Conf. on Uses of Radioisotopes in Physical Sciences and Industry*, paper 72, Copenhagen (1960 b).

—— unpublished work (1960 c).

GILL, R. A. Atomic Energy Research Establishment, Harwell, Report AERE C/R 2758 (1958).

GLENDENIN, L. E. *Nucleonics*, **2**, no. 1 (1948) 12.

GLENDENIN, L. E., and SOLOMON, A. K. U.S. Atomic Energy Commission Report AECD 735 (1950).

GLUECKAUF, E. *Trans. Farad. Soc.* **51** (1955) 34.

GLUECKAUF, E., KITT, G. P., and BARKER, K. H. *Disc. Farad. Soc.* **7** (1949) 199.

GOLD, R. *Nucleonics*, **15,** no. 7 (1957) 111.

GOLDBERG, E. D. *J. Geol.* **62** (1954) 249.

GOLDBERG, E. D., and ARRHENIUS, S. *Geochim. Cosmochim. Acta*, **13** (1958) 153.

GOLDBERG, E. D., and BROWN, H. *Anal. Chem.* **22** (1950) 308.

GOLDBERG, E. D., UCHIYAMA, A., and BROWN, H. *Geochim. Cosmochim. Acta*, **2** (1951) 1.

GOLDICH, S. S., and OSLUND, E. H. *Bull. Geol. Soc. Amer.* **67** (1956) 811.

GOLDSCHMIDT, B., and DJOURKOVITCH, O. *Bull. Soc. Chim. France*, **6** (1939) 718.

GOLDSCHMIDT, V. M. *Skrift. Norske Videnskaps-Akad. Oslo I, Mat. Natur. Kl*, no. 4 (1937).

GOLES, G. G., and ANDERS, E. *J. Geophys. Res.* **65** (1960) 4181.

GOODMAN, C. *The science and engineering of nuclear power*. Addison Wesley, Cambridge, Mass. (1947).

GOODMAN, C., and THOMPSON, G. A. *Amer. Min.* **28** (1943) 456.

GORDON, L., PETERSON, J. I., and BURTT, B. P. *Anal. Chem.* **27** (1955) 1770.

GORSUCH, T. T. *Analyst*, **84** (1959) 135.

GOTTE, H., and HATTEMER, J. A. *Z. Naturforsch.* **10B** (1955) 343.

GOVAERTS, J. *Ind. Chim. Belge*, **20** (1955) 284.

GRACE, J. D., and BATES, T. F. *Geochim. Cosmochim. Acta*, **17** (1959) 226.

GRAND, J. A., BAUS, R. A., BOGARD, A. D., WILLIAMS, D. D., LOCKHART, L. B., and MILLER, R. R. *J. Phys. Chem.* **63** (1959) 1192.

GRANDJEAN, P., LERCH, P., and MONNIER, R. *Helv. Chim. Acta*, **43** (1960) 848.

GRIFFON, H. *Ann. Pharm. Franc.* **13** (1955) 258.

GRIFFON, H., and BARBAUD, J. *C.R. Acad. Sci. Paris*, **232** (1951) 1455.

GRILLOT, E. *Ibid.* **234** (1952) 1775.

GUEBEN, G., and GOVAERTS, J. *Inst. Intern. Sci. Nucl., Brussels*, Monog. 2 (1957).

GUINN, V. P., and WAGNER, C. D. *Amer. Chem. Soc. meeting*, paper 567 (1957).

HAERDI, W., VOGEL, J., MONNIER, D., and WENGER, P. E. *Helv. Chim. Acta*, **43** (1960) 869.

HAIGH, C. P. *Nature*, **172** (1953) 359.

—— *Proc. Oxford Radioisotope Conference*, **2**, 101. Butterworth, London (1954).

HAISSINSKY, M. *Nature*, **136** (1935) 141.

HALBAN, H. VON, JOLIOT, F., and KOWARSKI, L. *Ibid.* **143** (1939) 680.

HALL, K. L., and MEINKE, W. W. *J. Inorg. Nucl. Chem.* **9** (1959) 193.

HAMAGUCHI, H., KURODA, R., and HOSOHARA, K. *J. Atom. Energy Soc. Japan*, **2** (1960) 317.

HAMAGUCHI, H., KURODA, R. *et al.* *Geochim. Cosmochim. Acta*, **23** (1961) 296.

HAMAGUCHI, H., REED, G. W., and TURKEVICH, A. *Ibid.* **12** (1957) 337.

HAMILTON, E. *Meddel. om Grønland*, **162**, no. 7 (1959 *a*).

—— *Meddel. Dansk. Geol. Foren.* **14** (1959 *b*) 188.

HAPP, W. W., and HORWOOD, J. L. *Science*, **115** (1952) 622.

HARBOTTLE, G. *Nucleonics*, **12**, no. 4 (1954) 64.

HARBOTTLE, G., and SUTIN, N. *Advances Inorg. Chem. Radiochem.* **1** (1959) 268.

HARRISON, G. E., and RAYMOND, W. H. A. *J. Nucl. Energy*, **1** (1955) 290.

HARVEY, H. W. *The chemistry and fertility of sea waters.* Cambridge University Press (1957).

HEATH, R. L. U.S. Atomic Energy Commission Report IDO 16408 (1957).

HEATH, R. L., and SCHROEDER, F. U.S. Atomic Energy Commission Report IDO 16419 (1957).

HERNEGGER, F., and WÄNKE, H. *Z. Naturforsch.* **12a** (1957) 759.

HERR, W. *Ibid.* **8a** (1953) 305.

—— *Ibid.* **9a** (1954) 907.

—— *Radioactivation analysis symposium*, 39. Butterworth, London (1960).

HERR, W., HINTENBERGER, H., and VOSHAGE, H. *Phys. Rev.* **95** (1954) 1691.

HERR, W., HOFFMEISTER, W., and LANGHOFF, J. *Z. Naturforsch.* **15a** (1960) 99.

HERR, W., HOFFMEISTER, W., LANGHOFF, J., GEISS, J., BIRT, B., and HOUTERMAN, F. G. *Conf. on uses of radioisotopes in physical sciences and industry*, paper 155, Copenhagen (1960).

HERR, W., and MERZ, E. *Z. Naturforsch.* **10a** (1955) 613.

—— *Radioisotopes in scientific research*, **2** (1958 *a*) 571.

—— *Z. Naturforsch.* **13a** (1958 *b*) 231.

HERR, W., MERZ, E., EBERHARDT, P., and SIGNER, P. *Ibid.* **13a** (1958) 268.

HESS, W. N. U.S. Atomic Energy Commission Report UCRL 3839 (1957).

HEVESY, G. VON, and LEVY, H. *Kgl. Danske Vidensk. Selsk. Math.-fys. Medd.* **14**, no. 5 (1936).

—— *Ibid.* **15**, no. 11 (1938).

HEWITT, E. J. *Sand and water culture methods used in the study of plant nutrition.* Commonwealth Agricultural Bureau (1952).

HEYNDRICKX, A., and SCHANVLIEGE, F. *Meded. Landbouw. Opzoeking*, **23** (1958) 795.

HILL, W. H., and SMITH, R. C. *J. Amer. Indust. Hyg. Ass.* **20** (1959) 131.

HILLERT, M. *Nature*, **168** (1951) 39.

HOFFMANN, J. I., and LUNDELL, G. E. F. *J. Res. Nat. Bur. Standards*, **22** (1939) 465.

HOFSTADTER, R., and MCINTYRE, J. A. *Phys. Rev.* **78** (1950) 619.

HOOD, S. L., PARKS, R. Q., and HURWITZ, C. *Ind. Eng. Chem., Anal. Ed.* **16** (1944) 202.

HOSTE, J. *Radioactivation analysis symposium*, 58. Butterworth, London (1960)

HOSTE, J., and VAN DEN BERGHE, H. *Microchim. Acta* (1956) 797.

HUDGENS, J. E. *Amer. Soc. Test. Mat., Special Tech. Publication*, **195** (1956) 11.

HUDGENS, J. E., and CALI, P. J. *Anal. Chem.* **24** (1952) 171.

HUDGENS, J. E., and DABAGIAN, H. J. *Nucleonics*, **10**, no. 5 (1952) 25.

HUDGENS, J. E., and MEYER, R. C. U.S. Atomic Energy Commission Report BNL 126 (1956).

HUGHES, D. J., and SCHWARZ, R. B. U.S. Atomic Energy Commission Report BNL 325 (1958).

HULCHER, F. *Anal. Chem.* **32** (1960) 1183.

HUMMEL, R. W. *Analyst*, **82** (1957) 483.

HUMMEL, R. W., and SMALES, A. A. Ibid. **81** (1956) 110.

HUTCHINSON, G. E. *Quart. Rev. Biol.* **18** (1943) 1, 128, 242, and 331.

HUTCHINSON, W. P. Atomic Energy Research Establishment, Harwell, Report AERE Med/R 2317 (1960).

IKEDA, N., and YOSHIHARA, K. *Radioisotopes (Tokyo)*, **5** (1956) 11.

—— Ibid. **7** (1958 *a*) 11.

—— Ibid. **7** (1958 *b*) 17.

—— Ibid. **7** (1958 *c*) 195.

—— Ibid. **8** (1959) 238.

IKEDA, N., YOSHIHARA, K., and MISHIO, N. Ibid. **7** (1958) 92.

IKEDA, N., YOSHIHARA, K., and SHIMADA, K. Ibid. **8** (1959 *a*) 17.

—— Ibid. **8** (1959 *b*) 24.

International Atomic Energy Agency. *Directory of nuclear reactors.* Vienna (1959).

International Commission on Radiological Protection. *Brit. J. Radiol.* **24**, Supplement (1951).

IREDALE, P. Atomic Energy Research Establishment, Harwell, Report AERE EL/M 96 (1957).

IRVING, H. *Quart. Rev.* **5** (1951) 200.

IRVING, H., and COX, J. J. *Analyst*, **83** (1958) 526.

IRVING, H., SMIT, J. VAN R., and SALMON, L. Ibid. **82** (1957) 549.

ISHIBASHI, M., and HARA, T. *Bull. Inst. Chem. Res. Kyoto*, **37** (1959) 179.

Isotope Division, Atomic Energy Research Establishment, Harwell. *Radioactive materials and stable isotopes*, **4** (1957) 8.

JAKOVLEV, J. V. *Proc. Int. Conf. on peaceful uses of atomic energy*, Geneva, 1955, **15** (1956) 54.

JAKOVLEV, J. V., KULAK, A. I., RYABUKHIN, V. A., and RYTCHOV, R. S. *Proc. 2nd U.N. Conf. on peaceful uses of atomic energy*, Geneva, 1958, **28** (1959) 496.

JAMES, J. A., and RICHARDS, D. H. *Nature*, **175** (1955 *a*) 769.

—— Ibid. **176** (1955 *b*) 1026.

—— *Anal. Chim. Acta*, **15** (1956 *a*) 118.

JAMES, J. A., and RICHARDS, D. H. *Nature,* **177** (1956 b) 1230.

—— J. *Electronics and Control,* **3** (1957) 500.

JARMIE, N., and SEAGRAVE, J. D. U.S. Atomic Energy Commission Report LA 2014 (1956).

JENKINS, E. N. *Analyst,* **80** (1955) 301.

JENKINS, E. N,, and SMALES, A. A. *Quart. Rev.* **10** (1956) 83.

JERVIS, R. E. Atomic Energy of Canada, Ltd., Report AECL 428 (1957).

JERVIS, R. E., and MACKINTOSH, W. D. *Proc. 2nd U.N. Conf. on peaceful uses of atomic energy,* Geneva, 1958, **28** (1959) 470.

JOHNSON, J. M., and BUTLER, G. W. *Physiol. Plant.* **10** (1957) 100.

JOLIOT, F., and CURIE, I. *Nature,* **133** (1934) 201.

JOWANOWITZ, L. S., MCCARLEY, R. E., and MARTIN, D. S. *133rd Amer. Chem. Soc. Meeting* Abstr. 71 (1958).

JOWANOWITZ, L. S., MCNATT, F. B., MCCARLEY, R. E., and MARTIN, D. S. *Anal. Chem.* **32** (1960) 1270.

KAISER, D. G., and MEINKE, W. W. *Talanta,* **3** (1960) 255.

KANT, A., CALI, J. P., and THOMPSON, H. D. *Anal. Chem.* **28** (1956) 1867.

KAPLAN, L., and WILZBACH, K. E. Ibid. **26** (1954) 1797.

KAR, K. R., and RANGAN, L. K. *J. Sci. Indust. Res. India,* **15B** (1956) 661.

KEHOE, R. A., CHOLAK, J., and STORY, R. V. *J. Nutrit.* **19** (1940) 579.

KEINBERGER, C. A., GREENE, R. E., and VOSS, F. S. U.S. Atomic Energy Commission Report K 1042 (1957).

KEITH, M. L., and DEGENS, E. T. *Researches in geochemistry.* Edited by Abelson, P. H. Wiley, New York (1959).

KEMP, D. M., and SMALES, A. A. *Anal. Chim. Acta,* **23** (1960 a) 410.

—— Ibid. **23** (1960 b) 397.

—— *Geochim. Cosmochim. Acta,* **18** (1960 c) 149.

KENNETT, T. J., and THODE, H. G. *Phys. Rev.* **103** (1956) 322.

KEOMLEY, G. *Magyar Kem. Lapja.* **11** (1956) 82.

KETELLE, B. H., and BOYD, G. E. *J. Amer. Chem. Soc.* **69** (1947) 2800.

KEYES, R. U.S. Atomic Energy Commission Report AECD 3000 (1950).

KEYNES, R. D., and LEWIS, P. R. *Nature,* **165** (1950) 809.

—— J. *Physiol.* **114** (1951) 151.

KIM, C. K. Univ. Michigan Progress Report 9 (1960).

KING, L. D. P., and HENDERSON, W. J. *Phys. Rev.* **56** (1939) 1119.

KING, R. C. *Amer. Nat.* **41** (1957) 319.

KLEINBERG, J. U.S. Atomic Energy Commission Report LA 1721 (1958).

KOCH, H. J., SMITH, E. R., SHIMP, N. F., and CONNOR, J. *Cancer,* **9** (1956) 499.

KOCH, R. C. *Activation analysis handbook.* Academic Press (1960).

KOHMANN, T. P. *Nuclear processes in geologic settings,* 14. Wisconsin (1953).

KOHN, A. *C.R. Acad. Sci. Paris,* **236** (1953) 1419.

—— *Chim. et Ind.* **71** (1954) 69.

KOHN, H. W., and TOMKINS, E. R. U.S. Atomic Energy Commission Report ORNL 390 (1949).

KOHN-ABREST, M. E. *Ann. Fals. et Fraudes,* **49** (1956) 407.

KOLTHOFF, I. M., and SANDELL, E. B. *Textbook of quantitative inorganic analysis.* 3rd ed. Macmillan, London (1952).

KOMLEV, A. I., and TSIMBALISTA, L. I. *Zhur. Anal. Khim.* **8** (1953) 217.

KÖNIG, H., and WÄNKE, H. *Geochim. Cosmochim. Acta,* **17** (1959 a) 350.

—— Z. *Naturforsch.* **14a** (1959 b) 866.

KRAUS, K. A., and NELSON, F. *Amer. Soc. Test. Mat. Special Tech. Publication,* **195** (1956) 27.

KRAUS, K. A., and NELSON, F. *Ann. Rev. Nucl. Sci.* **7** (1957) 31.

KRAUSKOPF, K. B. *Geochim. Cosmochim. Acta,* **9** (1956) 1.

KUNDU, D. N., and POOL, M. L. *Phys. Rev.* **73** (1948) 22.

KUNIN, R. *Ion Exchange Resins.* Wiley, New York (1958).

KUNIN, R., MCGARVEY, F. X., and FARREN, A. *Anal. Chem.* **28** (1956) 729.

KUSAKA, Y. *Radioisotopes (Tokyo),* **6** (1957) 1.

—— *Bunseki Kagaku,* **8** (1959) 111.

—— *Z. Anal. Chem.* **172** (1960) 199.

KUSAKA, Y., and MEINKE, W. W. Univ. Michigan Progress Report 9 (1960).

KUSNETSOV, V. I. *Utilization of organic co-precipitants in analytical chemistry.* Moscow (1955).

KUYKENDALL, W. E., WAINERDI, R. E. *et al. Conf. on uses of radioisotopes in physical sciences and industry,* paper 198, Copenhagen (1960).

LAING, K. M., JONES, R. E., EMHISER, D. E., FITZGERALD, J. V., and BACHMAN, G. S. *Nucleonics,* **9**, no. 4 (1951) 44.

LAL, D., RAMA, and ZUTSHI, P. K. *J. Geophys. Res.* **65** (1960) 669.

LBOV, A. A., and NAUMOVA, E. E. *Atomnaya Energiya,* **6** (1959) 468.

LEA, D. E. *Nature,* **133** (1934) 24.

LEDDICOTTE, G. W. *Nucleonics,* **14**, no. 5 (1956) 47.

—— *Radioactivation analysis symposium,* 65. Butterworth, London (1960).

LEDDICOTTE, G. W., and BROOKSBANK, W. A. U.S. Atomic Energy Commission Report TID 7531, part 1 (1957).

LEDDICOTTE, G. W., and MAHLMAN, H. A. *Proc. Int. Conf. on peaceful uses of atomic energy,* Geneva, 1955, **8** (1956) 250.

LEDDICOTTE, G. W., MULLINS, W. T., BATE, L. C., EMERY, J. F., DRUSCHEL, R. E., and BROOKSBANK, W. A. *Proc. 2nd U.N. Conf. on peaceful uses of atomic energy,* Geneva, 1958, **28** (1959) 478.

LEDERER, M. *An introduction to paper electrophoresis and related methods.* Elsevier (1955).

LEDERER, M., and LEDERER, E. *Chromatography.* Elsevier (1955).

LEIPUNSKAYA, D. I., GAUER, Z. E., and FLEROV, G. N. *Atomnaya Energiya,* **6** (1959) 315.

LELIART, G., HOSTE, J., and EECKHAUT, J. *Nature,* **182** (1958 a) 600.

—— *Anal. Chim. Acta,* **19** (1958 b) 100.

—— *Talanta,* **2** (1959) 115.

LENIHAN, J. M. A., and SMITH, H. *Proc. 2nd U.N. Conf. on peaceful uses of atomic energy,* Geneva, 1958, **26** (1959) 238.

LEVEQUE, P. *Proc. Int. Conf. on peaceful uses of atomic energy,* Geneva, 1955, **15** (1956) 78.

LEVEQUE, P., and GOENVEC, H. *Bull. Soc. Chim. France,* (1955) 1213.

LIBBY, W. F. *Radiocarbon dating.* Chicago Univ. Press (1955).

LIBBY, W. F., and LEE, D. D. *Phys. Rev.* **55** (1949) 245.

LINDNER, V. R., and PETER, O. *Z. Naturforsch.* **1** (1946) 67.

LINGANE, J. J. *Electroanalytical Chemistry.* Interscience (1953).

LISSITZKY, S., and MICHEL, R. *Bull. Soc. Chim. France* (1952) 891.

LOEVINGER, R., and BERMAN, M. *Nucleonics,* **14**, no. 5 (1951) 47.

LONG, J. V. P. *Analyst,* **76** (1951) 644.

LOUNAMAA, J. *Ann. Bot. Soc. Vanamo,* **29**, no. 4 (1956).

LOVERIDGE, B. A., WEBSTER, R. K., MORGAN, J. W., THOMAS, A. M., and SMALES, A. A. *Anal. Chim. Acta,* **23** (1960) 154.

LOVERIDGE, B. A., and SMALES, A. A. *Methods of biochemical analysis.* Ed. Glick, D. 5, 225. Interscience (1957).

LOVERING, J. F., NICHIPORUK, W., CHODOS, A., and BROWN, H. *Geochim. Cosmochim. Acta,* **11** (1957) 263.

LOWE, L. F., THOMPSON, H. D., and CALI, J. P. *Anal. Chem.* **31** (1959) 1951.

LUKE, C. L. *Ind. Eng. Chem., Anal. Ed.* **15** (1943) 602.

—— *Anal. Chem.* **20** (1949) 1369.

LUX, H. *Z. anorg. Chem.* **240** (1938) 21.

LYON, W. S., and REYNOLDS, S. A. *Nucleonics,* **13,** no. 10 (1955) 60.

MACGREGOR, M. H. Applied Radiation Co., Walnut Creek, Calif., Report AM–100 (1957 *a*).

—— *Nucleonics,* **15,** no. 11 (1957 *b*) 176.

MACKAY, H. A. C. Atomic Energy Research Establishment, Harwell, Report AERE C/M 23 (1957).

MACKINTOSH, W. D. *Anal. Chem.* **32** (1960) 1272.

MACKINTOSH, W. D., and JERVIS, R. E. Atomic Energy of Canada, Ltd., Report CRDC 704 (1957).

—— *Anal. Chem.* **30** (1958) 1180.

MACKLIN, R. L., and LYKINS, J. H. *J. Chem. Phys.* **19** (1951) 844.

MACKLE, W., SCOTT, E. W., and TREON, J. *Amer. J. Hyg.* **29A,** no. 3 (1939) 139.

MAGEE, R. J., and HEADRIDGE, J. B. *Analyst,* **80** (1955) 785.

MAHLMAN, H. A., and LEDDICOTTE, G. W. *Anal. Chem.* **27** (1955) 823.

MAILLARD, L., and ETTORI, J. *C.R. Acad. Sci. Paris,* **202** (1936) 594, 1459, and 1621.

MAKIN, S. M. *Conf. on Uses of Radioisotopes in Physical Sciences and Industry,* paper 26, Copenhagen (1960).

MARION, J. B. *Nucleonics,* **18,** no. 11 (1960) 184.

MARSHAK, R. E. *Phys. Rev.* **71** (1947) 443.

MARTIN, J. A., LIVINGSTON, R. S., MURRAY, R. L., and RANKIN, M. *Nucleonics,* **13,** no. 3 (1955) 28.

MASHIMA, M. *Japan Anal.* **5** (1956) 324.

MASON, B. *Principles of geochemistry.* Wiley, New York. 2nd ed. (1958).

MATEOSIAN, E. DER, and McKEOWN, M. U.S. Atomic Energy Commission Report BNL 605 (1960.)

MATSUMURA, S., KOKUBU, N., WATANABE, S., and SAMESHIMA, Y. *Mem. Fac. Sci. Kyushu* **C2** (1955) 81.

MATUSZEK, J. M., and SUGIHARA, T. T. *Anal. Chem.* **33** (1961) 35.

MAY, S., and LEVEQUE, P. *Radioisotopes in scientific research,* **2,** 190. Pergamon, London (1957).

MAYNEORD, W. V., MARTIN, J. H., and LAYNE, D. A. *Nature,* **164** (1949) 728.

MAYR, G. *Nucleonics,* **12,** no. 5 (1954) 58.

MAYR, G., BRUNER, H. D., and BRUCER, M. *Nucleonics,* **11,** no. 10 (1953) 21.

McCANCE, R. A., and WIDDOWSON, E. M. *The composition of foods.* H.M. Stationery Office, London (1960).

McDONALD, G. J. F. *Researches in geochemistry.* Edited by Abelson, P. H., Wiley, New York (1959).

McDONALD, H. J. *Ionography and electrophoresis in stabilised media.* Chicago Univ. Press (1955).

McISAAC, L. D. U.S. Naval Radiol. Defense Lab. Report USNRDL–TR–72 (1956).

MEINKE, W. W. U.S. Atomic Energy Commission Report AECD 2738 (1949).

—— *Anal. Chem.* **30** (1958) 686.

—— Univ. Michigan Progress Report 8 (1959 *a*).

—— *Nucleonics,* **17,** no. 9 (1959 *b*) 86.

—— *Conf. on uses of radioisotopes in physical sciences and industry,* paper 283. Copenhagen (1960).

MEINKE, W. W., and ANDERSON, R. E. *Anal. Chem.* **25** (1953) 778.

—— *Anal. Chem.* **26** (1954) 907.

MEINKE, W. W., and MADDOCK, R. S. *Anal. Chem.* **29** (1957) 1171.

MEITNER, L. *Arkiv Mat. Astron. Fys.* **27A** (1940) 18.

MEITNER, L., and FRISCH, O. R. *Nature,* **143** (1939) 239.

MELLISH, C. E., PAYNE, J. A., and OTLET, R. L. *Radioisotopes in scientific research,* **1**, 35. Pergamon, London (1958).

MELLON, M. G. *Anal. Chem.* **22** (1950) 1342.

MERZ, E., and HERR, W. *Proc. 2nd U.N. Conf. on peaceful uses of atomic energy,* Geneva, 1958, **28** (1959) 491.

MEZHIBORSKAYA, K. A. *Atomnaya Energiya,* **6** (1959) 567.

MICHON, R. *Ann. Fals. et Fraudes,* **49** (1956) 284.

MILLER, C. E. U.S. Atomic Energy Commission Report ORNL 2715 (1959).

MILNER, G. W. C., and EDWARDS, J. W. Atomic Energy Research Establishment, Harwell, Report AERE R 2965 (1959).

MILNER, G. W. C., and SMALES, A. A. *Analyst,* **79** (1954) 425.

MITCHELL, R. L. *Proc. Nutr. Soc.* **1** (1944) 183.

—— *J. Sci. Food Agric.* **11** (1956) 553.

MITCHELL, R. L., and SCOTT, R. O. *J. Soc. Chem. Ind.* **66** (1947) 330.

MOLJK, A., DREVER, R. W. P., and CURRAN, S. C. *Nucleonics,* **13**, no. 2 (1955) 44.

MONIER-WILLIAMS, G. W. *Trace elements in food.* Wiley, New York (1950).

MONNIER, D., HAERDI, W., and VOGEL, J. *Helv. Chim. Acta,* **43** (1960) 675.

MOORE, F. L., WHITE, J. C., and HYNEK, R. J. *Amer. Soc. Test. Mat. Special Tech. Publication* 258 (1958).

MORRIS, D. F. C., and BREWER, F. M. *Geochim. Cosmochim. Acta,* **5** (1954) 134.

MORRIS, D. F. C., and CHAMBERS, M. E. *Talanta,* **5** (1960) 147.

MORRIS, D. F. C., and FYFIELD, F. W. *Ibid.* **8** (1961) 612.

MORRIS, D. F. C., and KILLICK, R. A. *Anal. Chim. Acta,* **20** (1959 *a*) 587.

—— *Talanta,* **3** (1959 *b*) 34.

—— *Ibid.* **4** (1960 *a*) 51.

—— *Geochim. Cosmochim. Acta,* **19** (1960 *b*) 139.

MORRIS, D. F. C., and OLYA, A. *Talanta,* **4** (1960) 194.

MORRISON, G. H., and COSGROVE, J. F. *Anal. Chem.* **27** (1955) 810.

—— *Anal. Chem.* **28** (1956) 320.

MORRISON, G. H., and FREISER, H. *Solvent extraction in analytical chemistry.* Wiley, New York (1957).

—— *Ann. Rev. Nucl. Sci.* **9** (1959) 221.

MORTON, G. A. *R.C.A. Review,* **10** (1949) 525.

MÜLLER, J. H. *Radioisotopes in scientific research,* **3**, 667. Pergamon, London (1958).

MULLIN, J. B., and RILEY, J. P. *J. Marine Res.* **15** (1956) 103.

MUTH, H., RAJEWSKI, B., HANTKE, H. J., and AURAND, K. *Health Phys.* **2** (1960) 239.

NAKAI, T., YAJIMA, S., FUJII, I., and OKADA, M. *J. Chem. Soc. Japan,* **80** (1959) 49.

NATHANS, R., and HALPERN, J. *Phys. Rev.* **93** (1954) 437.

NELSON, L. C. U.S. Atomic Energy Commission Report NBL 117 (1956).

NELSON, L. C., and AARON, D. U.S. Atomic Energy Commission Report TID 7531 (part 1) (1957).

NEUFELD, A. H. *Canad. J. Res.* **14B** (1936) 160.

NEWMAN, W. F. *Pharmacology and toxicology of uranium compounds,* 701. McGraw-Hill (1949).

NILSSON, G. *Acta Chem. Scand.* **10** (1956) 94.

NOVEY, T. B. U.S. Atomic Energy Commission Report CC 1631 (1944).

OBRINK, K. J., and ULFENDAHL, H. R. *Int. J. Appl. Rad. Isot.* **5** (1959) 99.

ODEBLAD, E. *Acta Radiol.* **42** (1954) 391.

—— *Clin. Chim. Acta*, **1** (1956 a) 67.

—— *Acta Radiol.* **45** (1956 b) 396.

—— *Trace analysis*, edited by Yoe, J. H., and Koch, H. J. Chapman and Hall, London (1957).

ODEBLAD, E., and NATI, G. *Acta Radiol.* **43** (1955) 249.

ODEBLAD, E., and ODEBLAD, S. *Anal. Chim. Acta* **15** (1956) 114.

ODEBLAD, E., and TOBIAS, C. A. *Arch. Biochem. Biophys.* **49** (1954) 452.

ODEBLAD, E., WESTIN, B., and MALMFORS, K. G. *Acta Radiol.* **49** (1958) 137.

OGILVIE, K. W. *The Nucleus (Nat. Res. Foundation, Sydney)*, **5** (1959) 24.

OKADA, M. *Nature*, **187** (1960) 57.

OSMOND, R. G., and SMALES, A. A. *Anal. Chim. Acta*, **10** (1954) 117.

PANETH, F. A., REASBECK, P., and MAYNE, K. I. *Nature*, **172** (1953) 200.

PARKER, L. F. J. *Analyst*, **80** (1955) 638.

PATTERSON, C. *Geochim. Cosmochim. Acta*, **10** (1956) 230.

PAULY, J. *C.R. Acad. Sci. Paris*, **240** (1955) 2415.

PECK, R. A., and EUBANK, H. P. *Rev. Sci. Instr.* **26** (1955) 444.

PEIRSON, D. H. *Brit. J. Appl. Phys.* **6** (1955) 444.

—— *Atomics*, **7** (1956) 316.

PEIRSON, D. H., and IREDALE, P. *Brit. J. Appl. Phys.* **8** (1957) 422.

—— *Radioisotopes in scientific research*, **2**, 197. Pergamon, London (1958).

PETTERSEN, H. *Geochim. Cosmochim. Acta*, **17** (1959) 209.

PFANN, H., SALLEY, D., and MARK, H. *J. Amer. Chem. Soc.* **66** (1944) 983.

PHILLIPS, G., and CORNISH, F. W. Atomic Energy Research Establishment, Harwell, Report AERE C/R 1276 (1953).

PICCIOTTO, E., and STYVANDAEL, M. VAN. *C.R. Acad. Sci. Paris*, **232** (1951) 855.

PICKETT, E. E., and HANKINS, B. E. *Anal. Chem.* **30** (1958) 47.

PIJCK, J. U.S. Atomic Energy Commission Report NAS–NS 3007 (1960).

PLAKSIN, I. N., SMIRNOV, V. N., and STARCHIK, L. P. *Dokl. Akad. Nauk S.S.S.R.* **127** (1959) 618.

—— *Atomnaya Energiya*, **9** (1960) 361.

PLUMB, R. C. *Nucleonics*, **14**, no. 5 (1956) 48.

PLUMB, R. C., and LEWIS, J. E. Ibid. **13**, no. 8 (1955) 42.

PLUMB, R. C., and SILVERMAN, R. H. Ibid. **12**, no. 12 (1954) 29.

POINT, J. J. *Radioisotopes in scientific research*, **2**, 180. Pergamon, London (1958).

POLLARD, F. H., and McOMIE, J. F. W. *Chromatographic methods of inorganic analysis*. Academic Press, New York (1953).

POOLE, M. J., and RAE, E. R. *Nature*, **185** (1960) 280.

PRICE, J. *J. Soc. Chem. Ind.* **64** (1945) 283.

PURSER, P. R., RYGARD, J., and HORNNES, N. *Phys. in Med. and Biol.* **3** (1959) 361.

PUTMAN, J. L., and TAYLOR, W. H. *Int. J. Appl. Rad. Isot.* **1** (1957) 315.

—— *Trans. Soc. Glass. Technol.* **42** (1958) 84.

Radiochemical centre, Amersham, U.K. Catalogue (1960).

RANKAMA, K., and SAHAMA, T. G. *Geochemistry.* Chicago Univ. Press (1950).

REED, G. W. *Radioactivation analysis symposium*, 26. Butterworth, London (1960).

—— Personal communication (1959).

REED, G. W., HAMAGUCHI, H., and TURKEVICH, A. *Geochim. Cosmochim. Acta*, **13** (1958) 248.

REED, G. W., KIGOSHI, K., and TURKEVICH, A. *Proc. 2nd U.N. Conf. on peaceful uses of atomic energy*, Geneva, 1958, **28** (1959) 486.
—— *Geochim. Cosmochim. Acta*, **20** (1960) 122.
REED, G. W., and TURKEVICH, A. *Nature*, **176** (1955) 794.
REGNARD, C., and SCHLÖSUNG, T. *C.R. Acad. Sci. Paris*, **124** (1897) 302.
REID, A. F. *Rev. Sci. Instr.* **18** (1947) 501.
REIFFEL, L., and STONE, C. A. *J. Lab. Clin. Med.* **49** (1957) 286.
REYNOLDS, J. H. *Rev. Sci. Instr.* **27** (1956) 928.
RIEZLER, W. *Z. Naturforsch.* **4A** (1949) 545.
ROCHLIN, R. S. *Neutron activation data*. General Electric Co. Report (1957).
ROCHOW, E. G., HURD, D. T., and LEWIS, R. N. *The chemistry of organometallic compounds*. Wiley, New York (1957).
RONA, E. *Trans. Amer. Geophys. Union*, **38** (1957) 754.
RONA, E., HOOD, D. W., AKERS, L. K., and MUSE, L. *Radioactivation analysis symposium*, 76. Butterworth, London (1960).
ROWLAND, F. S., and HASKIN, L. *Amer. Chem. Soc. meeting*, Atlantic City, paper 15 (1959).
RUBIN, S., PASSELL, T. O., and BAILEY, L. E. *Anal. Chem.* **29** (1957) 736.
RUDNEV, N. A. *Anal. Chem. U.S.S.R.* **10** (1955) 223.
SAGANE, R., EGUCHI, M., and SHIGETA, J. *J. Phys.-Math. Soc. Japan*, **16** (1942) 383.
SAINT-RAT, L. DE. *C.R. Acad. Sci. Paris*, **227** (1948) 150.
SALMON, L. Atomic Energy Research Establishment, Harwell, Report AERE C/M 154 (1952).
—— AERE, Harwell, Report AERE C/R 1324 (1954).
—— AERE, Harwell, Report AERE C/M 323 (1957).
—— AERE, Harwell, Report AERE C/R 2377(3) (1957).
—— AERE, Harwell, Report AERE C/R 2377(1) (1959).
SALUTSKY, M. L. *Treatise on analytical chemistry*, edited by Kolthoff, I. M., and Elving, P. J. Interscience (1959).
SAMUELSON, O. *Ion exchangers in analytical chemistry*. Wiley, New York (1953)
SANDELL, E. B. *Colorimetric determination of traces of metals*. Interscience. 3rd ed. (1960).
SATTERLEE, H. S., and BLODGETT, G. *Ind. Eng. Chem., Anal. Ed.* **16** (1944) 400.
SCHAEFFER, O. A., and DAVIS, R. *Nat. Acad. Sci., Nat. Res. Council* publication no. 400 (1956) 172.
SCHINDEWOLF, U. Massachusetts Institute of Technology, Tech. Report 68 (1955).
—— *Geochim. Cosmochim. Acta*, **19** (1960) 134.
SCHINDEWOLF, U., and WAHLGREN, M. Ibid. **18** (1960) 36.
SCHLEICHER, A. *Elektroanalytische Schnellmethoden*. Enke, Stuttgart (1947).
SCHMEISER, K., and JERCHEL, D. *Angew. Chem.* **65** (1953 a) 366.
—— Ibid. **65** (1953 b) 490.
SCHMITT, R. A., MOSEN, A. W., SUFFREDINI, C. S., LASCH, J. E., SHARP, R. A., and OLEHY, D. A. *Nature*, **186** (1960) 863.
SCHONKEN, P. U.S. Atomic Energy Commission Report NP 6971 (1959).
SCHWARTZ, K., and FOLTZ, C. M. *Fed. Proc.* **17,** no. 1 (1958) 492.
SEABORG, G. T., and LIVINGOOD, S. *J. Amer. Chem. Soc.* **60** (1938) 1784.
SEAL, M. S., MILLS, W. A., and TERRILL, J. G. *Public Health Reports*, **72** (1957) 4.
SEYFANG, A. P. *Analyst*, **80** (1955) 74.
SEYFANG, A. P., and SMALES, A. A. Ibid. **78** (1953) 394.
SHCHERBOV, D. P., and SAGALOVICH, I. I. *Izvest. Akad. Nauk Kazakh. S.S.R.*, Ser. Khim. no. 8 (1953) 114.

SHELDON, J., and WILLIAMS, J. Atomic Energy Research Establishment, Harwell, Report AERE M/M 80 (1954).

SHIDELER, J., WAHLGREN, M., and MEINKE, W. W. Univ. Michigan Progress Report 9 (1960).

SHIMP, N. F., CONNOR, J., PRINCE, A. L., and BEAR, F. E. *Soil Sci.* **83** (1957) 51.

SHIOKAWA, T., and YAGI, M. *Kagaku,* **13** (1959) 321.

SHIPMAN, G. F., and MILNER, O. I. *Anal. Chem.* **30** (1958) 210.

SHORT, H. G., and WILLIAMS, A. I. *Analyst,* **83** (1958) 624.

SHVANGIRADZE, R. R., and MOZGOVAYA, T. A. *J. Anal. Chem. U.S.S.R.* **12** (1957) 727.

SIDGWICK, N. V. *Chemical elements and their compounds.* Clarendon Press, Oxford (1950).

SIEGBAHN, K. *Beta and gamma ray spectroscopy,* 26. North Holland, Amsterdam (1955 a).

—— Ibid. 33 (1955 b).

SIPPEL, R. F., and GLOVER, E. D. *Nucl. Instr. Methods,* **9** (1960) 37.

SLATTER, A. U., and STITCH, S. R. *Chem. and Ind.* (1956) 567.

SMALES, A. A. *Analyst,* **77** (1952) 778.

—— *Electronics,* **1** (1955) 327.

—— *Proc. Int. Conf. on peaceful uses of atomic energy,* Geneva, 1955, **9** (1956 a) 273.

—— Ibid. **15** (1956 b) 73.

SMALES, A. A., and BROWN, L. O. *Chem. and Ind.* (1950) 441.

SMALES, A. A., and LOVERIDGE, B. A. *Anal. Chim. Acta,* **13** (1955) 566.

SMALES, A. A., and MAPPER, D. Atomic Energy Research Establishment, Harwell, Report AERE C/R 2392 (1957).

SMALES, A. A., MAPPER, D., MORGAN, J. W., WEBSTER, R. K., and WOOD, A. J. *Proc. 2nd U.N. Conf. on peaceful uses of atomic energy,* Geneva, 1958, **2** (1959) 242.

SMALES, A. A., MAPPER, D., and SEYFANG, A. P. Atomic Energy Research Establishment, Harwell, Report AERE R 3313 (1960).

SMALES, A. A., MAPPER, D., and WOOD, A. J. *Analyst,* **82** (1957) 75.

—— *Geochim. Cosmochim. Acta,* **13** (1958) 123.

SMALES, A. A., MAPPER, D., WOOD, A. J., and SALMON, L. Atomic Energy Research Establishment, Harwell, Report AERE C/R 2254 (1957).

SMALES, A. A., and PATE, B. D. *Anal. Chem.* **24** (1952 a) 717.

—— *Analyst,* **77** (1952 b) 188.

—— Ibid. **77** (1952 c) 196.

SMALES, A. A., and SALMON, L. Ibid. **80** (1955) 37.

SMALES, A. A., SMIT, J. VAN R., and IRVING, H. Ibid. **82** (1957) 539.

SMALES, A. A., and WAGER, L. R. *Methods in geochemistry.* Interscience (1960).

SMALES, A. A., and WISEMAN, J. D. H. *Nature,* **175** (1955) 464.

SMITH, G. F. *Anal. Chim. Acta,* **17** (1957) 175.

SMITH, H. *Anal. Chem.* **31** (1959) 1361.

SOWDEN, E. M., and PIRIE, A. *Biochem. J.* **70** (1958) 716.

SOWDEN, E. M., and STITCH, S. R. Ibid. **67** (1957) 104.

SPECTOR, W. S. *Handbook of biological data.* W. B. Saunders, Philadelphia (1956).

SPENCER, R. P., MITCHELL, T. G., and KING, E. R. *J. Lab. Clin. Med.* **50** (1957) 646.

—— *Int. J. Appl. Rad. Isot.* **3** (1958) 104.

SPIESS, F. N. *Phys. Rev.* **94** (1954) 1292.

STARIK, I. E., and SHATS, M. M. *Geokhimiya,* **19** (1956) 2.

STEELE, E. Univ. Michigan Progress Report 9 (1960).

STEPHENS, W. E., and LEWIS, M. N. *Phys. Rev.* **69** (1946) 43.

STEVENS, R. E., NILES, W. W., CHODOS, A. A., FILBY, R. H., LEININGER, R. K., AHRENS, L. H., FLEISCHER, M., and FLANAGAN, F. J. *U.S. Geol. Survey Bull.* 1113 (1960).

STEVENSON, P. C., and HICKS, H. G. *Ann. Rev. Nucl. Sci.* **3** (1953) 221.

STEWART, D. C., and BENTLEY, W. C. *Science,* **120** (1954) 50.

STEWART, L. U.S. Atomic Energy Commission Report LADC 1117 (1953).

STITCH, S. R. Atomic Energy Research Establishment, Harwell, Report MRC/R 1952 (1956).

—— *Biochem. J.* **67** (1957) 97.

STOCK, A. *Biochem. Z.* **304** (1940) 73.

STOCKS, P. *Brit. J. Cancer,* **14** (1960) 397.

STOENNER, R. W., and ZÄHRINGER, J. *Geochim. Cosmochim. Acta,* **15** (1958) 40.

STRAIN, J. E., OLIVER, J. H., and LEDDICOTTE, G. W. *Radioactivation analysis symposium,* 72. Butterworth, London (1960).

STRICKLAND, E. H., and BENSON, A. A. *Arch. Biochem. Biophys.* **88** (1960) 344.

STROMINGER, D., HOLLANDER, J. M., and SEABORG, G. T. *Rev. Mod. Phys.* **30** (1958) 585.

SÜE, P. *Bull. Soc. Chim. France,* **D9** (1951).

—— *C.R. Acad. Sci. Paris,* **237** (1953) 1696.

—— *J. Phys. Radium,* **16** (1955 *a*) 734.

—— *C.R. Acad. Sci. Paris,* **240** (1955 *b*) 88.

—— Ibid. **242** (1956) 770.

SÜE, P., and ALBERT, P. Ibid. **242** (1956) 2461.

SUESS, H. E., and UREY, H. C. *Rev. Mod. Phys.* **28** (1956) 53.

SUNDERMAN, D. N., ACKERMANN, I. B., and MEINKE, W. W. *Anal. Chem.* **31** (1959) 40.

SUNDERMAN, D. N., and MEINKE, W. W. Ibid. **29** (1957) 1578.

SZEKELY, G. Ibid. **26** (1954) 1500.

SZILARD, L., and CHALMERS, T. A. *Nature,* **134** (1934) 462 and 494.

TAYLOR, K. J. Personal communication (1961).

TAYLOR, T. I., and HAVENS, W. W. *Nucleonics,* **6,** no. 4 (1950) 54.

—— *Physical methods in chemical analysis.* Edited by Berl, R. **3,** 539. Academic Press, New York (1956).

THIERS, R. E. *Trace analysis.* Edited by Yoe, J. H., and Koch, H. J. Chapman and Hall, London (1957 *a*).

—— *Methods of biochemical analysis.* Edited by Glick, D. **5,** 273. Interscience (1957 *b*).

TIPTON, I. H., FOLAND, W. D., BOBB, F. C., and McCORKLE, W. C. U.S. Atomic Energy Commission Report CF–53–8–4 (1954).

TOBIAS, C. A., and DUNN, R. W. U.S. Atomic Energy Commission Report AECD 2099 B (1948).

—— *Science,* **109** (1949) 109.

TOBIAS, C. A., WOLFE, R., DUNN, R. W., and ROSENFELD, I. *Unio. Int. Contra Cancrum Acta,* **7** (1952) 874.

TREADWELL, W., and FREY, G. *Helv. Chim. Acta,* **27** (1944) 42.

TRUEMPER, J. L. *Diss. Abstr.* **20** (1960) 2524.

TUREKIAN, K. K., GAST, P. W., and KULP, J. L. *Spectrochim. Acta,* **9** (1957) 40.

TURNER, R. C., RADLEY, J. M., and MAYNEORD, W. V. *Health Phys.* **1** (1958 *a*) 268.

—— *Brit. J. Radiol.* **31** (1958 *b*) 397.

TURNER, S. E. *Anal. Chem.* **28** (1956) 1457.

VALLEE, B. L., and GIBSON, J. G. *J. Biol. Chem.* **176** (1948) 435.

VARRES, K. S. *J. Chem. Educ.* **37** (1961) 391.

Vienna symposium, *Pure and Appl. Chem.* **1** (1960) 15.

VINCENT, E. A., and BILEFIELD, L. I. *Geochim. Cosmochim. Acta,* **19** (1960) 63.

VINCENT, E. A., and CROCKET, J. H. Ibid. **18** (1960 a) 130.

——— Ibid. **18** (1960 b) 143.

VINCENT, E. A., and SMALES, A. A. Ibid. **9** (1956) 154.

VINCENT, J. *Nature,* **184** (1959) 1332 S.

VINOGRADOV, A. P. *The elementary chemical composition of marine organisms.* Sears Foundation, New Haven, Conn. (1953).

——— *The geochemistry of rare and dispersed elements in soils.* Chapman and Hall, London (1959).

VOGEL, A. L. *A text book of macro and semimicro qualitative inorganic analysis.* Longmans, London. 4th ed. (1954).

WAGER, L. R., and DEER, W. A. *Meddel. om Grønland,* **105** (1939) 1.

WAGER, L. R., and MITCHELL, R. L. *Geochim. Cosmochim. Acta,* **1** (1951) 129.

WAGER, L. R., SMIT, J. VAN R., and IRVING, H. Ibid. **13** (1958) 81.

WAGER, L. R., VINCENT, E. A., and SMALES, A. A. *Econ. Geol.* **52** (1957) 855.

WAGNER, C. D., CAMPANILE, V. A., and GUINN, V. P. *Nucl. Instr. Methods,* **6** (1960) 238.

WAHL, A. C., and BONNER, N. A. *Radioactivity applied to chemistry.* Wiley, New York (1951).

WAHLGREN, M. Univ. Michigan Progress Report 8 (1959).

WALDRON, M. B. *Glove boxes and shielded cells.* Butterworth, London (1958).

WALTON, H. F. *Ann. Rev. Phys. Chem.* **10** (1959) 123.

WÄNKE, H. *Z. Naturforsch.* **13a** (1958) 645.

WÄNKE, H., and KÖNIG, H. Ibid. **14a** (1959) 860.

WÄNKE, H., and MORSE, E. U. Ibid. **10a** (1955) 667.

WARREN, H. V., and DELAVAULT, R. E. *Bull. Geol. Soc. Amer.* **61** (1950) 123.

WATTENBURG, H. *Z. anorg. Chem.* **236** (1938) 339.

WEISSBERGER, A. *Techniques of organic chemistry,* **4.** Interscience (1951).

WESTERMARK, T., and FINEMAN, I. *Proc. 2nd U.N. Conf. on peaceful uses of atomic energy,* Geneva, 1958, **28** (1959) 506.

WESTERMARK, T., and SJÖSTRAND, B. *Int. J. Appl. Rad. Isot.* **9** (1960 a) 1.

——— Ibid. **9** (1960 b) 78.

WETHERILL, G. W., and INGRAM, M. C. *Nuclear processes in geologic settings,* 33. Wisconsin (1953).

WHITEHOUSE, J. L., and PUTMAN, J. L. *Radioactive isotopes.* Clarendon Press, Oxford (1953).

WIELAND, T., and DOSE, K. *Physical methods in chemical analysis,* edited by Berl, W. G. **3** (1956) 29. Academic Press, New York.

WILKINSON, D. H. *Ionisation chambers and counters.* Cambridge University Press (1950).

WILLARD, H. H. *Anal. Chem.* **22** (1950) 1372.

WILLIAMS, A. I. *Analyst,* **84** (1959) 433.

WILLIAMS, I. R. Personal communication (1959).

WILSON, E. J. Personal communication (1960).

WILSON, E. J., DIBBS, H. P., RICHARDS, S., and EAKINS, J. D. *Nucleonics,* **16,** no. 4 (1958) 110.

WILSON, E. J., EVANS, C., CHADWICK, J., EAKINS, J. D., and TAYLOR, K. J. Atomic Energy Research Establishment, Harwell, Report AERE I/R 2216 (1955).

WILSON, E. J., and TAYLOR, K. J. Atomic Energy Research Establishment, Harwell, Report AERE I/R 2693 (1958).

WINCHESTER, J. W. *Trans. Amer. Geophys. Union*, **39** (1958) 536.

—— *J. Geophys. Res.* **64** (1959) 1130.

—— *Progress in inorganic chemistry*, edited by Cotton, F. A. **2**. 1. Interscience (1960).

WINTERINGHAM, F. P. W. *Analyst*, **75** (1950) 627.

WINTERINGHAM, F. P. W., HARRISON, H., and BRIDGES, R. G. *Nucleonics*, **10**, no. 3 (1952) 52.

WOLFE, R., DUNN, R. W., and TOBIAS, C. A. U.S. Atomic Energy Commission Report UCRL 480 (1949).

WOODMAN, F. J. U.K. Atomic Energy Authority, Windscale, Report ARDC/P 36 (1954).

YAMAGATA, N. *J. Chem. Soc. Japan*, **71** (1950) 288.

YAMAGATA, N. Japanese Atomic Energy Commission Report A/AC 82/G/L 476 (1960)

YAMAMOTO, D. *Kagaku*, **29** (1958) 208.

YOSIM, S., and DAVIES, T. H. *J. Phys. Chem.* **56** (1951) 599.

YOUNG, E. G., and LANGILLE, W. M. *Canad. J. Bot.* **36** (1958) 301.

YULE, G. U., and KENDALL, M. G. *An introduction to the theory of statistics*. Griffin, London (1947).

INDEX

abbreviations, 214.
absorber, 87.
absorption cross-section, 94–95.
accelerating machines, 17.
acetylacetonates, 115.
achondrites, 142, 146–7.
actinium, 17, 21.
activation analysis, 1, 8.
— — advantages, 11.
— — biological applications, 166–88.
— — disadvantages, 14–15.
— — errors, 3, 92–110.
— — geochemical applications, 141–65.
— — inorganic applications, 189–212.
— — sensitivity, 9–14.
— — specificity, 11.
— — theory, 5–15.
activation cross-section, 8, 10, 24, 95.
agate mortar, 133.
age determination, 161–3.
Algae, marine, 167, 170, 186–7.
alkyls, 115.
alloys, 191–2.
alpha particle, 35, 42.
— — activation by, 42–43.
— — (α, γ) reaction, 42.
— — (α, n) reaction, 16, 42, 164, 177, 179.
— — (α, p) reaction, 42.
aluminium absorbers, 87.
— analysis of, 132–3, 190–1.
— cans, 95, 128, 131.
— determination of, 179, 196, 221.
amalgams, 117–18.
americium, 17.
Amphibia, 177.
amplifier, 48, 76, 85.
ampoule, 95, 101–21, 108, 129, 131–3.
Angiosperms, 168, 187–8.
anticoincidence counter, 58–59, 85–86.
antimony, determination of, 196, 251–2.
— Sb^{124}/Be source, 16, 21, 215.
argon, 196, 223–4.
arsenic, determination of, 103–4, 180, 196–7, 236.
— standard, 101.
Arthropods, 167, 168.
Ascidians, 181.
ashing, 137–8, 213.
astatine, 114.
atomic bomb, 21.
atomic weight, 8–9.
automated analysis, 71.

autoradiography, 90–91, 149, 180.
Avogadro's number, 8.
axon, 184–5.

background, 10, 48, 59, 78–81, 85.
back-scattering, 47, 82.
Bacteria, 166, 168.
barium, determination of, 178, 197, 254–5.
barn, 10.
α-benzoin oxine, 116, 122, 243, 259.
BEPO, 10, 18, 92, 94, 105.
beryllium, determination of, 33, 42, 197, 215–16.
— neutron source, 16.
berylometer, 150.
beta absorption curves, 87–88.
— counters, 73.
— energy, 86–88.
— particle, 75; maximum range of, 88–89.
— spectrometer, 86.
— spectrum, 85–87.
Bethge apparatus, 113–14.
binding energy, 22, 35, 45.
biological applications, 166–88.
biological material, analysis of, 70.
— — composition of, 167–74.
— — solution of, 213.
biomass, 167.
bismuth, determination of, 197, 266–7.
blood, 176.
— analysis of, 178–80.
— collection of, 136.
— composition of, 171.
boron, determination of, 38, 178, 197, 216–17.
boron nitride mortar, 134.
boron trifluoride counter, 33, 214, 216.
brain, 171.
bremsstrahlung, 31.
British standard steel, 100.
bromine, determination of, 181, 198, 237–8.
Buchner funnel, 121.

cadmium, determination of, 183, 198, 248–9.
caesium, determination of, 177–8, 198, 254.
calcium, determination of, 198–9, 225–6.
canning materials, 19, 131–3.
carbon, determination of, 38, 41, 179, 199, 217.

U

PRINTED IN GREAT BRITAIN
AT THE UNIVERSITY PRESS, OXFORD
BY VIVIAN RIDLER
PRINTER TO THE UNIVERSITY